RY ROADS IN THE PROVINCE OF ALBERTA

P9-CJY-661

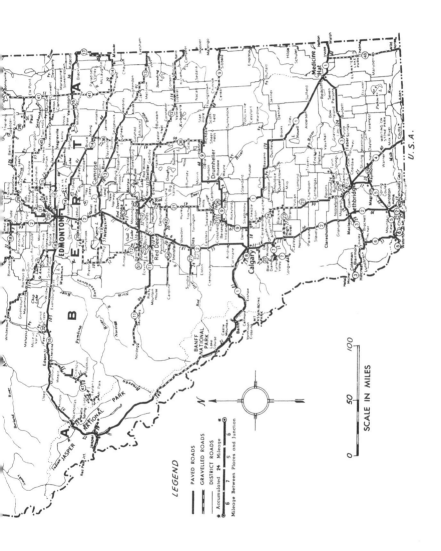

THE BIRDS
of
ALBERTA

BY

W. RAY SALT

AND

A. L. WILK

Second Edition

Revised By

W. Ray Salt

Illustrated with

Color Photographs by Cyril Hampson, Kathleen Hodges,
Stewart D. MacDonald, B. & J. Morgan, and others;

Color drawings by Allan Brooks, R. Chandler, W. Ray Salt,
T. M. Shortt, and others;

Black and white drawings by T. M. Shortt.

GOVERNMENT OF ALBERTA

First Edition, 1958.
Second (Revised) Edition, 1966.
Second Edition Reprinted, 1972.

Lithographed by Bulletin-Commercial Printers Ltd., Edmonton.

Available by mail order from
The Bookservice, Queen's Printer
Government of Alberta, Edmonton, T5G 2Y5

$5.00 per copy

CONTENTS

To

KATHLEEN

whose encouragement has carried
this book
through the travails of
its birth and its adolescence,

and to

DANIELLE

who has reopened my eyes
to the beauty of nature.

ACKNOWLEDGMENTS

THE assistance of a large number of contributions to the first edition of this book was acknowledged in that volume. That assistance, without which this revised edition would have been impossible, is again gratefully acknowledged. It is hoped that these original contributors have derived satisfaction from the reception given to the project which they fostered.

For information and records specifically provided for this second edition I am grateful to Drs. D. A. Boag, J. M. Ellis, E. O. Hohn, V. Lewin, R. Lister, H. A. MacGregor, and J. D. Soper, University of Alberta, Edmonton; Messrs M. V. Dahlgren, R. Gehlert, Edgar T. Jones, R. Lumsden, H. Pegg and Dr. R. Turner, Edmonton; Dr. M. T. Myres, University of Alberta, Calgary; Dr. D. Shute, Miss K. Hodges, Mr. R. Webb and Mr. D. A. Beacham, Calgary; Dr. T. H. Bassett, Dr. D. W. A. Roberts, and Mr. H. Sivyer, Lethbridge; Mr. R. K. Shaw, Cardston; Miss Myrtle Biggs, Beynon; Mr. G. Pegg, Glenevis; Mr. Paul H. Pohlman and the late Mr. Fred Martel, Jasper; the late Mr. Bernard Hamm, Sexsmith; Messrs R. J. Adams, G. Freeman and T. Sadler, Strathmore; Mr. Gavin Craig, Wembley; Dr. R. W. Nero, Regina, Sask.; Dr. E. L. Mills, Kingston, Ont.; Mr. A. J. Erskine, Wolfville, N.S.; Mr. J. Grant, Vernon, B.C.; Mr. David Stirling and Mr. Wm. Merilees, Victoria, B.C. To the many correspondents whose names do not appear on the above list I extend my thanks, with the hope that I may continue to receive from them the interesting bits of bird news which help to keep this project alive and flourishing.

To W. Earl Godfrey, Curator of Ornithology, National Museum of Canada, I am indebted for subspecific determination of specimens, for making available to me information and materials pertaining to the ornithology of Alberta, and for helpful criticism.

The illustrations in this book include many color photographs of birds taken in their natural habitat. The work of Professor Cyril Hampson in the field of nature photography has rightfully received international recognition. Dr. Hampson has again freely opened his collection of bird photographs to the author and has generously permitted their use for illustrations. Many recent examples of his artistry are reproduced herein for the first time. Miss Kathleen Hodges, Calgary, Mr. Stewart D. MacDonald, National Museum of Canada, Ottawa, and Mr. and Mrs. Barry Morgan, now of Brisbane, Australia, have also contributed many fine photographs from their extensive collections. That there is much talent currently being developed in the field of nature photography is evidenced by excellent photographs contributed by the following Alberta photographers: M. V. Dahlgren, R. Gehlert, Wm. Lea and A. Porcher of Edmonton, H. Sivyer, Lethbridge and Bruce Sparks, Calgary. The National Museum of Canada kindly gave access to the National Collection of Nature Photographs and as a result permission to reproduce photographs from this collection was generously granted by Miss Valerie J. May, Cultus Lake, B.C., Mr. Doug Gilroy, Saskatoon, Sask., Mr. Wm. I. Campbell, Waterdown, Ont., Dr. D. F. Parmelee, Emporia, Kansas, and Mr. J. M. Templeton, Islington, Ont. A beautiful photograph of Willow Ptarmigan by the late Dr. J. G. Beatty was sent to me several years ago expressly for inclusion in this book. To all of these photographers, and to the many others who kindly sent photographs for consideration, I am sincerely grateful.

Many illustrations are in the form of color drawings. Acknowledgment has been made of permission to reproduce some illustrations from Taverner's "Birds of Canada", published by the National Museum of Canada, Ottawa, and from "Birds of Canada's National Parks" published by the National Parks Service, Ottawa. Introduced in this volume are the first published examples of the work of Mr. Reg. Chandler, Edmonton, a newcomer in the field of bird art. It is a pleasure to acknowledge permission to reproduce these fine paintings.

To Mrs. Rachel Kilsdonk I am grateful for secretarial services faithfully and meticulously performed.

INTRODUCTION

THIS volume is intended to be an aid primarily to those who are not too well acquainted with the birds of Alberta and who would like to know them better. It is hoped, however, that those who already have a good knowledge of our birds will find in it something of value, even though it be only recognition of the fact that there are large gaps in our present knowledge and large areas of the province still to be explored ornithologically. In planning the volume it was found necessary to limit the amount of information to be presented in order that the book might not become too unwieldly in size. Selection of material was made with two major aims in mind: first, to assist the observer to identify any birds which he might see in Alberta; and second, to help him to find in the province those species which he wishes to observe. Other aims have been subordinated to these two.

USE OF THE BOOK

The book is so arranged that the text and the illustration for each species either face each other or are only one page apart. The order of presentation is that of the Fifth Edition of the A.O.U. Check-List of North American Birds. In general the popular names used are the vernacular names given to species in the A.O.U. Check-List but in certain cases where the A.O.U. Check-List name is not in common usage in Alberta the local name or that of the local subspecies is used. Below this the scientific name appears in italics. The abbreviation, subsp., followed by a page number means that the subspecies which occur in Alberta will be found in the Check-List of birds of Alberta by referring to that page.

The approximate distribution within the province of each species is outlined on a small map of Alberta. Dark areas on the map indicate that the species breeds in that region and it may be assumed that it migrates over more southerly regions to reach that area. A dotted outline means that the boundary of the breeding range is not known for that region. The letters signify relative abundance within the range: C stands for common, FC for fairly common and S for scarce. Dark circles show isolated nesting records, dark triangles isolated non-breeding records. Lines with arrows indicate that the species is only a migrant in the province. Horizontal lines show wintering areas.

Many species of birds show variation in plumage with age, sex, or season. Since description and illustration of all of these plumages is impossible in a work of this size emphasis has been placed on the plumage worn during the nesting season. In this section some abbreviations are used: ads. stands for adults; im. for immature; m. for male; f. for female.

Under the heading, Identification, an attempt is made to point out those characteristics of color and form which are the best means of separating a particular species from any other.

The locality and date at the end of a section on nesting habits gives a record of a nest with eggs which has been found in that locality on that date. Where possible an average nesting date is given.

Under the heading, Remarks, is grouped a variety of information which might be helpful in locating and identifying the species. Its distribution and status in the province is included here; so also is the type of habitat in which the species is most likely to be found. Any peculiarities of flight, habit, behavior, and voice are described in order to show that some birds identify themselves by behavior and song more readily than they do by color and form. Where space has permitted a brief account of the life-history is included.

In identification of species a variety of aids is offered: size, shape, color, special field-marks, peculiarities of flight, habit, and song and an illustration in color or in black and white of each species. The status and distribution of each species and the type of habitat it frequents are given to help the bird student to locate birds which are of special interest to him.

All species of birds known to have occurred at some time within the boundaries of Alberta are dealt with in the text. No other species are included. A check-list of species and subspecies is appended. This is a complete list of all species and subspecies known to occur, or to have occurred, in Alberta. It is based upon existing specimens taken in the province or, in a few cases, upon reliable photographic evidence. Where no such proof exists of the occurrence of a species in Alberta but sight records have been made, the name of the species has been placed on the hypothetical list. Since 1958 when the first check-list was published in this book, ten species have been added to the list of birds of Alberta only three of which had previously appeared on the hypothetical list.

STRUCTURE of BIRDS

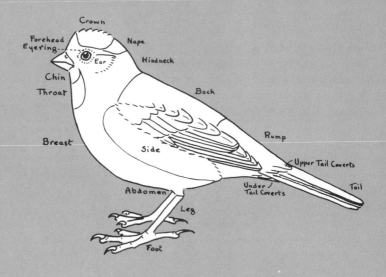

Crown
Forehead
Eyering
Ear
Nape
Hindneck
Chin
Throat
Back
Breast
Rump
Side
Upper Tail Coverts
Under Tail Coverts
Tail
Abdomen
Leg
Foot

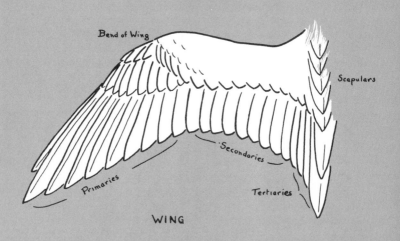

Bend of Wing
Scapulars
Secondaries
Primaries
Tertiaries

WING

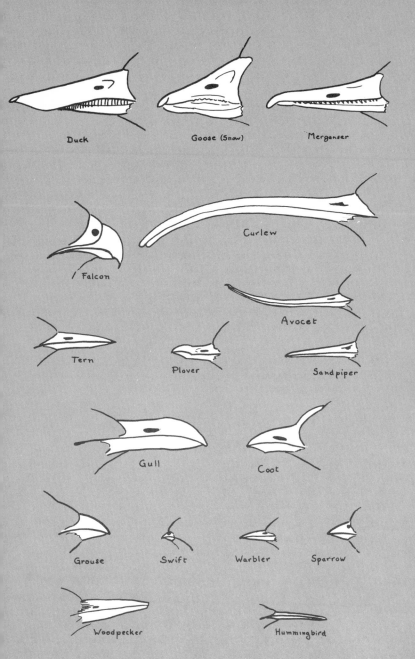

Duck

Goose (Snow)

Merganser

Falcon

Curlew

Tern

Avocet

Plover

Sandpiper

Gull

Coot

Grouse

Swift

Warbler

Sparrow

Woodpecker

Hummingbird

BEAKS

13

THE SECOND EDITION

T HE reception given to the first edition of "The Birds of Alberta" was taken as an indication that its aims were valid and that, in some measure, they had been achieved. In preparing this revised edition I have again kept these aims in mind. The text is still directed to the layman rather than to the scientist.

The revisions have been made from records contributed by a great many correspondents in all parts of the province, from articles published in ornithological journals, from the observations of members of the Edmonton Bird Club and the Calgary Bird Club, and from my own observations and records. New illustrations have been contributed by photographers and artists whose only reward is the satisfaction of having their work appreciated. Without the cooperation of these public-minded individuals the revision of this book would have been an impossible task. I have already expressed my gratitude for this cooperation; the future of this book will be heavily dependent upon its continuance and expansion. Any material sent to the author for use in "The Birds of Alberta" will be acknowledged with thanks and preserved for future reference, or, if requested, returned to the sender.

W. Ray Salt

Department of Anatomy
University of Alberta,
Edmonton, Alberta.

the
Birds of Alberta

An Account of all Species
of Birds Which Have Been
Found to Occur in Alberta

INDEX BY FAMILIES

(Complete Index—Pages 502-511)

COMMON LOON

WM. I. CAMPBELL

ARCTIC LOON

C. HAMPSON

17

LOONS — Family Gaviidae

Loons are heavy-bodied water birds with strong pointed beaks and short stiff tails. Only the last joint of the leg is free from the body and this is attached near the tail. Loons, therefore, move with great difficulty on the ground but are expert swimmers and divers. They usually sit low in the water; when alarmed they can completely submerge their bodies, leaving only the head above surface.

COMMON LOON
Gavia immer

Common Summer Resident.
Length 29-32 in.

DESCRIPTION: Breeding ads.—Head and neck glossy black, a few thin vertical white stripes on the lower throat, and a series of similar stripes forming an almost complete ring around the lower neck; back, wings and sides black with white spots and streaks, those on the back forming orderly rows of white squares; underparts white; beak and legs black; iris red. Winter ads. and im.—head and neck dark gray; throat, dirty white; back, wings and sides dark gray, some feathers edged with ashy-gray; underparts white; iris brown.

IDENTIFICATION: A large diving bird with heavy pointed beak, neck as thick as the head, and legs set close to the short tail; larger than the arctic loon and with all-black head.

RANGE: Northern part of northern hemisphere. Breeds throughout northern States and Canada. Winters as far north as open water may be found.

NESTING: On muskrat house or floating debris over water, or on ground near edge of water. Nest may be a mere depression in the ground but is often built up of aquatic vegetation. Eggs, 2, olive-brown sparsely spotted with black. (Belvedere, June 6.)

REMARKS: Although it formerly nested at most of the deep-water lakes of Alberta the common loon has gradually retreated before the advance of settlement until it now nests commonly only in the northern half of the province. The species also nests in small numbers in the mountains, particularly in the National Parks. On the prairies and in the parklands common loons occur mainly on migration.

On stormy nights migrating loons occasionally become so exhausted or confused that they come down on land. These birds face certain death for loons can take wing only from water and even there only after a long pattering take-off run. Water is their element. On the surface they move with ease and grace; beneath it they can outmanoeuvre a fish. In May common loons seek out for their nesting territory a quiet lake with an inaccessible bit of wooded shoreline or preferably a secluded island. At this season they become quite vocal. Their weird laughing calls echoing across the lake are wilderness music to some ears; to others they are crazy as a loon.

LOONS — Family Gaviidae

ARCTIC LOON   Scarce Transient.
Gavia arctica subsp. (p. 487)   Length 24 in.

DESCRIPTION: Breeding ads.—Crown and hindneck pearl gray, darker in female, throat and foreneck black, series of fine white streaks on lower throat and along sides of neck; back, wings and sides black with white marks, those of the back forming rows of white squares; breast and abdomen white; legs and beak black. Winter ads.—Similar to above but head and neck white to pale gray, lightest on throat and crown; back plain dull black. Im.—Like winter adults but some feathers of back with gray tips giving 'scaly' appearance.

IDENTIFICATION: Size will distinguish the arctic loon from the common loon. In immature and winter plumage arctic and red-throated loons are difficult to separate in the field. Arctic loons have a heavier beak and their backs are either plain black or slightly 'scaly'.

NESTING: Similar to that of the common loon.

RANGE: Northern parts of northern hemisphere. In western Canada breeds from the arctic south to about the sixtieth parallel of latitude. Winters on open waters of both coasts.

REMARKS: The arctic loon has been recorded in Alberta on only a few occasions. There is a single old record of nesting on Lake Athabasca east of Fort Chipewyan and there are sight records of the species in Wood Buffalo Park during the nesting season. Arctic loons probably move over northwestern Alberta on their migrations between the Pacific coast and their arctic nesting grounds. They could be expected to rest on some of the lakes of these regions before or after flights across the mountains. During the spring migration adults in their striking breeding plumage should be readily identified but in the fall arctic and red-throated loons are difficult to separate. At a distance the shape of the beak is about the best single feature. Observers in northern Alberta should check migrating loons carefully.

Although clumsy on land and ungainly in the air, arctic loons swim gracefully and dive expertly. Under water their feet normally propel them but when extra speed is required the wings are also used. While nesting arctic loons are not gregarious. On small northern lakes not more than one pair builds a nest; on large lakes their nesting territories are widely separated. For a short period during the summer the adults are flightless since they moult all of their primaries at the same time but by the time the young are fledged all are ready for the westward migration to the Pacific coast. The journey is made in stages with numerous stops on lakes and rivers for rest and feeding.

19

RED-THROATED LOON

RED-NECKED GREBE

LOONS — Family Gaviidae

RED-THROATED LOON   Scarce Transient.
Gavia stellata   Length 25 in.

DESCRIPTION: Breeding ads.—Head and neck soft slate-gray; an irregular series of black and white streaks on hindneck and a triangular patch of chestnut-red on foreneck; back, wings and sides dark gray with few faint light marks; breast and abdomen white; legs and beak black. Winter ads. and im.—Similar to above but head and neck dirty white to pale gray lightest on crown and throat; red patch lacking; fine white marks on back, largest on scapulars and wing coverts.

IDENTIFICATION: Likely to be confused with arctic loon only in fall and winter when red-throated loons have light spots on the back instead of the plain black or 'scaly' backs of arctic loons. At a distance the beak appears to be slightly upturned.

NESTING: Similar to that of other loons.

RANGE: Northern parts of northern hemisphere. In Canada breeds from arctic south to about the sixtieth parallel of latitude. Winters on open waters of both coasts.

REMARKS: In the spring of 1951 a flock of about 500 red-throated loons were seen on Bear Lake near Grande Prairie shortly after the ice had left the lake. These migrants were on their way to their nesting grounds to the north and northeast. Red-throated loons have been seen on several northern Alberta lakes in remote districts but whether they remain to nest has not yet been ascertained. This loon does not require such a long take-off run as the preceding species and hence it may nest on smaller ponds. In the late fall red-throated loons migrate over northern Alberta on their way to their wintering grounds on the Pacific coast. The species has been seen or collected as far south as the Edmonton area.

Except during the breeding season red-throated loons are gregarious birds usually found in flocks on coastal waters. On migration they may congregate for brief periods on any open waters along their route. During the summer, in the arctic, each pair occupies a small fresh-water lake or pond on which no other loons are allowed to intrude. However, even at this season, many pairs may gather on larger bodies of water which are used as common feeding grounds. Red-throated loons fly readily and rise from the water more easily than common loons. In flight they have the typical loon outline, the head and neck held lower than the body and the feet held well out behind to serve as a rudder. They invariably alight on the water and swim to the nest. On the land they move with great difficulty; their longest trip, fortunately, is the few inches from the edge of the water to their eggs.

21

GREBES — Family Colymbidae

In general appearance grebes are similar to loons but they are smaller and have no recognizable tail. The feet are not webbed but each toe bears a long flat lobe. Their pointed beaks separate them from the ducks. Like the loons, grebes are expert divers and can submerge their bodies at will. This ability has earned them the name of hell-divers.

RED-NECKED (HOLBOELL'S) GREBE　　　　Common Summer Resident.
Podiceps grisegena　subsp. (p. 487)　　　　　　　Length 19 in.

DESCRIPTION: Breeding ads.—Crown black, long feathers forming a puffy crest over each ear; hindneck, back and wings brownish-black, except secondaries which are white forming a white patch seen only in flight; throat and cheeks silvery-gray; foreneck and upper breast reddish-brown; abdomen grayish-white. Winter ads.— Crown dull black, crests reduced; throat and cheeks whitish; neck and upper breast gray; otherwise similar to above. Im.—Similar to winter adults but usually with dark and light stripes on sides of head, and showing a trace of brown on neck.

IDENTIFICATION: In any plumage separated from the western grebe by colored instead of white foreneck.

RANGE: Temperate and northern parts of northern hemisphere. In Canada breeds mainly from Manitoba westward, and north to arctic circle. Winters in coastal waters.

NESTING: In or near reedbeds on borders of lakes, usually over water. Nest a floating mass of reeds and water weeds anchored to aquatic vegetation. Eggs, 4-6, chalky white when laid but soon discolored. (Pine Lake, June 3.)

REMARKS: The red-necked, or Holboell's, grebe nests commonly on suitable lakes throughout Alberta, but only rarely in the mountains. The only mountain nesting record is that of a pair of red-necked grebes which had frequented the Vermilion Lakes near Banff for several years before their nest was discovered in 1965. On migration red-necked grebes may occur anywhere in the province. They usually migrate at night spending the daylight hours resting and feeding on any open body of water. Towards evening they patter along the surface for some distance before becoming airborne and then, on short, rapidly beating wings which look too weak to carry them over the mountains, they disappear into the twilight.

Holboell's grebe is the commonest diving bird on the larger lakes of central and northern Alberta. At such resorts as Sylvan, Gull, and Pigeon Lakes its raucous notes are well known to many people who may never have identified their source. Although the downy young are excellent swimmers and divers they often climb on the back of a parent for a rest or a ride. The young are fed on insects, crustaceans, and small fish, and it is perhaps only just that many of them in turn fall prey to large fish.

GREBES — Family Colymbidae

HORNED GREBE
Podiceps auritus subsp. (p. 487)

Fairly Common Summer Resident.
Length 13.5 in.

DESCRIPTION: Breeding ads.—Head black, dense feathers behind cheeks forming a 'ruff' and long, buffy feathers on sides of crown erectile to produce 'horns'; hindneck, back and wings brownish-gray except secondaries which are white; foreneck and sides chestnut; chest and abdomen white; beak black. Winter ads. and im.— Similar but lacking horns, ruffs, and chestnut sides and neck; throat, cheeks, and foreneck white to pale gray.

IDENTIFICATION: In spring and summer separated from eared grebe by buffy horns, puffed-out head, and reddish foreneck; in other seasons the two species are almost indistinguishable. The horned grebe may be identified by its shorter, stouter beak.

RANGE: Northern parts of northern hemisphere. Breeds across North America from northern states to the arctic. Winters mainly in southern states and on Pacific coast as far north as Alaska.

NESTING: Solitary, in reedy sloughs or lakes. Nest a floating mass of wet decaying vegetation anchored to reeds. Eggs, 5-7, bluish-white but soon discolored. (Calgary, May 22.)

REMARKS: The small prairie sloughs of the southern part of the province often support a pair of horned grebes, the weedy margin giving cover for the nest and the aquatic animal life providing food for the family. On larger bodies of water several pairs of horned grebes may nest at widely scattered points; they never form colonies as do eared grebes. When the nest is approached the female usually swims away but she may return toward the intruder erecting the horns and ruffs, lifting the body erect, and pattering along the water on rapidly moving feet. This display is similar to the courtship dance performed by mated pairs in unison earlier in the season.

Grebes are truly aquatic birds. They do not fly with ease and they can barely move on land for their legs are attached at the very end of their bodies. Once they are established on their nesting territories, therefore, horned grebes rarely leave the water. Their eggs are hatched in a floating nest and their ungainly downy youngsters are at home in and under the water from the very day they hatch. But later, as days shorten and temperatures drop, horned grebes exercise their wings with short evening flights. Usually before ice forms on the home pond they have flown to a larger lake. From here they start on the first lap of their migratory journey across the mountains.

Horned grebes nest locally throughout Alberta but breeding records for the mountain regions are few. Nests have been found in the foothills near Priddis, Cochrane and Entrance and horned grebes have been seen during the nesting season in the Banff and Barrier Lake areas.

EARED GREBE
Podiceps caspicus subsp. (p. 487)

Fairly Common Summer Resident.
Length 13 in.

DESCRIPTION: Breeding ads.—Head and neck black, feathers of crown forming a crest, a group of long, fine, yellow-brown feathers radiating from behind the eye over the cheeks; back and wings gray-black except secondaries which are white; breast and abdomen white; sides mixed gray and chestnut; beak black, slender. Winter ads. and im.—Similar but grayer and lacking 'ears' and chestnut sides; throat, cheeks and foreneck white to light gray.

IDENTIFICATION: In fall may be confused with horned grebe, but identified by longer, more slender beak which appears slightly upturned.

RANGE: Temperate parts of northern hemisphere. Breeds from Manitoba westward and in northwestern States. Winters on Pacific coast from Washington south.

NESTING: In loose colonies in large reedy sloughs or lakes. Nest a floating mass of water-soaked vegetation anchored to reeds. Eggs, 4-5, white but soon discolored. (Calgary, June 2.)

REMARKS: During the nesting season eared grebes become gregarious and show preference for the reedy margins of fairly large bodies of water. The size of the nesting colonies varies; in a shallow slough near Calgary about 100 birds built some 40-50 nests, but at Fairmont Lake in the Peace River district a colony estimated to contain 3,000 eared grebes had built over 1,200 nests and laid about 5,000 eggs. The birds rarely leave the water from the time they arrive at the nesting site until they leave in the fall. When alarmed they dive and take refuge in the reeds or, if caught in the open, they remain submerged with only the crown and nostrils above water. Such miraculous disappearances, common to all species of grebes, have earned for them the name hell-divers.

A nesting colony of eared grebes is usually quite accessible since the nests float on water only a foot or so deep. The birds slip off the nests when approached and form a protesting group on the open water of the slough. They will not return until the intruder has left. So frail are the nests that they barely support the incubating birds and they tip precariously as the grebes climb off or onto them. Although the eggs are often wet they hatch well. Downy grebes swim and dive readily a few hours after hatching. Among the reeds and water weeds they find adequate protective cover and plenty of insects, crustaceans and tadpoles for food.

HORNED GREBE
on nest

EARED GREBE

WESTERN GREBE
Aechmophorus occidentalis

Fairly Common Summer Resident.
Length 26 in.

DESCRIPTION: Ads.—Crown, hindneck, back, wings and sides grayish-black to black, feathers over ears forming two slight crests; secondaries pale gray forming light patch on opened wing; throat, cheeks, foreneck, breast and abdomen white; beak black, 3 in. long; legs black; iris red. Im.—Similar but slightly paler.

IDENTIFICATION: A large black and white grebe with very long neck and beak; swan-like on the water. Separated from red-necked grebe in autumn plumage by longer neck and longer, finer beak.

RANGE: Western North America. Breeds from prairie provinces and B.C. south to Minnesota and California. Winters mainly along coast from southern B.C. to Mexico.

NESTING: In colonies in reed-beds of larger lakes. Nest similar to that of other grebes. Eggs, 3-5, dull white but soon discolored. (Miquelon Lake, June 9.)

REMARKS: Of all species of grebes the western grebe has suffered most from the advance of civilization in Alberta; most of the large lakes formerly frequented by nesting colonies are now popular vacation resorts, and unlike the red-necked grebe, the western grebe appears to be unable to adjust itself to the disturbance of the reveller and his motor-boat. Today, nesting colonies are found only in quiet spots on the more remote lakes; western grebes are seen elsewhere mainly during migration periods. Flying south by night in the fall they sometimes land on a wet highway or a frozen slough, mistaking it for open water. Here they are doomed, for their legs are not built for walking and their short wings will lift them into the air only after a long take-off run.

Western grebes are gregarious birds. A large nesting colony may number in the hundreds with nests located only three or four feet apart but it is doubtful if colonies of this size exist in Alberta today. The young are precocious. Within a few hours of hatching they are able to swim and dive although they are fond of riding on the backs of their parents. They also have the peculiar grebe ability to change their buoyance which allows them to sink beneath the surface without actively diving.

The breast feathers of grebes and loons are tightly overlapped forming a warm waterproof covering. Before protective laws stopped the practice, grebes and loons were killed for the skin of the breast which was tanned with the feathers attached and made into collars, neck-pieces, and even blankets. Some fine examples of handwork in this medium are still in existence in Alberta.

GREBES — Family Colymbidae

PIED-BILLED GREBE Scarce Summer Resident.
Podilymbus podiceps subsp. (p. 487) Length 13 in.

DESCRIPTION: Breeding ads.—Head, neck, back and wings brownish-black or grayish-black, darkest on crown; throat jet black; secondaries edged with white but not enough to form a white patch in flight; breast and abdomen silvery white mottled with dusky-brown, most strongly on sides; beak short and stout, bluish-white with black band near tip; legs dark gray; iris brown. Winter ads. and im.—Similar but lacking black throat and band around beak; over-all color much browner becoming reddish-brown on lower neck and sides.

IDENTIFICATION: A small grebe with short, thick, blunt beak; head appears somewhat flattened; more indication of tail than in any other species of grebe.

RANGE: North and South America. Breeds throughout its range. Winters mainly in southern states and on Pacific coast north as far as B.C.

NESTING: Solitary, in reeds on water. Nest similar to that of other grebes. Eggs, 6-8, greenish-white but soon buffy by discoloration. (Belvedere, June 8.)

REMARKS: The pied-billed grebe is such a shy bird that it probably goes unnoticed much of the time. Recent observations indicate that it is more common in Alberta than was formerly believed. Even on migration it is rarely reported from the prairies but it has been found nesting in small numbers at lakes in the Brooks area and may nest at other prairie lakes where it has been seen during the summer. North and west of Edmonton, however, it breeds regularly if not commonly at least as far west as Entrance and north to Fairview and Lake Athabasca. It is rarely seen in the mountains. Recognition of its peculiar call, a series of guttural grunts and *khow - khow's,* is an aid to identification.

Pied-billed grebes often swim with their heads outstretched under the surface, apparently watching for food for which they can dive. At other times, especially when alarmed, they lower their bodies beneath the surface until only their heads remain above water. The head is then remarkably snake-like in appearance. This ability to disappear under water in a flash and apparently never to reappear has earned for them the name, hell-divers. When undisturbed pied-billed grebes act much like other grebes, swimming about among water-weeds and reeds and diving at intervals for the plant and animal matter which forms their food. The downy young swim with ease from the moment they are hatched but when attempting to dive they have difficulty in staying below the surface and keep bobbing up like corks.

C. HAMPSON

WESTERN GREBE

ALLAN BROOKS

PIED-BILLED GREBE
adult   *immature*

C. HAMPSON

WHITE PELICAN

C. HAMPSON

DOUBLE-CRESTED CORMORANT

29

PELICANS — Family Pelecanidae

Pelicans are very large aquatic birds most commonly found on sea-coasts or on large inland lakes. At all seasons they are communal in nature, and almost sheep-like in behavior. Although weighing as much as 16 lbs. they are as graceful in the air as in the water. The beak is much longer than the head. The most unusual structural feature, however, is a large distensible sac of colored skin extending between the mandibles and well back on to the throat.

WHITE PELICAN
Pelecanus erythrorhynchos

Scarce Summer Resident.
Length about 65 in.

DESCRIPTION: Ads. — Plumage pure white except primaries and outer secondaries which are black; often with a yellowish cast over the white; beak yellow, very long and somewhat flattened, with a horny crest half way to tip during breeding season; a yellow pouch along under surface of beak extending on to throat; legs orange; iris white. Im.—Similar to adults but with some gray feathers on head and back; iris brown.

IDENTIFICATION: Differs from swan in having shorter neck, very long beak, and black wing tips. Shows color pattern of whooping crane and snow goose in flight but may be identified by habit of carrying head back on shoulders as do the herons.

RANGE: Temperate North America. In Canada breeds mainly in prairie provinces and north to Great Slave Lake. Winters along coasts of Mexico, California and states bordering Gulf of Mexico.

NESTING: In colonies on islands in large lakes or rivers. Nest, a depression in the ground which may or may not be lined with sticks, rushes and grass. Eggs, 2-4, chalky white.

REMARKS: In 1789 when Alexander Mackenzie passed through northern Alberta on a trip which ultimately took him to the arctic he found a colony of white pelicans on an island in the Slave River above Fort Smith. Descendants of this group nest on the same island today. At the turn of the century nesting colonies of white pelicans could be found at many lakes in central Alberta including Lac Ste. Anne, Oliver, Miquelon and Buffalo Lakes. None of these exist today. Happily, white pelicans have established new nesting colonies at other lakes mainly north of Edmonton where local interest in conservation has guarded them against human depredation.

The pelican uses the pouch as a scoop to catch small aquatic animals such as crustaceans, frogs and fish. After a catch the water is squeezed out at the sides of the beak while the food is retained and swallowed. Later, partially digested food may be regurgitated into the pouch as food for the young.

CORMORANTS — Family Phalacrocoracidae

Cormorants are large aquatic birds with long sinuous necks and fairly long tails. Their slender beaks are strongly hooked and show no external nostrils. There is a small gular pouch. All four toes of the foot are joined by webs. Cormorants are gregarious birds. They spend much of their time perched upon rocks or in shore-line trees, occasionally diving into the water to capture a fish by pursuit.

DOUBLE-CRESTED CORMORANT   Scarce Summer Resident.
Phalacrocorax auritus subsp. (p. 487)   Length 36 in.

DESCRIPTION: Ads.—Entirely black, a greenish tinge over head, neck and underparts, brownish tinge elsewhere; in breeding season a crest on each side of the crown; bare skin of throat pouch and around eye yellow-orange; beak dark gray with yellow mottling; legs black; iris pale green. Im.—-Similar but no greenish tinge, instead head, neck and underparts brownish, remainder gray-black; no crests until second spring when they first breed.

IDENTIFICATION: With long tail, long neck, and hooked beak, not likely to be confused with any other species; in the hand the union of all four toes by three webs is distinctive.

RANGE: North America. Breeds across Canada north to sub-arctic. Winters along both coasts.

NESTING: In colonies on rocks or cliffs of islands or shores; occasionally in trees. Nest a bulky mass of sticks and rushes lined with coarse grass. Eggs rough; bluish-white; variable in number but most commonly 4-5. (Lake Newell, June 10.)

REMARKS: Few colonies of double-crested cormorants nest in Alberta today. Cormorants nested at Buffalo, Ministik, and Miquelon Lakes, and at Lac la Biche early in the century but the colonies have disappeared. At Miquelon Lake the cormorants left the island when the pelicans deserted it in 1909, but continued to nest in spruce trees along the shore until 1937. Cormorants still seen in summer on Lac la Biche, Cold Lake, and Lesser Slave Lake are believed to nest in the vicinity. In the last few years a small colony of double-crested cormorants which had become established at Lake Newell appears to have been driven off by human interference.

Cormorants fly low over the water with strong steady wingbeats somewhat like the larger diving ducks. Usually however, they string out in a line one behind the other and their long tails give them an extended appearance which is characteristic. When swimming they are easily mistaken for loons. They dive either from the air or from the water often remaining below for several minutes in pursuit of the small aquatic animals which are their food.

GREAT BLUE HERON

SNOWY EGRET

HERONS, EGRETS, BITTERNS—Family Ardeidae

The members of this family are long-legged, long-necked, wading birds of considerable size. They are usually found in marshes or in the shallows edging large bodies of water, where they wade about with cautious tread ready to pick up an unwary fish or frog in their strong pointed beaks. In flight their long legs extend far beyond the tail but their necks are curled over the shoulders giving them a neckless appearance which readily distinguishes them from the cranes.

GREAT BLUE HERON   Fairly Common Summer Resident.
Ardea herodias subsp. (p. 487)   Length 36-42 in.

DESCRIPTION: Breeding ads.—Neck and legs very long; tail short; head mostly white, a black stripe extending back from eye into long black plumes; neck ashy brown with black streaks on under side; back, wings and tail bluish-gray; breast white streaked with black; abdomen black streaked with white; thighs chestnut. Im.—Similar but plumes lacking and overall markings less definite.

IDENTIFICATION: To be confused only with the sandhill crane. The light neck and black head-streak are good field marks. Flight outline (as above) is positive identification.

RANGE: North and Central America. Breeds from B.C. to Newfoundland, south to Mexico and Florida.

NESTING: In colonies in trees. The nest is a bulky mass of twigs and reeds placed near the top of a tree. Eggs, 4-5, pale blue (Lake Isle, June 15.)

REMARKS: During the past ten years many heronries in central Alberta have been deserted or destroyed. Water drainage, tree cutting and harassment of the nesting birds have been major factors in their disappearance. Heronries still exist at scattered points in Alberta as far north as Lake Athabasca but most are of small size. They deserve rigid protection. On migration great blue herons may occur throughout the province although they are seldom seen in the mountains. They do not migrate in flocks as do the cranes; rarely are more than two or three birds seen together at these times.

In the shallows near the lakeshore the great blue heron stalks with stately grace, his movements slow and deliberate. Suddenly he stops, his beak pointed to the water before him; then snake-like his neck shoots out to grasp a luckless frog or minnow. Often he stands motionless for minutes at a time apparently asleep yet always alert for any prey which may swim within his reach. When alarmed he takes flight with slow ponderous wing beats and loud guttural croaks. Surprisingly he may alight in a tree down the lake, somewhat awkwardly it is true but he probably feels at home for the first few weeks of his life were spent in trees.

33

HERONS, EGRETS, BITTERNS — Family Ardeidae

CATTLE EGRET
Bubulcus ibis

Accidental Wanderer.
Length 20 in.

SNOWY EGRET
Leucophoyx thula   subsp. (p. 487)

Accidental Wanderer.
Length 20-27 in.

COMMON EGRET
Casmerodius albus   subsp (p. 487)

Accidental Wanderer.
Length 37-42 in.

IDENTIFICATION: The cattle egret and the snowy egret are white, long-legged birds, about the size and build of a bittern, which are unlikely to be confused with any other ·species. The cattle egret has a yellow beak, yellow or greenish legs and feet. Adult cattle egrets may have buffy on head and back; immature cattle egrets have blackish legs with feet the same color. Breeding snowy egrets have fluffy plumes on head, upper breast and back, those on the back being very long and recurved.

The common egret is about the size and build of the great blue heron but has pure white plumage; legs and feet black; beak yellow; plumes on back and breast in breeding plumage. Might be mistaken for whooping crane but lacks black wing tips and red crown.

REMARKS: The cattle egret is a European species which first appeared in the United States in 1952 after previously showing up in South America. It is apparently an inveterate wanderer and has now spread widely in the Americas. On Nov. 12, 1964, a cattle egret was picked up alive near Iron Springs, Alberta. Despite attempts to keep it alive it died a few days later and was preserved as a specimen. This is the only record for the province; in fact it is the first known appearance of the species in western Canada.

The snowy egret is indigenous to North and South America, breeding from California, Utah and North Carolina south to Central and South America. Early in the century this species was in danger of extinction after many years of slaughter of breeding birds for their plumes. Today, under rigid protection thousands of snowy egrets nest in the bayous of the southern States. There are but two known records for Alberta. A specimen was collected in May, 1901, near Pincher Creek and another was collected at Sandy Lake in May, 1909. There are no recent records of the species in Alberta.

The common, or American, egret breeds from Oregon and North Carolina south to Patagonia. On May 6, 1954, a common egret was observed and photographed near Cowley. During the last week of August, 1954, a common egret was observed for several days at a lake about 15 miles northwest of Edmonton. This bird also was photographed. These are the only records of the species for Alberta.

HERONS, EGRETS, BITTERNS — Family Ardeidae

BLACK-CROWNED NIGHT HERON   Fairly Common Summer Resident.
Nycticorax nycticorax   subsp. (p. 487)   Length 23-28 in.

DESCRIPTION: Heron-like but shorter neck and legs. Breeding ads.—Crown and back black with greenish sheen; wings, rump and tail bluish-gray; forehead, face, neck and underparts grayish-white; narrow white plume extending from crown to back; iris red; beak black; legs yellow. Im.—Upper parts grayish-brown, darkest on crown and back, streaked with buffy on head and neck and spotted with white on back and wings; tail gray with rufous tip; underparts white or buffy white broadly streaked with grayish-brown; no plumes; iris yellow.

IDENTIFICATION: Adults are distinctive. Young black-crowned night herons resemble bitterns but are grayer, the bittern having richer browns and yellows and often showing black neck stripe.

RANGE: Almost cosmopolitan. In North America breeds from southern Canada, except B.C., south throughout United States.

NESTING: In colonies in trees near water or in rushes over water. Nest a platform of twigs or reeds. Eggs, 3-6, pale blue. (Tofield, June 9, 1959.)

REMARKS: Black-crowned night herons were first observed in Alberta near Strathmore during the summer of 1958. Since that time the species has been observed and specimens have been taken at various points as far north as Edmonton. A nesting colony of black-crowned night herons was discovered at Beaverhill Lake in 1959. The herons chose nesting sites in rushes over water in preference to the bushes which bordered the marsh. Nesting colonies have since been found near Strathmore, Brooks, Tilley and Iron Springs. It is probable that the above dates reflect fairly accurately the invasion and dispersion of this species in Alberta since it is unlikely that such a distinctive bird could long have escaped detection by the many competent observers in the province.

Extensive marshes overgrown with rushes and cattails are the haunts of black-crowned night herons. Here they wade in the shallow water from which most of their food is obtained or walk on tangled masses of stems. A rock, a fence-post or anything which protrudes above the surface is an acceptable perch for sunning on warm days. Quill-covered young, as repulsive in habits as in appearance, disgorge a partially digested meal of fish or frogs when disturbed and clamber off into the rushes. Mortality is very high for the parents apparently make no attempt to find their wandering offspring and give little enough protection to those which remain in the nest.

HERONS, EGRETS, BITTERNS — Family Ardeidae

AMERICAN BITTERN
Botaurus lentiginosus

Common Summer Resident.
Length 28 in.

DESCRIPTION: A heron-like bird but neck shorter and thicker, and legs shorter than in the true herons. Breeding ads.—above, mainly brownish-gray with brown and tawny streaks on hindneck and fine vermiculations of the same colors on back and wings; crown black with brown feather edgings; a blacker stripe from beak down side of neck; below, white grading to tawny on the abdomen, the whole broadly striped with brownish-gray feathers edged with black; iris small and yellow; beak yellowish; legs yellow-green. Im. and fall ads.—Similar but browner and lacking the black neck stripe.

IDENTIFICATION: Likely to be confused only with the immature black-crowned night heron. Bitterns have an overall buffy-brown appearance; young night herons are more grayish-brown. Both species in flight have slow floppy wing beat and head drawn back on shoulders.

RANGE: North America. Breeds from California and Florida north to the Arctic Circle. Winters in extreme south of its range but occasionally north on Pacific coast to British Columbia.

NESTING: Solitary, on the ground in or near marshes. Nest of grass and rushes often lined with feathers. Eggs, 3-7, buffy olive. (Chestermere Lake, May 28.)

REMARKS: Although the bittern is reasonably common in suitable habitat throughout Alberta, it is not very well known probably because its haunts are difficult of access to man. In the spring it betrays its presence in the marsh by a series of notes reminiscent of the noise made by an old-fashioned wooden water-pump—*pump-er-lunk, pump-er-lunk;* hence the names 'thunder-pump' and 'slough-pumper'. In the fall the duck hunter wading the marshes may be startled by a large bird which rises with a harsh *crawk* and flaps cumbrously away. When it drops again into the reeds it stands with neck extended and beak pointed to the sky, its colors and markings blending so perfectly with the dead reeds that only a keen eye will detect it. Insects, frogs, mice, fish, and any other small animal life of the marsh and its adjacent waters and fields are the food of the bittern. These it catches in typical heron fashion. Unlike the great blue heron, however, it rarely ventures into the open. Instead it prefers to skulk in the rushes and cattails stalking its prey slowly and deliberately or standing motionless until an unwary creature comes within range of the swift thrust of its beak.

Bitterns have been seen at Jasper, Entrance and Banff during the summer months but so far no nests have been found in the mountains.

BLACK-CROWNED NIGHT HERON

C. HAMPSON

ALLAN BROOKS

AMERICAN BITTERN

SWANS, GEESE, DUCKS — Family Anatidae

The members of this family are long-necked, short-tailed, aquatic birds. Their beaks have serrated edges which form a sieve allowing water to be strained from food. The feet are webbed. Except during the nesting season most species are quite gregarious, the migrating flocks often being spectacularly large. Many species are equally at home on land and water; the geese especially feed regularly on the uplands.

WHISTLING SWAN
Olor columbianus

Fairly Common Migrant.
Length up to 55 in.

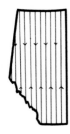

DESCRIPTION: Ads.—Large, long-necked birds weighing from 10 to 20 lbs. Plumage entirely white, occasionally a trace of rusty-orange on head and neck; tail of 20 feathers; beak black, bare skin extending back to eye, sometimes a yellow spot in front of eye; legs black. Im.—Similar but with ashy-gray wash over upper parts; head and neck light brownish-gray.

IDENTIFICATION: Large size, pure white plumage, extremely long neck, and short legs should identify as a swan on land or water. The two species of swans are inseparable in the field except by a skilful judge of size and voice. In flight, absence of black wing-tips separates the swans from any other species of comparable size.

RANGE: North America. Breeds on islands and coastal regions of arctic. Winters on both coasts of southern U.S.A. Migrates mostly through interior of continent.

NESTING: On the ground on the tundra. Nest of moss and grass lined with down. Eggs, 2-7, usually 4-5, white.

REMARKS: Whistling swans migrate in numbers through the province during April and October, stopping over at favorite sloughs and lakes for several days at a time. The spring migration is quite regular; observers in Calgary and Edmonton should have little difficulty in locating whistling swans within a few miles east of the cities around the middle of April. In flocks they fly to the surrounding fields to glean in the stubble or to tear up the green winter annuals. Little more than thirty years ago the sportsman could hunt them legally and their numbers were diminishing towards the point where the species was threatened. Today, protected at least in settled areas, they are on the increase.

Spring arrival of the swans can hardly go unnoticed. Their great white bodies, necks extended, gleam against a blue sky; their slowly beating pinions flash in the sun; and as they plane down to join some earlier migrants an exchange of bugled greetings echoes for miles across the lake. There is little in this deep harmonious clamor to justify the name whistling swan but once they have landed on the rotting ice or in open strips of water they change to conversational tones from which their name may have been derived.

SWANS, GEESE, DUCKS — Family Anatidae

TRUMPETER SWAN Scarce Summer Resident.
Olor buccinator Length about 65 in.

DESCRIPTION: Ads.—Very large, long-necked birds weighing up to 36 lbs. Color and general appearance same as whistling swan; tail of 24 feathers; nostril usually closer to eye than tip of beak. Im.—Similar to adult but many grayish feathers on back and wings and often a brownish tinge on head and neck.

IDENTIFICATION: Identified as a swan by large size, long neck, short legs and pure white color. There is no reliable way of separating the two species of swans in the field by sight alone.

RANGE: Formerly central and western North America. Today confined to a few localities in Alberta, B.C., and Wyoming. Winters mainly in the last two regions.

NESTING: On the ground on islands or on the shores of lakes and sloughs. Nest a large mound of rushes, reeds, roots and grass; depression lined with down. Eggs, usually 4-5, white. (Clairmont, June 10).

REMARKS: On the verge of extinction thirty years ago, the trumpeter swan is making a remarkably steady recovery in Canada under well-enforced protective laws. Thanks are due to the people of the Peace River District who have co-operated in protecting the trumpeter swans which nest in that area and have thus helped to preserve and increase one of the three major remnants of this threatened species. If this flock had not to endure the dangers of migration it would probably consist of more than the presently estimated 25 pairs. However, migration may result in the repopulation of other areas, for trumpeter swans have recently raised young successfully in the Cypress Hills. Swans which remain in central Alberta past the middle of May are probably trumpeter swans. If unmolested they may extend their breeding grounds more widely.

One usually associates the remnants of a threatened race with wilderness areas. It comes, therefore, as something of a surprise to find trumpeter swans nesting in northwestern Alberta near rather small bodies of water and often quite close to a farmyard. Incubating birds are usually conspicuous for their color and size make concealment difficult; fortunately both male and female guard the nest carefully and are more than a match for most predators. Greatest losses occur when the cygnets are quite small but a few are raised to maturity each year. Only a few hundred trumpeter swans remain in the world today; these require constant protection if the species is to be perpetuated.

WHISTLING SWAN

C. HAMPSON

S. MACDONALD

TRUMPETER SWAN

CANADA GOOSE

C. HAMPSON

WHITE-FRONTED GOOSE

KAY HODGES

41

CANADA GOOSE Fairly Common Summer Resident, Common Migrant.
Branta canadensis subsp. (p. 487) Length 24-39 in.

DESCRIPTION: Ads. and im.—Head and neck black with white cheek patches usually meeting across throat; back and wings grayish-brown with lighter feather edging; breast and sides light grayish-brown; abdomen and upper and lower tail coverts white; tail black; beak and legs black.

IDENTIFICATION: White cheek patches on black head and neck identify this goose at rest or in flight at all seasons.

RANGE: North America. Breeds from northern states to the arctic. Winters in southern part of range but occasionally north to southern B.C. and Alberta.

NESTING: On ground preferably on islands in lakes or rivers; occasionally in trees on deserted nests of other large birds. Nest a mass of reeds, grass, and leaves lined with down. Eggs, 4-7, creamy white. (Miquelon Lake, May 18.)

REMARKS: The subspecies of the Canada goose vary greatly in size, the smallest weighing about 4 lbs., and the largest up to 17 lbs., but the average of those found in the sportsman's bag is probably between 7 and 8 lbs. Although hunters prize this goose above all waterfowl, the species is holding its own against present hunting pressure. As long as game regulations are based upon sound principles of game management the existence of a species should never be threatened by the sportsman.

While the goose is incubating the gander remains on guard in the vicinity of the nest and vigorously defends it when necessary. A blow from the bend of his wing is sufficient to discourage all but the largest marauders. From observation of Canada geese in captivity it is believed that the birds mate for life. In the fall, flocks of northern and locally raised Canada geese make regular morning and evening flights from the lakes to the stubble fields, feeding in the same spot for several days if unmolested. After a time they mount high in the sky and in V-formation move southward a few hundred miles to settle in another favorable location for a few days. Thus they migrate. Small numbers of Canada geese winter regularly on the open waters of the Bow River near Calgary, their survival in severe winters being dependent upon the kindness of a few citizens. Some of the geese remain to nest in the area.

BRANT—See page 45.

SWANS, GEESE, DUCKS — Family Anatidae

WHITE-FRONTED GOOSE
Anser albifrons subsp. (p. 487)

Fairly Common Migrant.
Length 27 in.

DESCRIPTION: Ad.—Head, neck, back and wings grayish-brown, darkest on lower back; white band around face at base of beak from which its name is derived; breast and abdomen light grayish-brown with transverse blotches of black and white, giving rise to the local name specklebelly; upper and lower tail coverts white; tail brownish-black; beak pink with yellow edges; legs yellow-orange. Im.—Similar but lacking the white face and the black marks on the abdomen which is grayish-white.

IDENTIFICATION: A gray goose without black head and neck. If seen, the orange legs are a good identification mark.

RANGE: Northern hemisphere. In Canada breeds in arctic from eastern Mackenzie to Yukon. Winters mainly in southern states from Mississippi to California.

NESTING: On the ground on the tundra. Nest similar to that of other geese. Eggs, 4-7, creamy-white.

REMARKS: Apparently white-fronted geese rarely migrated through Alberta until about thirty years ago, for prior to that time they were seldom shot by goose hunters. Today these gray geese with yellowish legs often form an appreciable part of the hunter's bag and though rarely weighing over 6 lbs. they are a fine addition to the table.

White-fronted geese are most commonly seen in relatively small flocks which often associate loosely with other species of geese. During the spring migration a few flocks of from half a dozen to half a hundred white-fronts are usually found among the thousands of lesser snow geese which stop over at Beaverhill Lake in April. As the flocks pass noisily overhead on their way to the feeding grounds the white-fronts are easily distinguished from the snows by both color and voice; from Canada geese they are not so easily separated. In this area four species of geese may be found feeding together in the same field, each species however, keeping its own company within the large flock. White-fronted geese, like Ross' geese, form only a small part of this aggregation but they form interesting objects of study during this period when they are not alarmed by the hunter's gun.

For a species whose numbers are not great the white-front bears a surprising number of vernacular names including speckle-belly, wavey and gray wavey. The last two names are believed to be a corruption of the Indians' interpretation of its call, a high-pitched, rapidly-repeated *wa-wa*.

43

SNOW GOOSE

BLUE GOOSE

SWANS, GEESE, DUCKS — Family Anatidae

BRANT
Branta bernicla subsp. (p. 487)

Scarce Migrant.
Length 23-26 in.

BLACK BRANT
Branta nigricans

DESCRIPTION: Ads.—Head, neck and upper breast black with partial collar of white streaks around neck; back and wings brownish-gray; underparts pale gray becoming white towards tail; flanks and rump white; tail black; beak and legs black. The black brant has much darker underparts. Im.—Similar but the white collar reduced or lacking and many pale feather edgings on back and wings. IDENTIFICATION: A small, dark goose with white 'necklace'. The black of the upper breast forms a sharp line of contrast with the pale lower breast in the common brant; in the black brant the black of the underparts fades gradually towards the tail leaving no sharp line of contrast.

RANGE: Europe and North America. The common brant breeds in arctic regions of eastern North America and Europe. Black brant breeds in arctic regions of western North America.

NESTING: On the ground on the tundra. Eggs, 2-6, white.

REMARKS: There are only three records of brant in Alberta. A brant was shot from a small flock near Grande Prairie on Oct. 7, 1957. On Oct. 18, 1959 a brant was photographed near Jasper. A specimen was shot at Cooking Lake on Sept. 24, 1960. The last two were lone birds. Of these three brant one appears to be a common brant, one a black brant and one an intermediate form.

BRANT

C. HAMPSON

45

SNOW GOOSE
Chen hyperborea subsp. (p. 487)

Common Migrant.
Length 27 in.

DESCRIPTION: Ads.—Entirely white except primaries which are black, often with rusty marks on head and neck; beak deep pink, serrated edges black giving appearance of a grin; legs purplish-red. Im.—Similar but with a wash of light blue-gray over back and wings.

IDENTIFICATION: White plumage with black wing-tips separates this from all other species except whooping crane, white pelican and Ross' goose. At rest and in flight short legs distinguish it from the crane. From the pelican distinguished by its short beak and outstretched neck in flight. Impossible to separate from Ross' goose in the field unless both species are together for comparison of size.

RANGE: North America and northeastern Asia. Breeds in arctic from Baffin Island west to Alaska. Winters in southern states from California to Florida.

NESTING: On the ground on the tundra. Nest similar to that of other geese. Eggs, 4-7, creamy-white.

REMARKS: There is no more beautiful sight in nature than that of thousands of snow geese strung out in skeins against the spring sky, or settling like a white cloud on golden stubble. Nor could the changing seasons be more fittingly heralded than by the wild high-pitched gabble of the migrating flocks. Each year in April they move slowly through the province stopping over for days at a time on favorite lakes at which their arrival may be predicted almost to the day. In September the migration is less predictable; the flocks are smaller and more widely scattered, but they move south in the same leisurely fashion.

During the summer lesser snow geese graze on the grasses and lichens of the tundra. On migration they commonly feed in the grain fields. Yet even there, their preference for green vegetation can be attested by the disgruntled hunter who has downed a 5 lb. prize, only to find it reeking with the taste and odor of stinkweed.

Like other geese, lesser snow geese undergo a summer moult in which so many of the flight feathers are lost simultaneously that the birds cannot fly. At this time they remain on water as much as possible, hiding when danger threatens. However, they are by no means helpless on land for they can easily outrun a man.

The snow goose and the blue goose are probably conspecific. They are identical in size and conformation. They are usually found together as they migrate through Manitoba and hybridization is known to occur on their breeding grounds in the arctic.

SWANS, GEESE, DUCKS — Family Anatidae

BLUE GOOSE
Chen caerulescens

Scarce Migrant.
Length 27 in.

DESCRIPTION: Ads.—Head and upper neck white; lower neck, breast, sides and back grayish-brown; wings and rump blue-gray; abdomen and tail white; beak dark pink with black 'grinning' mark; legs purplish-red. Im.— Chin white; remainder of head, neck, back and wings sooty-gray with brown feather edging; underparts dusky gray, lightest on abdomen; beak grayish-black; legs dark gray to pinkish-gray.

IDENTIFICATION: White head and neck and gray body of adults is distinctive. Immatures of blue and white-fronted geese are not readily separable in the field; in the hand, the beak of this species shows 'grinning' mark and the legs are never yellowish.

RANGE: Interior North America. Breeds on Baffin Island, mouth of Hudson Bay, and adjacent islands. Winters mainly on Gulf coast marshes of Louisiana.

REMARKS: Blue geese migrate along a narrow flyway through Manitoba and the Mississippi valley. There is apparently very little deviation from this route for the species has been seen in Alberta on very few occasions. During the fall migration blue geese are occasionally seen in the Hanna district and in September, 1956, a specimen was collected. Others have been observed at Cooking Lake, Beaverhill Lake, and in the Lake Athabasca region.

ROSS' GOOSE
Chen rossii

Scarce Migrant.
Length 21-25 in.

DESCRIPTION: Like a small snow goose. In all plumages Ross' goose and the snow goose are identical in color. The beak of Ross' goose lacks a 'grinning' patch and in the adult is covered with small excrescences at the base.

IDENTIFICATION: Inseparable from the snow goose in the fields except by size and voice. The feather line on the sides of the beak is straight and recedes towards the crown; in the snow goose this line forms a strong forward curve.

RANGE: Breeds in a restricted area of the arctic coast from Perry River to Banks Island. Winters in California. Migrates along narrow flyway between these two regions.

REMARKS: The smallest of our geese is also the rarest. Only a few thousand Ross' geese, all that remain of the species, migrate through Alberta and the other prairie provinces each year. Though protected by law many are shot by hunters who do not recognize them even in their bag. Discovery of their resting places along the migration route and restriction of shooting in these areas is reducing hunting pressure on the species.

SURFACE-FEEDING DUCKS — Family Anatidae
(Description on page 50)

MALLARD Common Summer Resident.
Anas platyrhynchos subsp. (p. 487) Length 21-24 in.

DESCRIPTION: Ad.m. — Head and upper neck iridescent green separated by white ring from chestnut lower neck and breast; back and wings brownish-gray; speculum iridescent purple bordered front and back by an inner band of black and an outer band of white; underparts and sides light gray; tail-feathers gray with white borders; upper and under tail coverts black. In eclipse plumage similar to female. Ad. f.—Upperparts brown streaked with black, most heavily on crown and back; wings as in male; throat and foreneck buffy; lower neck and sides buffy-brown with dark feather centers; underparts buffy-gray indistinctly spotted with gray-brown. Im.—Like female. Legs orange-red in all plumages.

IDENTIFICATION: The breeding male is unmistakable. In other plumages large size, purple speculum, and orange legs will identify. In the field the white under-surface of the wings and the white borders of the speculum show well.

RANGE: The northern hemisphere. Breeds throughout North America except in southeastern states. Winters from southern Canada to Panama.

NESTING: On the ground often far from water. Nest of grass and leaves lined with down. Eggs, 8-12, buffy-green. (Lethbridge, May 8.)

REMARKS: Mallards arrive early in the spring and by mid-April they have spread throughout the province even into the mountains. Families are raised on any bodies of water, large or small, except fast-moving streams. Mallards show preference, however, for grassy prairie sloughs.

While the duck is performing the family duties the drake withdraws to some secluded marsh to loaf with others of his sex and to moult. Like all species of ducks mallards moult twice a year. In early summer the males lose their bright breeding coat and assume a duller garb similar to that of the female. This eclipse plumage is worn until late fall when, after a second moult, the colorful breeding plumage again appears.

In the fall large flocks of mallards make regular morning and evening flights into the grain fields, becoming a problem of some importance to the farmer whose fields they invade. They remain long after freeze-up keeping open a hole in a large lake, and, unless a storm sets them on their way, many seem to lose the migratory urge and settle down to stay the winter. Mortality is high among such flocks unless their wintering spot is particularly favorable. Ducks which winter on the Bow river near Calgary survive reasonably well.

ROSS' GOOSE

MALLARDS

49

SURFACE-FEEDING DUCKS — Family Anatidae

Surface-feeding ducks frequent grassy sloughs, marshes, and the shallow margins of lakes where they can reach the bottom by tipping-up rather than by diving. Many species feed regularly on land. They spring into flight with ease from either land or water. Bristles on the borders of the beak enable them to strain excess water from the food. Brightly colored secondaries form an area on the wing, called the speculum, which is an excellent aid in identification of species.

BLACK DUCK Scarce Summer Resident.
Anas rubripes Length 21-24 in.

DESCRIPTION: Ads.—Crown black lightly streaked with buff; remainder of head and neck buff streaked with dull black; upperparts blackish-brown, each feather with light edges; speculum iridescent purple bordered front and back with black; under surface of wings creamy-white; underparts sooty-brown, the feathers edged with buff more heavily on lower breast and abdomen; legs orange-red. Sexes alike. Im.—Similar to adults but lighter below with much dark streaking.

IDENTIFICATION: Like a very dark female mallard but the speculum bordered broadly with black only. In the field shows no white except on under surfaces of wings.

RANGE: Eastern North America. Breeds from northern states to northern Manitoba and Quebec. Winters mainly on Atlantic coast and in eastern states.

NESTING: On the ground often some distance from water. Nest of grass and reeds lined with down. Eggs, 8-12, buffy-green.

REMARKS: The black duck replaces the mallard in eastern Canada. It is scarce west of Manitoba but in recent years there have been increasingly frequent reports of its appearance in Saskatchewan and Alberta. A specimen was taken at Lac la Nonne in the late 1920s. In the fall of 1940 a black duck was collected on the delta of the Athabasca river and another was seen there. In 1950 a pair was reported nesting near Kelsey and that fall a specimen was shot in that vicinity. More recently black ducks have been seen or collected at several places in Alberta including Strathmore, Big Valley and Hanna.

The name, black duck, is misleading since the species is not truly black in color. Black mallard, used in some parts of eastern Canada, is a more appropriate name for this species and dusky mallard would be even better. Scoters are sometimes called black ducks because of their color and confusion can arise from the use of this misnomer. Black ducks are most likely to be seen with mallards in Alberta since the two species are similar in habits and behavior. They tip up for food in shallow sloughs during the summer and fly to the grainfields to feed in the fall. It is from such flights of mallards that black ducks are occasionally shot.

SURFACE-FEEDING DUCKS — Family Anatidae

GADWALL
Anas strepera

Common Summer Resident.
Length 20-21 in.

DESCRIPTION: Ad. m.—Head and neck pale buff streaked and spotted with brownish-gray most heavily on crown; upper back, breast and sides brownish-gray finely barred with wavy lines of white; inner feathers of speculum white, outer ones black; speculum bordered in front with a heavy band of black in front of which is a large patch of chestnut; lower back black; abdomen white; legs yellow. Eclipse plumage like female. Ad. f.—Upperparts buffy-brown streaked with brownish-black; wing as in male but only a trace of chestnut and black replaced by dark gray; throat, foreneck, upper breast and sides buffy streaked and barred with brownish-black; remainder of underparts white. Im.— Similar to female but underparts streaked and spotted with gray.

IDENTIFICATION: In the fall this species is often confused with the mallard; yellow legs, and the white and black speculum are distinctive.

RANGE: The Northern Hemisphere. In North America breeds in northern states and in Canada mainly west of Great Lakes. Winters in southern states and Mexico.

NESTING: On the ground not far from water. Nest of grass lined with down. Eggs, 7-12, cream or pale buff. (Hay Lakes, June 1.)

REMARKS: The gadwall is a true puddle duck, most commonly found on the stagnant sloughs of the parklands and prairies. Mucky, algae-filled shallows are its delight for these abound with the aquatic insects and vegetation which form most of its food. Where there are adjacent cultivated fields the gadwall may wander into them to eat the grain, but it does not fly long distances to feed in the stubble as do the mallard and pintail. The taste of its flesh reflects the nature of its food, and it is not highly prized by most sportsmen. The gadwall is not a very wary species and many are shot early in the fall. This may account for a noticeable decrease in numbers of the species during the past three or four decades.

In some areas gadwalls are quite appropriately called gray ducks. It is perhaps because they never wear the striking spring colors assumed by so many other species of ducks that they are not well known. Gadwalls are reasonably common in southern Alberta but less so in the north. In the mountains they have been seen on rare occasions near Banff and Jasper. They rarely occur in large flocks but small groups of one or two females followed by courting males are often seen in the spring. Later in the summer a female and her fledged brood form a little band. When the nights get cold and a scum of ice forms on small ponds gadwalls move southward; most have left by the end of September.

BLACK DUCK

GADWALL

ALLAN BROOKS

PINTAIL
male   *female*

C. HAMPSON

GREEN-WINGED TEAL
female

53

SURFACE-FEEDING DUCKS — Family Anatidae

PINTAIL
Anas acuta

Common Summer Resident.
Length 22-28 in.

DESCRIPTION: A large duck with long thin neck and pointed tail feathers, the central two much longer than others in male. Ad. m.—Head and upper neck dark brown extending down hindneck as a dark stripe bordered with white; back and sides delicately barred black and white; wings gray with heavily striped black and white tertiaries; speculum iridescent green bordered in front with cinnamon, behind with white; underparts white except black under tail coverts; tail black margined with gray. In eclipse plumage like female. Ad. f.—Head and neck buffy striped with brown except on throat; upperparts brownish-black, the feathers edged and marked with buffy; speculum grayish-brown with green edged in front with buff, behind with black and white; upper breast and sides of buffy brown with lighter feather edges; rest of underparts whitish with brown streaks; tail feathers pointed. Im.—Like female.

IDENTIFICATION: Long neck and slender build are the best field marks. The bronzy-green speculum with buffy front border is distinctive.

RANGE: North America. Breeds mainly west of the Great Lakes from central states to arctic coasts. Winters from southern states to Central America and West Indies.

NESTING: On the ground. Nest of grass and weeds lined with down. Eggs, 8-12, olive-buff. (Craigmyle, April 27.)

REMARKS: Except in the mountains and foothills where it is scarce, the pintail is one of the commonest ducks in Alberta. It prefers the grassy sloughs of the prairies and the grassy or reedy shallows bordering the northern lakes. An early migrant, the female is usually laying by the end of April and many nests are destroyed by spring farming operations. The males take no share in family duties but gather in secluded spots to moult into the eclipse plumage. Newly hatched pintails clothed in grayish down with paler patches here and there may have to follow their mother on an overland journey to reach the nearest water. They are most vulnerable at this time. When the journey is long the entire brood may be wiped out by crows, magpies, gulls and mammalian predators. Once they reach water, however, their inborn ability to swim and dive and hide greatly increases their chance of survival.

The pintail is one of the two species of ducks which commonly flock into the grain fields during the fall. Stubble-shooting, the finest form of waterfowl hunting, produces a mixed bag of mallards and pintails until late in October; about that time most of the pintails move southward, usually before the males have assumed their beautiful breeding plumage. Grain-fed pintails are an epicurean's delight.

54

GREEN-WINGED TEAL　　　　　　　Common Summer Resident.
Anas carolinensis　　　　　　　　　　Length 14-15 in.

DESCRIPTION: Ad m.—Head and neck chestnut except a patch of iridescent green extending from eye down side of neck; back and wings gray, many feathers delicately barred with black and white; speculum iridescent green bordered in front with light brown and on the sides with black; upper breast pinkish with black spots; sides delicately barred with black and white but a definite white vertical stripe in front of wing; remainder of underparts white; a white patch bordered with black on side of tail at base. In eclipse plumage similar to female. Ad. f.—Upperparts grayish-brown with buffy feather margins; wings as in male but duller; throat white; breast buffy spotted with brownish-black; sides grayish-brown, the feathers edged with buffy; remainder of underparts white. Im.—Like female.

IDENTIFICATION: A very small duck similar to the blue-winged teal but lacking the blue shoulder patch; the underparts in any plumage are largely white.

RANGE: North America. Breeds in northern United States and across Canada mainly west of Hudson Bay. Winters in southern states, Mexico and West Indies.

NESTING: On the ground not far from water. Nest of grasses lined with down. Eggs, 6-12, white or buffy-white. (Winterburn, May 24.)

REMARKS: Although the green-winged and the blue-winged teal both nest throughout the province, the former is more abundant in the north while the latter is more common in the south. Neither occurs commonly in the mountains. The green-winged teal is the hardier species; it arrives early in the spring and stays so late in the fall that hunters occasionally take males in full breeding plumage. The flight of teal is so swift and erratic that only the expert marksman can score consistently; they fly in such close formation, however, that one shot may bring down several birds.

Green-winged teal spend much of their time in the shallows tipping-up to reach the food on the bottom. They are fond of sunning themselves on the shore, drowsily standing on one leg with beak tucked under a wing. It is surprising what a small body of water will attract a pair of green-winged teal. In the parklands they much prefer a roadside puddle or a small weed-choked creek to the larger open waters. In the north small muskeg sloughs are favorite resorts and in the mountains beaver ponds often support a family or two. This choice of breeding habitat has allowed this species to hold its own so far against the ravages of mass drainage and cultivation of sub-marginal lands.

BLUE-WINGED TEAL   GREEN-WINGED TEAL
female — male   *female — male*

CINNAMON TEAL
male

SURFACE-FEEDING DUCKS — Family Anatidae

BLUE-WINGED TEAL
Anas discors subsp. (p. 488)

Common Summer Resident.
Length 15-16 ins.

DESCRIPTION: Ad. m.—Crown black; remainder of head and upper neck bluish-gray except a large white crescent between eye and beak; back brownish-black, the feathers of upper back outlined with buffy; large patch on front of wing light blue; speculum iridescent green bordered by white on front and black on sides; underparts brown spotted and barred with black; tail black, a distinct white patch on each side of its base. In eclipse plumage similar to female. Ad. f.—Upperparts grayish-brown, the feathers edged with buffy; wings as in male but duller; throat white; foreneck and upper breast buffy streaked with brown; remainder of underparts white streaked with brown, most heavily on sides. Im.—Like female.

IDENTIFICATION: A very small duck with, in all plumages, a large light blue patch at the bend of the wing which shows at rest or in flight. In spring the white crescent on the face of the male is conspicuous.

RANGE: North America and northern South America. Breeds across Canada and northern United States. Winters in southern states, Central America and northern half of South America.

NESTING: On the ground not far from water. Nest of grasses lined with down. Eggs, 8-12, white or buffy-white. (Tofield, June 18.)

REMARKS: This little duck is found throughout the province but it is more common on the pot-holes and sloughs of the prairies and park-lands than on the northern lakes. It is scarce in the mountains. Blue-winged teal are quite tame during the nesting season and broods are often raised on stock-ponds close to the farm house. They dabble in the muddy water picking up water insects and algae, but when their appetites are satisfied they like to sit on the bank preening and sunning themselves. Teal are rarely seen far from water. In summer brief trips along a creek or a short flight from one pond to another are their longest jaunts. Like all the ducks blue-winged teal are flightless for several days during the summer moult and at this time they keep out of slight skulking in the marginal vegetation. Towards fall, however, males, females and young, all looking alike, begin to gather on larger sloughs in preparation for the southward migration. Most of them are gone by early October.

In the fall small flocks of teal flying fast and low over the water provide excellent sport for the gunner, and he is a good shot who can show a sizeable bag from such targets. Many hunters have never seen the male in his bright breeding plumage for the blue-winged teal usually migrates before the eclipse plumage is shed.

SURFACE-FEEDING DUCKS — Family Anatidae

CINNAMON TEAL   Scarce Summer Resident.
Anas cyanoptera subsp. (p. 488)   Length 15-17 in.

DESCRIPTION: Breeding m.—Crown brownish-black; head, neck, underparts and sides chestnut somewhat grayed on abdomen; back and tail brownish-black, feathers of back with light edges; wing as in blue-winged teal. Male in eclipse plumage similar to female. Ad. f.—Similar to adult female blue-winged teal but more heavily marked on sides of head and chin, and with a faint tinge of chestnut on underparts. Im.—Similar to female.

IDENTIFICATION: The male in winter and spring is unmistakable. Females, young, and males in eclipse plumage cannot be separated in the field from blue-winged teal; in the hand they usually show a suggestion of chestnut.

RANGE: North and South America. Breeds in western North America from southern B.C. to California. Winters from California through South America to the Falkland Islands.

NESTING: On the ground usually near water. Nest of grass lined with down. Eggs, 9-13, creamy white.

REMARKS: Of the few records of the cinnamon teal in Alberta the majority are from the south. Single specimens have been shot near Edmonton and Red Deer and a male was observed near Camrose. These are the only northerly records. Other specimens have been taken near Calgary and "from southwestern Alberta near the mountains". Recently the species has been observed regularly but in small numbers in the area south of a line through Stirling and Mountain View where it probably breeds. Cinnamon teal have been seen in the Strathmore irrigation district during the summer and a few nesting pairs have been reported from the Brooks area. The difficulty of identification in the fall may account for the paucity of records of this species at that season.

The habits and behavior of the cinnamon teal are similar to those of the other two species of teal. All three species may occasionally be found together but cinnamon teal more commonly associate with blue-winged teal in southern Alberta. They dabble in shallow prairie sloughs or sit about on their muddy shores during the heat of the day. The male cinnamon teal standing on one leg with his head tucked over his breast makes a beautiful picture of contentment. In the fall small numbers of cinnamon teal are undoubtedly shot in southern Alberta. These are easily mistaken for blue-wings unless the hunter notices the few traces of cinnamon on the sides and underparts.

SURFACE-FEEDING DUCKS — Family Anatidae

AMERICAN WIDGEON
Mareca americana

Common Summer Resident.
Length 19-20 in.

DESCRIPTION: Ad. m.—Crown white, remainder of head and neck speckled black and white except an iridescent green mark behind eye; back, upper breast and sides reddish-brown delicately barred with black on back and sides; large white patch at front of wings; speculum black with small spot of green and innermost feather light gray; underparts white; under tail coverts black. In eclipse plumage like female. Ad. f.—Head and neck speckled grayish-brown and white, lighter on crown; back barred with light and dark brown; wings as in male but white patch marked with gray; upper breast and sides buffy-brown; underparts white. Im.—Like female.

IDENTIFICATION: In the field the white patch on the front of the wing shows well, as does the white belly bordered with brown. The black speculum with light innermost feather is distinctive.

RANGE: North America. Breeds throughout except in northeast. Winters from middle states south to Central America.

NESTING: On dry ground near water. Nest of grass and weeds lined with down. Eggs, 8-12, cream. (Claresholm, May 11.)

REMARKS: The name American widgeon comes from its close resemblance to the European widgeon; another common name, baldpate, is derived from the shining white crown of the breeding male. The species occurs throughout the province but has been recorded rarely from the mountains.

Baldpates arrive early in the spring a few days after the mallards and pintails and settle down on the prairie sloughs or in the marshes bordering the larger lakes. They are friendly little ducks often raising broods on pot-holes near the farmyard. The female quacks in the usual duck fashion but the male whistles a soft, *whew, whew, whew.* Baldpates usually pass through southern Alberta in large flocks towards the middle of October, providing excellent shooting for the waterfowl hunter. Plump and tasty, they form a fine addition to the bag.

EUROPEAN WIDGEON
Mareca penelope

Accidental Wanderer.
Length 17-20 in.

The male European widgeon has a reddish brown head with a pale buffy crown but otherwise is similar to the American widgeon. Females are difficult to separate; the head of the European widgeon is tinged with reddish while that of the baldpate is gray.

Although there were previous sight records in the province an adult male European widgeon collected at Valhalla Lake, northwest of Grande Prairie, on April 27, 1959, is the only authenticated record for Alberta. This bird was in company with a few baldpates.

SURFACE-FEEDING DUCKS — Family Anatidae

SHOVELER
Spatula clypeata

Common Summer Resident.
Length 19-21 in.

DESCRIPTION: Beak long, narrow at base becoming very wide at tip, hence the local name 'spoonbill'. Ad. m.—Head and neck iridescent green; back brownish-black; front of wing light blue separated from iridescent green speculum by white band; upper breast white; remainder of underparts chestnut; tail and tail coverts black except small white patch at each side of base; legs orange. Ad. f.—Upperparts brownish-black, the feathers margined and irregularly marked with buff; underparts buffy streaked and spotted with brown, lightly on throat and heavily on sides; wing as in male but shoulder and speculum duller; legs orange. Im. and male in eclipse plumage.—Similar to female.

IDENTIFICATION: Often mistaken for the mallard in flight but the blue shoulders and long 'spoonbill' are evident to the careful observer. The blue-winged teal has blue shoulders but is much smaller.

RANGE: Occurs on every continent. In North America breeds mainly west of the Great Lakes. Winters on Pacific coast and southern states south of northern South America.

NESTING: On the ground not far from water. Nest of grass and weeds lined with down. Eggs, 6-12, buffy-olive. (Walsh, May 28.)

REMARKS: The shoveler occurs throughout the province in suitable habitat but is scarce in the mountains and the woodlands. It is most frequently found on the muddy sloughs and pot-holes of the prairies and parklands, often in company with gadwall and blue-winged teal. In the stagnant algae-filled shallows its large beak is put to good use straining from the water the small plants and animals which form its food. This diet imparts a flavor to the flesh which is not relished by most sportsmen, but the shoveler presents such an easy target that large numbers are taken early in the shooting season.

Among the ducks shovelers are rather late spring migrants. The males are very energetic in their courtship activities. A female is often pursued in erratic flight by several males all proclaiming their ardour with nasal grunts, *took, took, took,* a sound which will identify them readily at this season. But the females have little time for frivolities; egg laying, three weeks of incubating and several weeks' attendance on growing ducklings keep them busy for most of the summer. Then they must moult and grow new plumage before migration. As with most species of ducks the males do not assist in raising the family. They shed their bright plumage early and spend the summer in company with other indolent males. Most shovelers have left the province by early October.

ALLAN BROOKS

AMERICAN WIDGEON
female   male

KAY HODGES

SHOVELER

61

SURFACE-FEEDING DUCKS — Family Anatidae

WOOD DUCK
Aix sponsa

Rare Summer Visitor.
Length 18-20 in.

DESCRIPTION: A small duck with long flowing crest on head and long tail. Ad. m.—Crown and crest iridescent green and purple; rest of upperparts dark iridescent green with bronze reflections; speculum and much of wing iridescent blue-green; face metallic purple with two white marks extending up from white throat and foreneck; upper breast purplish-brown edged with white in front of wings; sides olive barred with black and white; rest of underparts white. Ad. f.—Crown dark brown; rest of upperparts brownish-olive glossed with green; wing as in male but duller; face brownish-gray except a white ring around eye; throat white; upper breast and sides dull brown mottled with white; rest of underparts white.

IDENTIFICATION: The brightly colored male is unmistakable. The female may be distinguished by the greenish tinge in her plumage.

RANGE: United States and southern Canada. Breeds in northern part of range; winters in southern states and Mexico.

NESTING: In cavities in trees or stumps. The bottom of the cavity is lined with down. Eggs, 10-14, buff.

REMARKS: The wood duck has been seen in Alberta on very few occasions. One was shot near Ft. Chipewyan in 1904, another was seen on a small slough near Embarras Portage about thirty years later, and in 1951 a male was observed on Stirling Lake near Stirling. In 1956 a pair of wood ducks nested near Midnapore. They successfully raised a brood of young, some of which were banded.

The bufflehead and the goldeneye, both of which also nest in holes in trees, are sometimes called wood ducks, a name which is properly applied only to this species. Neither looks like the true wood duck which, in breeding plumage, is the most colorful and the most beautiful of our waterfowl. Once threatened with extinction through over-shooting the wood duck is now protected by law in the United States and its numbers are increasing. Its normal habitat is woodland lakes and ponds where it may be found dabbling in the shallows or perched in the trees bordering the pool. Since this type of habitat is rapidly disappearing before the onslaught of the bulldozer wood ducks and other tree-nesting species are being forced back into wilderness areas to find suitable nesting sites. Cottagers who erect nest boxes and hollow logs in woods adjacent to our resort lakes should attract these species. Chances are that the tenants will be buffleheads or goldeneyes rather than wood ducks but the appearance of a family of any of these species will prove ample compensation for the work involved.

DIVING DUCKS — Family Anatidae

Diving ducks are heavy-bodied ducks which frequent the larger lakes and rivers. They secure their food by diving beneath the surface, often to considerable depths. They can take flight only after pattering along the surface of the water. The flattened web of the hind toe is much larger than in the surface-feeding ducks. They lack a well-marked speculum.

REDHEAD
Aythya americana

Scarce Summer Resident.
Length 19-23 in.

DESCRIPTION: Breeding m.—Head and upper neck chestnut; lower neck, breast, and upper back brownish-black; back, wings, and sides white with fine wavy black bars producing a dark gray effect; lower breast and abdomen white; tail and adjacent areas above and below brownish-black. In late summer and early fall the male assumes a plumage similar to the female. Ad. f.—Head and neck dull reddish-brown, paler on foreneck and white on chin; back and wings dark grayish-brown; upper breast and sides brownish, remainder of underparts white with some brown mottling. Im.—Like female.

IDENTIFICATION: A large diving duck most easily confused with the canvasback. The forehead rises abruptly above the beak in the redhead, whereas it slopes gradually back in the canvasback.

RANGE: North America. Breeds from northern Manitoba and B.C. to Michigan and California. Winters from southern B.C. to Mexico and West Indies.

NESTING: In clumps of rushes and reeds over water. Nest a mass of reeds only high enough above water to keep the eggs dry, lined with down. Eggs, 8-14, cream or buff. (Zep Lake, June 12.)

REMARKS: During the nesting season the redhead is confined to lakes with extensive reedy margins surrounding deeper open water, the type of lake which man finds least attractive for recreation and which is, therefore, the first to be drained in his senseless rush to rid the earth's surface of water. So great has been the destruction of this type of habitat that the population of redheads has now reached dangerously low levels. Today, although an occasional pair may be found in central Alberta redheads nest mainly in the unspoiled northern parts of the province. They are rarely seen in the mountains and only on migration.

Redheads dive for their food tearing up roots and bulbs of water vegetation and catching aquatic insects and crustaceans. When available seeds of surface plants are added to their diet. The downy ducklings soon learn to forage for themselves among the reeds either on or beneath the surface. They escape most dangers by diving but unfortunately they are then most vulnerable to underwater foes and many fall prey to voracious pike.

ALLAN BROOKS

WOOD DUCK
female   *male*

RAY SALT

REDHEAD

RING-NECKED DUCK
male   *female*

RAY SALT

RAY SALT

CANVASBACK
male   *female*

65

DIVING DUCKS — Family Anatidae

RING-NECKED DUCK Fairly Common Summer Resident.
Aythya collaris Length 16-18 in.

DESCRIPTION: Ad. m.—Head and neck black with purplish iridescence; a thin collar of brown around lower neck; upperparts brownish-black; speculum gray; breast black; rest of underparts and sides white with some fine dark barring on sides; beak slaty-blue with white at base and a white band near tip. In fall like female. Ad. f.— Upperparts blackish-brown, browner on hindneck and upper back, blacker on rump; speculum gray; sides of head grayish; foreneck, throat, and ring around base of beak whitish; breast brown mottled with white and buff; sides brown; rest of underparts white vaguely marked with brown. Immature like female.

IDENTIFICATION: Similar to scaup but male has black back and white of underparts extends up as a crescent in front of wing; females are almost indistinguishable in the field; in all plumages the ring-neck's speculum shows gray, the scaup's white in flight.

RANGE: North America. Breeds from B.C. to western Ontario south to Arizona and Wisconsin. Winters in southern B.C., the western states and Central America.

NESTING: In marshes or edges of sloughs. Nest of grasses, reeds, and rushes lined with down. Eggs, 6-12, olive-buff.

REMARKS: As a breeding bird the ring-necked duck has never been observed south of Edmonton but in the northern half of the province it is a fairly common but rather local nester. A record of ring-necked ducks west of Turner Valley at the end of May suggests the possibility of nesting in the foothills. In the mountains the species has been seen at Jasper and Banff. Throughout the prairies it occurs as a migrant.

In the almost inaccessible muskeg regions of northern Alberta are numerous ponds and lakes on whose quaking margins waders and wildfowl nest in comparative safety. Here, where the stagnant water teems with mosquito larvae and other aquatic insects, the ring-necked duck builds its nest and raises its family. When the young are awing and the adults have assumed their eclipse plumage they all look very much like scaups. The two species have similar habits and are commonly associated. In the fall both may be shot over decoys near the reedy margins of deep-water lakes; during spring migration a pair of ring-necks may often be seen only a few yards from a pair of lesser scaups providing an excellent opportunity for comparison of the two species; and in the summer both scaup and ring-neck families may be raised on the same muskeg slough.

DIVING DUCKS — Family Anatidae

CANVASBACK
Aythya valisneria

Fairly Common Summer Resident.
Length 22 in.

DESCRIPTION: Ad. m.—Head and neck dark reddish-brown; lower neck and upper breast black; rump and tail region black; rest of back white finely barred with pencillings of black, producing a canvas-gray effect; sides and rest of underparts white; iris red. Males in eclipse plumage are similar to females. Ad. f.—Head, neck, and upper breast brown with a tinge of reddish on head and chest and chin very light; back, wings and sides brown, the feathers edged with whitish producing a brownish-gray effect; rest of underparts grayish-white mottled with dusky; tail brown; iris brown.

IDENTIFICATION: A large diving duck with reddish-brown head and neck and canvas-colored back, lighter in all plumages than the redhead. At all seasons large size and shape of head will distinguish the canvasback; the crown slopes gradually back from the beak, a line from the middle of the beak to the back of the crown being practically straight.

RANGE: North America. Breeds mainly in central Canada and the north-central states. Winters in southern states, Mexico, and up Pacific coast as far as B.C.

NESTING: In rushes or reeds over shallow water. Nest a bulky mass of rushes and reeds held slightly above water level and lined with down. Eggs, 7-9, pale olive-green. (Pine Lake, June 1).

REMARKS: Deep-water lakes with extensive reedy margins and rich supplies of pondweed beneath their surface are the summer home of the canvasback. While females incubate in the shelter of the rushes the males, their white backs flashing in the sun, lie in flotillas well out on the lake or dive deep to tear up the roots and succulent shoots of water lillies and pondweeds. By the time the young have hatched the males have lost their beautiful breeding plumage and until the October moult restores the bright colors they are almost indistinguishable from females. Few canvasbacks remain in Alberta late enough in the fall to show the fresh breeding plumage in which they pass the winter. Heavy-bodied canvasbacks must patter along the water before taking to the air, but once awing their flight is swift and direct. They rarely fly at any great height and, except on migration, soon return to the water.

Except in the mountains and in the southern prairies where it appears only as a migrant, the canvasback nests in small numbers throughout Alberta. Overshooting and destruction of habitat in the early 1900s must share the blame for the present scarcity of canvasbacks. The first evil is now controlled; in control of the second lies the fate of the species. Construction of large irrigation reservoirs on the prairies, as at Brooks, has created suitable habitat and allowed the canvasback to extend its breeding range southward in recent years.

B. & J. MORGAN

GREATER SCAUP
male

ALLAN BROOKS

LESSER SCAUP
male   *female*

68

DIVING DUCKS — Family Anatidae

GREATER SCAUP

Aythya marila subsp. (p. 488)

Rare Migrant.
Length 17-20 in.

DESCRIPTION: Males in breeding plumage are almost identical with male lesser scaups but the iridescence on the head is greenish, there is more white at the base of the primaries, and the sides have less barring. Females and young of the two species have no color differences. The two species are separated on the basis of size (although there is overlapping of this character) and on shape and structure of beak.

IDENTIFICATION: A fairly large duck with black head, neck, and chest, gray wavy-barred back, and white abdomen. So like the lesser scaup that it is almost impossible to separate them in the field; in flight the white speculum and large amount of white at base of primaries form a broader streak through wing than is seen on lesser scaup; however even this is not an infallible means of separating the two species in the field for some lesser scaups may have white extending onto the primaries. The greater scaup has a much broader "nail" on the beak than the lesser.

RANGE: Northern parts of northern hemisphere. Breeds in North America from northern states north in Canada to edge of arctic. Winters mainly along Atlantic coast from New York south to northern South America.

NESTING: The nest and eggs are similar to those of the lesser scaup but average slightly larger.

REMARKS: There are few authentic records of the greater scaup in Alberta; in fact the only unquestionable record is of two males collected at La Saline between Ft. McMurray and McKay Lakes on May 13, 1920. There are a number of sight records from various parts of the province including Lake Athabasca where it was thought to nest. Recent investigations have failed to confirm this. On October 9, 1961, a female greater scaup was shot at Lake Saskatoon near Wembley.

The greater scaup is more of a maritime species than the lesser. It is a scarce migrant over inland regions and could be expected to nest only on very large bodies of water. Present records indicate that the greater scaup is more likely to occur in the northern half of the province. Observers in this area, particularly those who are familiar with the greater scaup, would do well to scrutinize all scaups closely. Hunters who find scaups of large size in their bags might save a wing for checking by an ornithologist. From such information the exact status of the greater scaup in Alberta will be learned.

69

DIVING DUCKS — Family Anatidae

LESSER SCAUP
Aythya affinis

Common Summer Resident.
Length 16½ in.

DESCRIPTION: Ad. m.—Head, neck and foreparts of back and breast black, the head and neck with purplish iridescence; back finely barred with wavy lines of black and white producing a gray effect; flight feathers dark grayish-brown, speculum white; lower back and region around tail black; rest of underparts and sides white with fine wavy bars of brown towards tail; iris yellow; beak pale blue. In eclipse plumage, male resembles female. Ad. f.—Wide white area around base of beak; rest of head and neck brown shading to grayish-brown on back and upper breast; wings as in male; sides brown; region around tail grayish-brown; rest of underparts white shading into adjacent colors; iris dark yellow; beak bluish.

IDENTIFICATION: Breeding males may be confused only with male ring-necked ducks but scaups have gray backs and white speculum. Females and males in fall plumage are difficult to distinguish in the field from ring-necked ducks, except in flight when the white speculum shows; this same character separates them from larger redheads and canvasbacks.

RANGE: North America. Breeds mainly from Alaska to Hudson Bay south to north-central United States. Winters in southern states, Central America and the Pacific coast north to B.C.

NESTING: On dry ground not far from water. Nest of grasses and reeds lined with down, hidden in grass or reeds. Eggs, 8-12, olive-buff. (Ministik Lake, June 24.)

REMARKS: The lesser scaup prefers the larger lakes in which pondweed grows to within a few feet of the surface. As a breeding bird it is quite abundant in the northern half of the province, but in the south it nests only near some of the large lakes and irrigation reservoirs. As a migrant it may appear anywhere, usually, however, showing preference for open water rather than grassy sloughs.

The lesser scaup is a late nester and haying operations in early July destroy many nests. Immediately after hatching the young are led to the lake where they join with other families to form rafts of as many as a hundred downy scaups. The females are solicitous for the welfare of all and apparently no attempt is made to separate their own offspring from the group. As the young increase in size the flock is reduced in numbers for disease and predation take their toll. Losses are not excessive, however, for flocks of bluebills, as the hunter calls them, provide excellent shooting over decoys in the early fall. By the time ice is forming on the lakes, lesser scaups have usually left Alberta for more favorable wintering grounds.

COMMON GOLDENEYE
Bucephala clangula subsp. (p. 488)

Fairly Common Summer Resident.
Length 17-20 in.

DESCRIPTION: A medium-size duck with rather short neck and moderately puffy head. Ad. m.—Head and upper neck black with green iridescence except a large white spot between beak and eye; rest of neck and all underparts white; rest of upperparts black except white streaks on scapulars and large white area on wing; iris yellow. In fall like female. Ad. f.—Head and neck chocolate brown; rest of upperparts grayish-black, the wings with much white mainly on the secondaries; upper breast and sides gray; rest of underparts white; iris yellow. Im.—Similar to female.

IDENTIFICATION: The male is larger than the bufflehead and lacks white in the crest; similar to Barrow's goldeneye but white near eye never forms crescent. Females of common and Barrow's goldeneye are separable in the field only by the expert; the common goldeneye is lighter all over with more white on wings.

RANGE: North America. Breeds in northern states and across Canada. Winters on coasts and in interior as far north as southern Canada.

NESTING: In holes in hollow trees or stumps. The eggs are laid on a mass of down at the bottom of the cavity. Eggs, 8-12, grayish-green. (Camrose, May 11.)

REMARKS: During the breeding season the common goldeneye occurs on the rivers and lakes of the northern woodland areas and, less commonly, in the parklands where suitable nesting trees are scarce. On the prairies and in the mountains it occurs as a migrant and as an occasional winter resident although it has been seen in summer at Jasper and Banff. Small numbers winter on open water at Edmonton, Calgary, Banff, and Drumheller.

Common goldeneyes arrive with the first suggestion of spring breakup. Frequenting at first the open edges of the lakes they move to the small woodland streams as the thaw progresses. In an intensive search for nesting sites the females will even explore chimneys, sometimes with disastrous results. They can squeeze their bodies through a four-inch aperture in a tree but the cavity within must be larger. A few hours after the young hatch they tumble some twenty or thirty feet to the ground and are led off to a stream in whose tangled borders they can find safety. In the fall whistlers, as the hunter calls them, move south on whistling wings, stopping over on the parkland lakes long enough to provide good shooting and, for the successful sportsman, excellent dinners.

DIVING DUCKS — Family Anatidae

BARROW'S GOLDENEYE Fairly Common Summer Resident.
Bucephala islandica Length 20-22 in.

DESCRIPTION: Ad.m.—Feathers of head long giving puffy effect especially on crown; head and upper neck black with purple iridescence; a crescent-shaped patch of white between beak and yellow eye; neck all around, and entire underparts white, tinged with gray under tail; back and wings black with row of white spots at base of wing, white bar on wing, and white speculum; legs bright orange. Ad.f.—Head and neck dark brown with no white patch; white ring around lower neck; upperparts sooty black some feathers tipped with gray; speculum white; underparts white with gray wash over breast, sides, and under tail. Males in eclipse plumage and young resemble female.

IDENTIFICATION: A large duck with distinct black and white markings, usually seen in the mountains. Resembles common goldeneye but has purplish head with white crescent or triangle near eye, and less white on back in form of spots instead of streaks.

RANGE: North America and Europe. Breeds in North America from central Alberta and B.C. south to California, and along coast of Labrador. Winters mainly along seacoasts near breeding grounds.

NESTING: In hollow stumps and trees or in cavities in the rocks. Nest lined with down. Eggs, 6-11, dull greenish. (Waterton, May 25.)

REMARKS: During the nesting season Barrow's goldeneye occurs in the mountains and foothills from the international boundary to north of Jasper. It has also been seen at this season in association with common goldeneyes on lakes northeast of Grouard and near Fairview but no evidence of nesting was found although both males and females were present. There are scattered records during migration periods from Camrose, Elk Island Park, Beaverhill Lake, and Wood Buffalo Park. The species occasionally winters in the province in small numbers.

Secluded mountain lakes and pools where woods crowd the water's edge are the home of Barrow's goldeneye during the summer. In our mountain parks the drab female leads her newly hatched young to a nearby beaver pond where the pretty black and white balls of fluff soon learn to dive for insects, roots, and pondweeds, which comprise most of their food. In such surroundings it would seem that their survival would be assured yet the species never seems to be abundant. When lakes and rivers begin to freeze most Barrow's goldeneyes cross the mountains, often in company with common goldeneyes, to spend the winter in the warmer waters of the Pacific coast. Occasionally a few winter near Calgary, Banff and Exshaw.

72

COMMON GOLDENEYE
male

BARROW'S GOLDENEYE *(male, front)*
(common goldeneyes, rear)

73

DIVING DUCKS — Family Anatidae

BUFFLEHEAD
Bucephala albeola

Fairly Common Summer Resident.
Length 14 in.

DESCRIPTION: Spring m.—Feathers of head long giving it puffy appearance, black with purple and green sheen, except large white V from eye across top of head; back black shading to light gray on tail and bordered with white at base of wings; wings black except large white patch on coverts and secondaries; neck, underparts, and sides white. Ad.f.—Head not so puffy; head, neck and upperparts brownish-black except white speculum and small white patch behind and below eye; underparts grayish-white becoming dark gray on sides and under tail. Immature birds are like female but browner. Males in eclipse plumage resemble females but have more white on wing.

IDENTIFICATION: A small duck with large puffy head. Winter and spring males are unmistakable. Females may be identified by white cheek patch and large white mark on wing. In flight small size, rapid wing beat, and large amount of white on wing will identify.

RANGE: North America. Breeds from California and Montana north to western arctic. Winters on Pacific and Atlantic coasts and on Great Lakes; occasionally inland.

NESTING: In hollow trees or stumps. Nest at bottom of cavity in tree or in nest box. Eggs, 9-14, buffy or creamy white. (Lake Isle, June 10).

REMARKS: On migration the bufflehead occurs fairly commonly on the larger sloughs of the prairies and the northlands, but less frequently in the mountains and the foothills. During the breeding season when distribution is restricted by the availability of nesting sites it is found on small lakes and ponds in the wooded regions of northern Alberta.

Cavities drilled in trees by pileated woodpeckers are favorite nesting places of the bufflehead. The female clings to the tree, almost like a woodpecker, to inspect her future home. An aperture only three inches wide will admit her but the cavity must not be too deep, for the young have to scramble up its sides to the opening shortly after they are hatched. Pausing for just a moment to get their first view of this new world they jump to the ground perhaps fifty feet below and follow their mother to the nearest water. In settled areas buffleheads appear early in the spring, floating well out on the water or diving for food beneath the surface. In the fall they stay so late that males in the beautiful breeding plumage are often shot by hunters who call them 'butterballs'. Each year a few buffleheads spend the winter on the Bow River just southeast of Calgary.

74

DIVING DUCKS — Family Anatidae

OLDSQUAW
Clangula hyemalis

Fairly Common Migrant.
Length 16-22 in.

DESCRIPTION: Spring m.—Face pale brownish-gray except white eyelids and patch behind eye; rest of head, neck, and breast brownish-black; abdomen white; back and wings black, many feathers edged with rusty-brown; white borders of lower back continue into white outer tail feathers; remainder of tail black, central two feathers very long. Spring f.—Similar to male but black largely replaced by brownish-gray, more white on head, less rusty on back, and lacking long central tail feathers. Winter ads.—Both sexes have a distinct winter plumage in which there is much more white on head, neck and back. The male retains the long central tail feathers.

IDENTIFICATION: Long tail feathers of male distinguish from all ducks except pintail; shorter neck and very dark head, neck, and breast identify the oldsquaw; the beak is black at base and tip, pinkish-orange in middle. Females are brownish ducks with a piebald appearance around head and neck, mostly white below but with brownish chest band.

RANGE: Northern hemisphere. In North America breeds in arctic from Alaska to Labrador. Winters along both Atlantic and Pacific coasts and on Great Lakes.

NESTING: On the ground. Nest, a depression lined with down. Eggs, 5-9, greenish or olive-buff.

REMARKS: The oldsquaw is a northern nesting duck which apparently by-passes southern Alberta on migration. It is a fairly regular migrant in that part of the province lying north of the Athabasca River, being recorded each spring at Belvedere, Athabasca, Lesser Slave Lake, and on the Athabasca delta, sometimes in considerable numbers. Farther south it has been recorded occasionally at Elk Island Park, Beaverhill Lake and Sylvan Lake and in the mountains at Jasper and Banff. It is seen more commonly in the spring than in the fall.

On their migrations between the Pacific coast and the Mackenzie regions oldsquaws apparently travel in northeast-southwest directions which take them across northern Alberta but not the south. They show preference for large bodies of water at all times. Oldsquaws are already paired when they appear on our lakes and rivers in mid-May waiting for more favorable weather farther north. Males are performing the antics which are a necessary part of the breeding cycle in most species of ducks. They jealously guard the female fighting off unattached males with a vigor which never seems to harm the participants. Summers are so short on their arctic nesting grounds that these preliminaries to the raising of a brood must be completed before they arrive. Once the eggs are laid however, the males become as disinterested in family duties as any other male duck.

RAY SALT

BUFFLEHEAD
male

C. HAMPSON

OLDSQUAW
female

HARLEQUIN DUCK
male   *female*

KING EIDER
female

DIVING DUCKS — Family Anatidae

HARLEQUIN DUCK
Histrionicus histrionicus

Fairly Common Summer Resident.
Length 17 in.

DESCRIPTION: Ad. m.—General color deep slate-blue becoming almost black on crown, rump and tail; a crescent in front of and over eye, spot behind ear, stripe down side of neck, ring around base of neck, and a long stripe in front of wing white margined with black; line between back and wing, and some secondaries also white; stripe down each side of nape chestnut; sides and flanks chestnut. Ad. f.—Dull dark brown all over except white at base of beak extending under eye, small white spot in front of eye, a large white spot behind ear, and much white mottling on underparts. Im.—Like female.

IDENTIFICATION: The adult male is unmistakable. The female is superficially like the females of several other species but the three white areas on the head and lack of white on the wings are distinctive; the female ruddy has a light stripe under eye and white throat; the female bufflehead has one white mark behind ear and white on the wings.

RANGE: Coasts of northern North America and northeastern Asia, Rocky Mountains and interior B.C. Winters mainly on coastal waters.

NESTING: On the ground, in holes or under rocks, or in holes in trees. Nest of grass and leaves lined with down. Eggs, 6-8, cream or light buff. (Gorge Creek, June 10.)

REMARKS: The harlequin duck is a maritime species which moves inland during the breeding season. It occurs regularly on the eastern slopes of the Rockies from the International boundary to north of Jasper. There are very few records away from the mountains. The species has been seen at Cooking Lake, Beaverhill Lake and Lake Athabasca.

The cold waters of high mountain streams and lakes are the home of the harlequin duck in Alberta. They may be found in all of our Mountain National Parks. Here early summer visitors may see the beautifully colored males swimming on the blue of a lake or sunning themselves on gray rocky shores. The females in somber hues are easily missed or ignored. But this is as it should be for the females attend to all family duties and, especially while incubating, their obscure colors are their best protection. The downy young are often led up a mountain stream a short time after hatching to seek the shelter of overhanging vegetation. Their persistence in breasting the current and in overcoming obstacles forms a fine lesson in perseverance for the human observer. On a quiet evening, however, they are often seen with their mother in calm waters diving for food and bobbing up like corks every few minutes. What they lack in color they make up for in energy, grace and an obvious joie de vivre.

DIVING DUCKS — Family Anatidae

KING EIDER
Somateria spectabilis

Accidental Wanderer.
Length 22-24 in.

DESCRIPTION: Ad. m.—Top of head and hindneck pearl-gray; rest of head, all underparts, and front half of back white, tinged with green on face and with buffy on breast; a black V from base of beak to middle of throat; rest of upperparts black except white patch on front of wings and white patch on each side of rump; beak reddish with a large bulbous orange projection at base bordered with black. Ad.f.—Entirely reddish-brown streaked and barred above and barred below with black; feathers of forehead and cheeks extend well down onto beak which is yellowish tipped with white. Im.—Like female.

IDENTIFICATION: A large bulky duck mainly white in front black at rear and with large projection at base of beak; females mainly brown and black with sloping forehead.

RANGE: Northern part of northern hemisphere. Breeds along arctic coast of North America. Winters on Atlantic coast south to Gulf of St. Lawrence and on Pacific mainly near Aleutian Islands.

NESTING: On the ground. Nest of down. Eggs, 6, olive-gray.

REMARKS: The king eider has been recorded in Alberta only once: an immature male was shot near Calgary on November 4, 1894. According to the collector it was accompanied by another much whiter bird which may have been an adult male. The king eider is a maritime species which is mainly arctic in distribution. Its appearance in Alberta must be considered accidental.

Females build their nest entirely of down plucked from their breasts. In some regions part of this down is collected from each nest and sold. As the finest and lightest natural insulating material known it is usually used in the manufacture of quilts and sleeping bags. The flesh of eider ducks is not relished by maritime sportsmen since it reflects the nature of their food. Molluscs, crustaceans, and other sedentary aquatic animals form the greater part of their diet. Eiders are skillful divers and can remain under water for considerable lengths of time. In the air, however, they manoeuvre with difficulty; they fly a few feet above the water in direct and cumbersome flight.

79

WHITE-WINGED SCOTER
male   *female*

SURF SCOTER

B. & J. MORGAN

DIVING DUCKS — Family Anatidae

WHITE-WINGED SCOTER Common Summer Resident.
Melanitta deglandi subsp. (p. 488) Length 20-22 in.

DESCRIPTION: Ad. m.—Entirely black sometimes with brownish tinge and usually paler on underparts; a thin white crescent starting below eye and extending behind eye towards crown; speculum white; beak orange at tip, black at base where there is a prominent knob; iris white or gray; legs dull red. Ad. f.—Upperparts blackish-brown with vague whitish mark behind eye; speculum white; underparts grayish-brown; beak and legs brownish-black; iris brown. Young birds resemble females but are lighter below.

IDENTIFICATION: A large very heavy-bodied black or brownish-black duck with large white patch on hindwing most noticeable in flight. May be confused only with surf scoter but larger, with large white patch on wing, and lacking white on crown and nape.

RANGE: North America. Breeds from northern states through Canada except in arctic. Winters on both sea-coasts from Alaska to California and Gulf of St. Lawrence to Carolina, and on Great Lakes.

NESTING: On the ground in light woods or on prairies. Nest, a depression lined with grass and down, often some distance from water. Eggs, 6-10, pinkish buff. (Pine Lake, June 30.)

REMARKS: In the mountains and foothills the white-winged scoter occurs irregularly as a migrant. Elsewhere it breeds on all the large lakes of the province. Its numbers have not changed appreciably during the past fifty years and vacationers at central Alberta lake resorts have ample opportunity to observe white-winged scoters in their natural haunts.

They are sociable birds; large flocks of males and non-breeding females congregate well out on open water, rarely approaching shore unless it be to preen on a rock or small island. Land is of no importance to them for they obtain their food, crustaceans, molluscs, and insects, by diving to considerable depths. Occasionally small flocks patter along the surface, wings beating strenuously to raise their bulky bodies into the air. Once awing they fly direct to their destinations as though unable to manoeuvre their unwieldy mass. In the fall such large lumbering birds make easy targets for the hunter, but few are shot for their flesh has a strong fishy flavor.

Although adult white-winged scoters are ungainly birds their black and white downy young are as appealing as any young ducklings. They are led out on the open water in the first few days of their life. Instinctively they kick up their heels to submerge bobbing to the surface a few moments later with a speed which indicates their buoyancy. What they do below the surface can only be surmised but their rapid growth indicates that the demands of appetite receive much attention.

81

SURF SCOTER
Melanitta perspicillata

Fairly Common Summer Resident.
Length 18-22 in.

DESCRIPTION: Ad. m.—A small patch on forehead between eyes and a triangular patch across nape and pointing down hindneck, white; remainder entirely black or brownish-black usually paler below; beak very heavy at base, marked with red, orange, black, and white; iris white; legs red or orange. Ad. f.—Top of head to lower level of eyes, black; vague white patch on ear and another near base of beak; abdomen mottled light and dark gray; rest of head, neck and body dusky-brown; beak slaty-black; iris brown; legs black tinged with yellow.

IDENTIFICATION: A heavy-bodied duck appearing entirely black at a distance, even in flight. Most likely to be confused with white-winged scoter but lacks white on wings; close observation is required to pick out white marks on head. Females can best be separated in flight when lack of white on wing identifies the surf scoter.

RANGE: North America. Breeds mainly in Alaska and northern Canada south to northern parts of provinces. Winters on both seacoasts south to California and Florida and on Great Lakes.

NESTING: On the ground usually on islands in lakes. Nest lined with down. Eggs, 5-8, cream.

REMARKS: Although there is no actual nesting record the surf scoter probably breeds in the Lake Athabasca region for it occurs in numbers during June and July on the delta of the Athabasca River and on the islands and open water of Lake Athabasca. The species migrates through the western part of the province being seen regularly at Belvedere, Obed Lake and Fairview in the spring. Less regularly it has been recorded near Calgary, Banff, Red Deer, Camrose, Pigeon Lake, Lamont, Lac Ste. Anne, Jasper, Athabasca and Lesser Slave Lake. Unusual records include adult males in breeding condition taken at Barrier Lake south of Seebe on May 25 and June 28, 1962, and two males seen in the Grouard area on July 20, 1964. There is also a record of nesting at Elk Island Park. These occurrences suggest that the breeding range of the species may extend farther south than is generally believed.

Surf scoters spend most of their time on the open water of deep-water lakes, disappearing from view as they dive to the bottom for crustaceans and molluscs and reappearing suddenly some moments later. In diving they arch their necks and kick with their legs appearing to rise from the water momentarily before making the plunge. Usually a small group stays together. There is much bickering and displaying by the males when they pass through the province in mid-May especially if the sexes are not equally represented in the group. If disturbed surf scoters move off, swimming and diving, but when hard pressed they rise fairly easily and fly away close to the water. The whistle of their wings as they take off can often be heard for two or three hundred yards.

DIVING DUCKS — Family Anatidae

RUDDY DUCK
Oxyura jamaicensis subsp. (p. 488)

Fairly Common Summer Resident.
Length 15-17 in.

DESCRIPTION: Spring m.—Crown and nape black; face, cheeks, and chin white; neck and upperparts reddish-chestnut becoming blackish on rump and tail; underparts grayish-white with wavy brownish bars most distinct on sides; white under tail; beak large, bright blue. Spring f.—Upperparts dull black, darkest on crown and with some faint barring and speckling with chestnut; face, cheeks, and chin dull white, an indistinct dusky line from base of bill through ear; foreneck and sides grayish-brown barred with dusky; rest of underparts grayish. Fall ads. and im.—Similar to spring female but duller without chestnut shades.

IDENTIFICATION: A small duck with large broad beak and fairly long tail. In spring the male is unmistakable. In any plumage ruddy ducks may be identified by large amount of white on face and cheeks, with or without a dark line through it.

RANGE: North America. Breeds from B.C. to Manitoba south to Texas and California. Winters from northern states mainly west of Mississippi south to Central America.

NESTING: Usually over water. Nest, a woven mass of reeds and rushes securely fastened to rushes a few inches above water. Eggs, 6-10, very large, creamy white. (Pine Lake, June 24.)

REMARKS: During the breeding season the ruddy duck frequents deep-water lakes whose borders have extensive beds of cat-tails and rushes. It may be found at this time from the parklands to the northern boundary of the province, but it is scarce in the southern prairie regions where such habitat is uncommon. On migration it occurs throughout the province. Ruddy ducks are rarely seen in the mountains; there are records from Banff, Exshaw and Jasper.

As he swims back and forth before his mate with his beak pressed against his breast and his spread tail cocked over his back the male ruddy duck is a picture of clownish self-importance in the spring. Later in the summer, however, in company with others of his carefree sex, he loses both his jaunty manner and his bright colors. The duck, meanwhile, is left to care for her growing brood. Not far from the shelter of the reed beds she watches the little balls of down disappear beneath the surface one after another to bob up again like corks a few moments later. In this way they learn to dive for the pondweeds and water insects which comprise their food. Ruddy ducks appear in hunters' bags at the beginning of the shooting season, but most have left the Province by the end of September.

MERGANSERS — Family Anatidae

Mergansers are fish-eating ducks with long narrow beaks 'toothed' along their edges and slightly hooked at their tips. They are popularly known as saw-bills or fish-ducks. In flight the entire body from tip of beak to tip of tail, is held in a straight line producing a distinctive flight outline.

HOODED MERGANSER
Lophodytes cucullatus

Scarce Summer Resident.
Length 17-19 in.

DESCRIPTION: Ad. m.—Head with high rounded crest, black except large white patch from eye over most of crest; back brownish-black becoming browner towards tail; tertiaries with long central white stripes and much white on secondaries; underparts white except two vertical black bars extending from back in front of wing; sides reddish-brown with fine black lines; iris yellow. In eclipse plumage head and crest resemble female and sides are grayish. Ad. f.—Head with smaller crest, grayish-brown; upperparts dark grayish-brown with white patch on secondaries; throat, neck, and upper breast pale grayish-brown; sides brown; rest of underparts white; iris brown.

IDENTIFICATION: Smallest of the mergansers and with largest crest. Identified as merganser by narrow, 'toothed' beak, as hooded by brown on sides in both sexes at any age.

RANGE: North America. Breeds in United States and southern Canada. Winters from southern states to Central Mexico.

NESTING: In holes in trees and stumps. Nest of grass lined with down. Eggs, 6-10, white.

REMARKS: Breeding records of the hooded merganser in Alberta have all come from the mountain regions before the turn of the century. It was found nesting at Banff in 1891, and females with young were observed at Waterton Lake in 1895 and in the Crow's Nest Pass in 1897. It has been seen frequently in summer near Barrhead and is suspected of nesting there. Other records, mostly during migration periods, are from Camrose, Sullivan Lake, Strathmore, Red Deer, Elk Island Park and Athabasca. A male was taken at Iosegun Lake southeast of Valleyview in September, 1960.

During spring and summer the hooded merganser graces those shady slow-running streams or quiet mountain pools whose margins are well wooded. While the males are disporting themselves on or under the water the females are attending to family duties in the woods nearby. Dead trees containing nesting holes large enough for birds of this size are usually deliberately destroyed in settled areas; as a consequence the species is confined to wilderness areas and to the National Parks for sanctuary.

RUDDY DUCK
female   *male*

HOODED MERGANSER
female   *male*

MERGANSERS — Family Anatidae

COMMON MERGANSER
Mergus merganser subsp. (p. 488)

Fairly Common Summer Resident.
Length 23-26 in.

DESCRIPTION: Ad. m.—Head and upper neck glossy greenish-black without evident crest; lower neck and underparts white with delicate pink blush; back black becoming light gray on rump and tail; most of wing and coverts white with single black bar; primaries brownish-black; iris, beak and legs, reddish. In eclipse plumage like female but retaining much white on wing. Ad. f.—Feathers of nape extended to form crest. Head and neck reddish-brown except white throat and cheeks; upperparts light gray, most feathers with dark centres; feathers of lower neck and sides gray tipped with white; rest of underparts white, tinted with pink; iris, beak, and legs, reddish.

IDENTIFICATION: A large merganser with much white above and below. Males differ from red-breasted merganser in lacking crest and reddish breast; from common goldeneye in lacking white patch near beak. Females similar to red-breasted merganser but white of throat more extensive and well-defined.

RANGE: North America, Europe, Asia. In North America breeds from middle states to Alaska and Newfoundland. Winters from southern Canada to Mexico.

NESTING: Usually on the ground under boulders or in woods; sometimes in hollow trees. Nest of grass lined with down. Eggs, 9-16, pale buff.

REMARKS: The breeding range of the common, or American, merganser in Alberta is not well known. It nests fairly widely in the mountains but elsewhere accurate nesting records are few, perhaps because of the difficulty of distinguishing females of common and red-breasted mergansers. Common mergansers have been observed in June on the lower reaches of the Athabasca River, on its delta, and around Ft. Chipewyan, suggesting that the species nests in that region. It does not nest on the upper reaches of the same river near Belvedere and Athabasca. In this area and in the south of the province it occurs only as a migrant. A few American mergansers may usually be found wintering on the Bow River near Calgary and Banff.

Common mergansers pass through the settled parts of the province early in the spring and late in the fall. They frequent clear-water rivers and deep lakes where small fish are available as food. Often they work as a team advancing in line over the water and diving for the fish which are driven before them. In the fall mergansers are occasionally shot by hunters who have failed to recognize them in the air. Their flesh is not palatable.

MERGANSERS — Family Anatidae

RED-BREASTED MERGANSER
Mergus serrator

Fairly Common Summer Resident.
Length 20-24 in.

DESCRIPTION: Ad. m.—Head and upper neck glossy greenish-black; long, double-pointed crest on crown and nape; back black becoming gray on rump; two rows of white spots near bend of wing; wing, except primaries, mostly white with two black wing bars; reddish-brown ring around lower neck, separated from dark head by white ring; rest of underparts white, the sides finely barred with black; iris, beak, and legs red. Ad. f.—Ragged crest, head and neck brown fading to whitish on throat; rest of upperparts grayish-brown, the feathers with light edges and dark centers; speculum white bordered in front by black then white stripes; feathers of upperbreast and sides brownish-gray edged with white; rest of underparts white; iris, beak, and legs red.

IDENTIFICATION: Double crest on head and reddish band across upper breast distinguish male; females are similar to female common mergansers but white on throat does not extend to cheeks and borders are ill-defined.

RANGE: Northern hemisphere. In North America breeds in northeastern states, across Canada to Alaska. Winters along Atlantic and Pacific coasts, Great Lakes, and Gulf of Mexico.

NESTING: In a crevice in rocks or in dense growth near water. Nest of grass lined with down. Eggs, 8-10, olive-buff.

REMARKS: The red-breasted merganser migrates through southern and central Alberta in fair numbers and has been seen in the mountains at Banff and Jasper. Female mergansers observed with broods in various parts of Northern Alberta have been ascribed to this species but none has been collected and field identification in most cases was uncertain. Accurate information on the breeding range of the red-breasted and the common mergansers is much to be desired.

Red-breasted mergansers frequent rivers and large lakes which are well supplied with coarse fish and other aquatic animals. Like other mergansers they dive for their food. In flight they have the rapid wing-beat and straight-necked outline typical of mergansers. Often they arrive in Alberta before the ice has entirely disappeared from our lakes and, being forced to stay along the open margins, they are easily observed. At this season females can be identified by observing the males which accompany them; on the nesting grounds however, identification is more difficult for they are usually left by themselves to care.for eggs and young while the males undergo a partial moult.

COMMON MERGANSER
female   *male*

ALLAN BROOKS

RED-BREASTED MERGANSER
female   *male*

TURKEY VULTURE

GOSHAWK

89

VULTURES — Family Cathartidae

At a distance vultures resemble large hawks or eagles; at close range their small unfeathered heads and weak feet lacking sharp talons identify them. When soaring on motionless wings high overhead they have an almost headless appearance. Vultures are scavengers; in tropical countries where they are abundant they do good service by destroying carrion.

TURKEY VULTURE Scarce Summer Resident.
Cathartes aura subsp. (p. 488) Length 28-32 in.

DESCRIPTION: Ads.—Head small, the crown sloping back in a straight line with beak, unfeathered except for a few short bristles, the skin rough and red; remainder of body covered with brownish-black plumage, some feathers with grayish edges; beak grayish-white; legs pale gray tinged with yellowish; iris brown. Im.—Similar to adults but skin of head blackish with gray down and beak blackish.

IDENTIFICATION: Most likely to be confused with eagle which it resembles in color. Unfeathered head is best field mark; in flight the under surface shows no white areas.

RANGE: North and South America. Breeds from northern Mexico north to southern Canada. Winters in southern states south to South America.

NESTING: On the ground, in, under, or beside logs, among rocks, or on ledges. No nest is made. Eggs, 1-3, white blotched with brown. (Mann Lake, June 9.)

REMARKS: Although it was never abundant the turkey vulture used to nest more commonly in Alberta than it does today. A pair nested under a fallen tree on an island in Astotin Lake at Elk Island Park in 1919. Turkey vultures also nested at Ministik Lake and, as late as 1944, at Miquelon Lake. In wild country some 150 miles northeast of Edmonton two pairs of turkey vultures have nested for several years. These are the most northerly nesting records in the province and perhaps for the species. Turkey vultures are seen fairly regularly in the badlands of the lower Red Deer River. Individuals have been seen outside this area at Rife, Belvedere, Smoky River, Calgary and Banff. The only winter record is a specimen shot at Lake de May north of Camrose, on January 1, 1911.

Turkey vultures are skilled in finding rising air currents which will carry them to great heights on motionless wings. Here they circle for hours at a time in favorable weather, feeling in some remarkable way the slightest changes in pressure and adjusting to them with minor flexures of the wings. So keen is their sight that they can spot a dead animal miles away. Upon such carrion they live for, by nature as well as in build, they are incapable of capturing their own food.

90

ACCIPITERS — Subfamily Accipitriinae

In flight the accipiters or short-winged hawks show short, rounded wings and long tails. At rest the wing-tips fall far short of the tip of the tail. They are woodland hawks usually seen darting through the trees or along the edges of the clearings. A few strokes of the wings followed by a glide give a characteristic flight. They capture their prey by surprise or by outright pursuit. In all species of hawks and owls the female is larger than the male. In the accipiters this difference in size is especially noticeable.

GOSHAWK

Accipiter gentilis subsp. (p. 448)

Fairly common resident.
Length 20-26 in.

DESCRIPTION: Ads.—Crown black; line over eye and across nape white with black streaks; remainder of upperparts dark slate-blue; underparts white finely vermiculated and barred with light slate-blue, giving a light-bluish effect at a distance; iris red. Im.—Quite different. Crown brown streaked with black; line over eye and across nape cream with black streaks; remainder of upperparts gray-brown with light feather edges; tail with 8-9 wide bars of dark and light gray-brown; underparts cream or buffy heavily streaked with dark gray-brown; iris yellow.

IDENTIFICATION: Adults, dark slate-blue above and light slate-blue below cannot be mistaken. Immature birds are best identified in the field or in the hand by short wings and large size.

RANGE: Northern hemisphere. Breeds in wooded regions across Canada.

NESTING: In tall trees. Nest a flat platform of twigs lined with shreds of bark near the top of deciduous trees. Eggs, 3-5, rough bluish-white, unmarked. (Belvedere, April 27.)

REMARKS: The goshawk breeds most commonly in the heavily wooded areas of the northern and western parts of the province. It is resident throughout its range, but during the winter it commonly wanders into the parklands and even occasionally into the wooded coulees of the prairies. It is common in the mountains.

Its large size permits the goshawk to prey upon most of the woodland birds and mammals. Snowshoe rabbits and ruffed grouse form a large part of the food but mice, chipmunks, squirrels and various birds are also taken. While it prefers to kill its own food the goshawk will eat any freshly killed flesh.

As settlement has advanced the goshawk has moved before it into the wilder areas where its effect upon man's economy is not felt. Its appearances in settled areas are largely confined to the fall and winter when, its natural food being in short supply, it may occasionally prey upon barnyard flocks. Fortunately the species is not sufficiently numerous to make these depredations very serious.

91

SHARP-SHINNED HAWK
immature   *adult*

COOPER'S HAWK

SHARP-SHINNED HAWK
Accipiter striatus subsp. (p. 488)

Fairly Common Summer Resident.
Length 10-14 in.

DESCRIPTION: Ads.—Above dark slate-gray or brown-ish-gray, darkest on crown; below white finely streaked with brown on throat and heavily barred with brown elsewhere; tail slate-gray with four broad dark bars, feathers all approximately the same length forming a square tail tip; iris red. Im.—Above brownish-gray with brown edges and concealed white spots on feathers, streaked with buffy on crown; below white, each feather with a central streak of gray-brown; tail as in adult; iris yellow.

IDENTIFICATION: May be separated from adult pigeon hawk by less bluish back, barred underparts, short wings, and untoothed beak; immatures of the two species are best separated in the field by wing length. Sharp-shinned hawks are the same color as Cooper's hawks of corresponding ages; the squared tail tip identifies this species.

RANGE: Wooded regions of North America except extreme north-east. Winters mainly south of Canada into Mexico.

NESTING: In trees. Nest a flat platform of twigs lined with bark; sometimes uses old nests of other large birds. Eggs, 4-5, bluish-white heavily blotched with brown. (Edmonton, May 24.)

REMARKS: The sharp-shinned hawk keeps to the depths of the mixed-wood forests in which it finds food and shelter for its nest. It may appear in the clearings as it dashes from one grove to the next, but it never rises into the sky to watch for prey or to soar on the air currents. Even on migration across the prairies it follows the wooded coulees or darts at low level from one farm plantation to the next.

Small woodland birds are the usual prey of the sharp-shinned hawk, but insects, mice, chipmunks, squirrels and bats are also taken. If the first attack is unsuccessful it relentlessly pursues its quarry whose only escape is into a thicket which the hawk cannot penetrate. Since the species is nowhere abundant and since it is too small to kill gamebirds, its depreda-tions do not ordinarily attract attention.

Bird lovers often find it difficult to reconcile themselves to the fact that predators are an essential part of any faunal environment. A full appreciation of this fact brings recognition that the sharp-shinned hawk is a thing of beauty admirably fitted to its role in nature. Piercing eyes to follow every movement, short wings for pursuit among the branches, long legs and claws to reach out and grasp and kill, all combine to form an efficient woodland hunter. The hunt is neither wanton nor sporting; it is deadly serious. Upon its success depends the existence of the indi-vidual and, indeed, of the species.

93

ACCIPITERS — Subfamily Accipitriinae

COOPER'S HAWK
Accipiter cooperii

Scarce Resident.
Length 15-20 in.

DESCRIPTION: Ads.—Above dark slate-gray usually with a brownish cast, almost black on crown; throat white finely streaked with brown; remainder of underparts white heavily barred with brown; tail slate-gray with four broad dark bars, outer feathers about an inch shorter than central, forming round tail tip; iris red. Im.— Above gray-brown with chestnut edges and concealed white patches on feathers; below white, each feather with a broad central streak of gray-brown; tail as in adult; iris yellow.

IDENTIFICATION: Cooper's and sharp-shinned hawks of corresponding ages are identical in color; the tail-tip of Cooper's is rounded. Large immature Cooper's hawks are similar to small immature goshawks; rounded tail-tip is the best identification.

RANGE: United States and southern Canada. Winters in southern states.

NESTING: In trees. Nest a flat mass of twigs lined with shreds of bark and grass. Eggs, 3-5, bluish-white, unmarked or faintly blotched with brown and violet. (Seebe, June 19.)

REMARKS: In the first edition of this book it was suggested that Cooper's hawk might be more common in Alberta than was thought at that time. This has proved to be true. Information provided by many observers shows that the species is not uncommon and that it has a much wider distribution in the province than was formerly supposed. Cooper's hawks nest regularly in the mountain and foothill regions of Alberta at least as far north as Jasper. Nests have been found recently at several places within about sixty miles of Edmonton. There are sight records of Cooper's hawks from many parts of the province except the extreme north, some during the nesting season, indicating that the breeding range may be more extensive than is yet known. During the winter of 1963-64 several Cooper's hawks were live-trapped in the Edmonton area where the species is apparently resident throughout the year.

In all of the accipiters the male is about two-thirds the size of the female. Thus a small male Cooper's hawk may be about the same size as a large female sharp-shin and a large female Cooper's hawk may be almost as large as a small male goshawk. Size, therefore, is not a reliable criterion for identification although it is helpful when used in conjunction with the shape of the tail-tip. Nor are habits or habitat distinctive. Cooper's hawk is a woodland bird which spends little time in the open and rarely rises above treetop height. It is well equipped for survival; quick strokes of its short wings give it speed, a long tail gives it maneuverability among the branches, long sharp talons penetrate the vitals of its prey, and a hooked beak tears the meal into manageable pieces.

BUZZARDS AND EAGLES — Subfamily Buteoninae

The buteos or buzzards are heavy-bodied, wide-winged hawks of rather sluggish habits. They spend a great deal of time sitting on poles, trees or cliffs, and even more circling high overhead on motionless wings. At rest the tips of their wings reach almost to the tip of the tail. Identification of species is difficult since there is wide individual color variation; it is further complicated by the fairly common occurrence of a dark phase in each species. The eagles are large counterparts of the buteos; color variation is slight and there is no dark phase.

RED-TAILED HAWK
Buteo jamaicensis subsp. (p. 488)

Fairly Common Summer Resident.
Length 20-23 in.

DESCRIPTION: Ads. — Above dark grayish-brown streaked and barred with white, brown and dull black; underparts cream to buff streaked with brown, most heavily streaked on abdomen and sides; tail brick-red with or without black bands. There is much variation from the above, some birds being very light and others approaching the dark phase which is entirely brownish-black. Im.—Above streaked and barred with gray, black and white, showing much less brown tinge than in adult; below white streaked with black, most heavily on abdomen; tail light to dark gray with 8-10 black bars, occasionally a suggestion of red.

IDENTIFICATION: A large hawk with red tail and dark streaks forming an indistinct band across abdomen, not as definite as in American rough-leg, and lower down than in Swainson's hawk. Separated from rough-legs by unfeathered legs and from Swainson's by 4 notched primaries.

RANGE: North America north to tree limit. Breeds in northern half of range, winters in southern half.

NESTING: In trees. Nest a mass of twigs near the top of a tree. Eggs, 2-4, white blotched with brown. As with all the Buteos the amount of coloring decreases with each egg laid, the first being well marked, the last often being plain. (Beynon, May 2.)

REMARKS: The red-tailed hawk is most commonly found in the parklands and mixed-wood forests but it occasionally nests in the wooded valleys of the prairies. It feeds mainly on mice, chipmunks, squirrels, ground-squirrels (gophers), rabbits and carrion. Despite this, in some areas it is unjustly called chicken-hawk, a misnomer which has resulted in its persecution by misguided farmers and hunters. Immature birds are often shot as they sit unsuspectingly on a pole or tree; fortunately the adults are more wary.

Red-tails, like all the buteos, are adept at soaring. In summer they rise on the warm air currents and circle aloft for hours without a single stroke of the wings.

95

HARLAN'S HAWK
Buteo harlani

Scarce Migrant.
Length 20-23 in.

DESCRIPTION: All black except the tail which is white finely mottled with black and brown toward the tip. A light phase is similar to the red-tailed hawk but grayer and lacking the browns.

IDENTIFICATION: The only reliable identification mark is the white tail mottled terminally with black and brown. Impossible to separate in the field from some of the color variants of the red-tail.

RANGE: Western North America. Breeds in northern B.C., Yukon, and Alaska. Winters in southwestern states.

NESTING: Similar to that of the red-tailed hawk.

REMARKS: Little is known of the exact status of Harlan's hawk. Classed until recently as a subspecies of the red-tailed hawk it is similar to that species in size, structure and behavior. Where extremes of color variation occur the professional ornithologist may find it difficult to classify certain specimens in his cabinet and impossible to identify some in the field. This is true for the red-tail group. Harlan's hawk has long puzzled the experts; the amateur should be cautious in making positive identification.

It is not certain that Harlan's hawk has nested in Alberta. There is a somewhat doubtful breeding record from the Red Deer area. The breeding range of the species should include northeastern Alberta but very little is known of the avifauna of this region. As further ornithological work is carried on in these wilderness areas the status and range of Harlan's hawk may become clarified.

During recent years specimens of buteos which have been referred to this species have been collected in Alberta mainly during fall migration periods. The collection of these specimens has shed little light on the breeding distribution in Alberta since young hawks habitually wander during the pre-migratory period and their peregrinations may take them in any direction from their birthplace. Unfortunately there are no new records of Harlan's hawk during the nesting season, the time at which both plumage differences and behavioral characteristics are most likely to show. Authenticated nesting records with observations of both parents and young would form valuable contributions to ornithological knowledge. Anyone with information of this sort should see that it is brought to the attention of an ornithologist for full investigation.

RED-TAILED HAWK

RAY SALT

HARLAN'S HAWK

S. D. MACDONALD

97

BROAD-WINGED HAWK Scarce Summer Resident.
Buteo platypterus subsp. (p. 489) Length 15-18 in.

DESCRIPTION: Ads.—Upper parts dark brownish-gray, darkest on crown, back and primaries; under surface of wings white, primaries tipped with black, secondaries lightly barred with black; underparts white barred with brown, most profusely across upper breast; throat and abdomen white; tail broadly barred with 6-7 black and white bars of equal width. Dark phase is dark chocolate brown, almost black on head and back, lighter on underparts. Tail barred with black and dark gray. Im.—Similar to adult above but grayer; below white streaked, not barred, with grayish-brown; tail brown with gray bars.

IDENTIFICATION: Small size and broad contrasting tail bars identify the adult. In flight in any plumage the great breadth of the wings in relation to their length, and the wide but relatively short tail give a very bulky appearance.

RANGE: Eastern North America south of the 60th parallel. Breeds across Canada west to Rockies. Winters in southeastern states and northern South America.

NESTING: In trees. Nest of twigs lined with shredded bark; usually a new nest is built each year. Eggs, 2-4, buffy-white splotched with brown. (Elk Island Park, June 4.)

REMARKS: This small buteo is a woodland hawk which shows a preference for deciduous groves or the more open parts of mixed-wood forests. It spends a great deal of its time perched, not openly in the tree-tops, but at lower levels within the confines of the woods; it avoids human habitations and it soars less commonly than other buteos. In these respects the broad-winged hawk differs markedly from its larger and commoner relative the red-tailed hawk. Perhaps these habits account for its apparent scarcity even in those regions where it occurs regularly. Like all of the buteos the broad-winged hawk is a beneficial species. It feeds mainly on mice, chipmunks, squirrels, insects and carrion.

The broad-winged hawk nests in the mixed-wood forests from Miquelon Lakes north at least to Hines Creek and Cold Lake, but perhaps farther since adults have been seen during the breeding season near Lake Athabasca. Westward it ranges to Jasper National Park. Occasionally it migrates in numbers. On April 21, 1940, a flight of 100 broad-winged hawks was observed near Edmonton moving slowly northward in scattered groups; 78 passed the observation point within a period of 15 minutes. A lone red-tailed hawk accompanied the broad-wings.

SWAINSON'S HAWK Fairly Common Summer Resident.
Buteo swainsoni Length 18-20 in.

DESCRIPTION: Ads.—Head, back and wings dark brownish-gray with subdued irregular marks of black and buff; underparts creamy-white, a wide band of brown across upper breast and some brown barring of feathers of sides; tail gray with several indistinct dark bars; lateral upper tail coverts white. The dark phase is entirely dark brown, slightly lighter on the abdomen. Im. — Head creamy-white broadly streaked with brownish-black; back and wings brownish-black with some buffy feather edges; underparts rusty-white with streaks of dark brown heaviest on upper breast where they form an indistinct band; tail as in adult.

IDENTIFICATION: Separated from rough-legs by unfeathered legs, from the red-tail by a distinct or indistinct dark band across upper breast and 3 notched primaries. In flight the light upper tail coverts help to identify the adult.

RANGE: Western North America. Winters in South America.

NESTING: In trees or bushes, rarely on the ground. Nest a large mass of twigs; a shallow depression in the top lined with grass. Eggs, 3-5, white splotched with chocolate. (Rosebud, June 20.)

REMARKS: Swainson's hawk is the common buteo of the prairies as the red-tailed is of the woods. It feeds mainly on mice, gophers (Richardson's ground-squirrels), and rabbits, but, at least in the fall, grasshoppers and crickets are included in the diet. Mice are eaten whole; larger rodents are torn to pieces small enough to swallow. Vitamins not present in meat are provided by fur and feathers which, however, are not digested. All undigested matter is regurgitated daily in the form of a pellet. This process, common to all hawks and owls, is known as casting. Near Drumheller a Swainson's hawk was observed to cast a pellet containing the hard shells of over 50 grasshoppers and crickets.

On the prairie the crown of a lone willow may be the only available nesting site yet this is adequate protection from all marauders except man. Swainson's hawk is a late nester; young rarely leave the nest until towards the end of July. They are fed largely on Richardson's ground-squirrels often picked up dead by their parents. If these rodents have been poisoned the poison is transmitted to the young usually resulting in their death. Those that survive may be seen sitting on fence posts or telephone poles much of the time or else lazily soaring overhead. The family scatters to the four winds later in the summer before turning southward on a journey which may end as far south as the Argentine.

BROAD-WINGED HAWK

SWAINSON'S HAWK

ROUGH-LEGGED HAWK

M. V. DAHLGREN

FERRUGINOUS HAWK

KAY HODGES

ROUGH-LEGGED HAWK
Buteo lagopus subsp. (p. 489)

Common Migrant.
Length 20-22 in.

DESCRIPTION: Ads.—Head creamy-white streaked with brownish-black; back and wings a mixture of buffy, rusty-brown and brownish-black; underparts creamy-white to buffy streaked with brownish-black, a wide black band across abdomen; under surface of wings creamy-white with black patch at bend of wing; legs feathered to base of toes (hence, rough-leg), buffy; basal half of tail white, terminal half black. There is much variation from the above; the dark phase is entirely black except for a few narrow white bars on the tail. Im.—More buffy but of same general pattern.

IDENTIFICATION: The wide black abdominal band is a good identification mark at any time. In flight the black terminal half of the tail contrasts with the white basal half and the black patch at the bend of the wing is obvious. Legs feathered as in the eagles but this is a much smaller bird.

RANGE: Northern hemisphere. In North America breeds in arctic regions across the continent. Winters in most of U.S.A. and extreme southern Canada.

NESTING: On cliffs, in trees, or on the ground. Nest a mass of twigs lined with mosses. Eggs, 2-5, white with brown splotches.

REMARKS: This species is usually known as the American rough-legged hawk in Alberta. Fair numbers of American rough-legs move south through the province in October and November and pass north again in March and April. A few spend the winter as far north as Red Deer if the weather is not too severe. The species does not nest in Alberta.

It is sometimes said that hawks which winter in Alberta are harmful. This is not so. Like all of the buteos American rough-legs are beneficial hawks. Mice, gophers, and rabbits form the greater part of their food, but they also eat carrion and will pick up birds left by hunters and animals killed on the highways. This latter habit, common to many of the buteos, often proves their undoing for, as they sit on nearby fence-posts or telephone poles to devour their food, they make easy targets for the thoughtless person with a rifle. As the result of wanton destruction during the past few decades some species have been reduced to dangerously small numbers. It is greatly to the credit of the Alberta Government that in 1953 all hawks were placed under complete protection.

The rough-legged hawk often hovers on heavily beating wings while it scans the stubble below. The habit is so characteristic of this species that it forms a good means of field identification.

BUZZARDS AND EAGLES — Subfamily Buteoninae

FERRUGINOUS HAWK
Buteo regalis

Scarce Summer Resident.
Length 24-26 in.

DESCRIPTION: Ads.—Head and neck white broadly streaked except on throat with gray-brown; back and wings irregularly marked with gray-brown, rusty-orange and white; outstretched wings show much white especially on under surface; underparts white, a few brown bars on abdomen and sides; legs feathered to base of toes, rusty-brown with dark brown bars; tail white with light rusty-brown on terminal half of upper surface. There is much individual variation, some birds showing more white, others more brown; the dark phase is entirely chocolate brown. Im.—Similar but usually lighter.

IDENTIFICATION: A large, very light hawk with much rusty on back. In flight appears white except brown legs which form a dark V with apex under the tail. Legs feathered to toes; beak more than 1.7 in. wide across gape.

RANGE: Southwestern states north to southern parts of prairie provinces. Winters in southern parts of range.

NESTING: On cliffs where available, otherwise in trees or on hillsides. Nest, a mass of twigs to which more is added each year until old nests may become 8-10 feet in height; depression lined with grass and, almost invariably, dry manure. Eggs, 3-5, white blotched with brown. (Rosebud, May 7.)

REMARKS: The steep clay cliffs of the badlands are the preferred home of the ferruginous rough-legged hawk. Until the late 1930s, when many adults and young were shot during the nesting season, the species was common in the valleys of the Rosebud and Red Deer rivers. Today the bulky nests still stand on the cutbanks but only rarely is one occupied.

Mice, rabbits and gophers are the staple food of this large hawk. Birds are rarely taken. Families of ferruginous rough-legs are raised within a quarter mile of the poultry yard without any depredation.

Ferruginous rough-legged hawks leave the nesting territory when the young have become strong on the wing and, after some preliminary wandering, they move south late in August. Mortality is high on migration; of 144 young ferruginous rough-legs banded in Alberta 28 were killed before they were 10 months old. Birds banded in the Rosebud valley have been shot during the winter in Oklahoma, Kansas, Texas, New Mexico and California.

103

GOLDEN EAGLE

BALD EAGLE
immature flying

BUZZARDS AND EAGLES — Subfamily Buteoninae

GOLDEN EAGLE
Aquila chrysaetos subsp. (p. 489)

Scarce Resident and Migrant.
Length 30-40 in.

DESCRIPTION: Ads.—All dark brownish-black except golden-brown feather edges on hindneck, tawny feathers on legs extending to base of toes; primaries black; tail black mottled with white at base; feet and cere yellow. Im.—Similar but more white on tail, the black forming a wide terminal band.

IDENTIFICATION: Large size (7-14 lbs.) and great expanse (6½-7½ ft.) identify this as an eagle. Cannot be confused with adult bald eagle. In flight white at base of tail and, in immature, a light area at base of primaries distinguishes from the immature bald eagle. In the hand feathering to the base of the toes will identify at any age.

RANGE: Northern parts of Northern hemisphere. In North America breeds in all mountainous areas south into Mexico.

NESTING: Usually on cliffs, occasionally in trees. Nest, a mass of twigs set on a ledge, lined with bark and grass. Eggs, 2-3, chalky white splotched with brown. (Sheep Creek, May 10.)

REMARKS: The golden eagle nests in the mountains and in the remote regions of northern Alberta. During late fall it moves out onto the prairies where many individuals spend the winter. At this season it feeds largely on carrion, and eagles are often caught in traps set for coyotes around dead farm animals. On its nesting territory it captures ground squirrels, rabbits and marmots; at one nest in the mountains 68 Columbian ground squirrels were brought to a single young bird in a ten-week period. Hunters persecute the golden eagle because it may occasionally take a young big-game animal.

On a warm October day when southbound raptors circle in the air-currents high overhead it is not unusual to find among the distant forms a golden eagle whose size sets it apart from the smaller buteos. We see it clearly only with the aid of good binoculars yet its eyes can spot the movement of a rodent on the ground below and as the hungry bird plunges earthward for a meal—for eagles rarely capture air-borne prey—the immensity of its proportions becomes more obvious and its identity is firmly established. The stoop of the eagle, once seen, is never forgotten.

The golden eagle is a magnificent and picturesque bird whose numbers, like those of certain other species of hawk, are rapidly approaching a dangerously low level. These species are unable to change their predatory nature; therefore, if they are to exist, man must change his. The survival of a predatory species is as important in the mind of the conservationist as is the survival of such game species as the whooping crane and trumpeter swan.

BALD EAGLE
Haliaeetus leucocephalus subsp. (p. 489)

Scarce Resident and Migrant.
Length 32-40 in.

DESCRIPTION: Ads.—Head, neck, tail coverts and tail white; remainder dark brown to brownish-black; legs feathered only half way to base of toes; lower legs, cere and beak yellow. Im.—Entirely brownish-black save where lighter bases of feathers show on surface; white bases show most on flight feathers and on throat and breast. White head and tail are not acquired until about three years of age.

IDENTIFICATION: Large size (7-12 lbs.) and great expanse (7-8 ft.) identify as an eagle; white head and tail as a bald eagle. Immature birds are similar to golden eagles but do not show as much white at base of tail and primaries. In the hand the unfeathered lower leg is positive identification.

RANGE: North America. Breeds north as far as tree limit, south to Florida and Mexico. Winters mainly in southern part of range.

NESTING: In tops of tall trees. Nest a bulky mass of sticks 6-8 ft. across. Eggs, 2-3, white splotched with brown.

REMARKS: Except on migration the bald eagle is rarely found far from large bodies of water. It formerly nested near various rivers and lakes of central Alberta, but today it is confined during the breeding season to the northern part of the province and to a few localities in the mountains. Nests have been observed at Waterton Lakes and Jasper but not at Banff, although adults are seen there nearly every summer. On migration it is widespread but it is less numerous than the golden eagle. It winters here rarely.

Although it is quite capable of capturing small rodents up to the size of a rabbit the bald eagle feeds largely on carrion. Poisoned rodents picked up and eaten by adults or fed to the young may be partially responsible for a decrease in numbers in recent years. On the coasts fish is a staple part of the diet. A poor fisherman itself, the bald eagle commonly harries a successful osprey until the screaming hawk drops its fish whereupon the eagle catches the meal before it reaches the ground. In Alberta such a sight is rare but when the sun in a blue October sky glints on dazzling contrasts of head and body and tail as a bald eagle wings slowly over the stubble or sits majestically in the crown of a dead tree the sight is not readily forgotten. It is understandable then, that our neighbors to the south chose the bald eagle as their national emblem but incomprehensible that the species is not protected in many of the states. Despite its size it is a harmless, beneficial bird which well deserves the protection given to all eagles in Alberta.

HARRIERS — Subfamily Circinae

The harriers are large hawks of slight build with long wings, long tails and long legs. A ring of feathers behind and below the eye forms an owl-like facial disc. They hunt in the open country, gliding or slowly flapping their widely spread wings a few feet above the grass. At other times they rise high in the air and perform remarkable gymnastics. Only one species of harrier occurs in North America.

MARSH HAWK   Common Summer Resident.
Circus cyaneus subsp. (p. 489)   Length 18-22 in.

DESCRIPTION: Ad. m.—Above pale grayish-blue becoming black on tips of primaries; upper tail coverts white; throat pale grayish-blue; remainder of underparts white with flecks of light brown; under surface of wings white. Ad. f.—Above grayish-brown mottled with reddish-brown; tail broadly barred in same colors; upper tail coverts white; below cream or buffy lightly streaked with brown. Im.—Similar to female but more heavily streaked with reddish-brown above and below.

IDENTIFICATION: The white rump patch is the best field mark. Swainson's hawk may have some white on rump but it is not as distinct as in the marsh hawk.

RANGE: North America. Breeds in United States and Canada except northeastern Canada. Winters mainly in southern states and Central America.

NESTING: On the ground. Nest, a mass of reeds, grasses or leaves, hidden in tall grass or low shrubs. Eggs, usually 5-7, bluish-white. (Winterburn, May 26.)

REMARKS: While there is no doubt that the marsh hawk prefers the damp meadows where mice, frogs, insects and small birds abound, it is quite able to support itself and its family on the open prairie far away from water. Here the tangled thickets of rose and snowberry, locally known as buckbrush, give ideal cover for the nest while grasshoppers, crickets, mice and ground squirrels provide a good food supply. When the male appears near the nest with food the female rises to meet him and the prey is transferred in mid-air. Often he drops the mouse he is bringing and she catches it before it has fallen far.

In the fall when marsh hawks and duck hunters share the same hunting grounds the immature birds offer tempting targets as though aware that hawks are protected by law in Alberta. Adults are more wary. The ducks on which marsh hawks may feed at this time of year are those lost or crippled by the hunters.

Although the marsh hawk is widely distributed throughout the province it is less common in the mountains and in the woodlands. Ordinarily the marsh hawk moves south in the fall but occasionally individuals winter here. A nestling banded at Rosebud was shot on the Pacific coast at Oak Harbor, Washington, when it was only 93 days of age.

OSPREYS — Family Pandionidae

OSPREY   Scarce Summer Resident.
Pandion haliaetus   subsp. (p. 489)   Length 23 in.

DESCRIPTION: Head white except brownish-black streaks across crown from eye to eye and black bar extending through eye, across ear to sides of neck; rest of upperparts dark grayish-brown; underparts white except a band of rusty streaks across upper breast; tail dark grayish-brown with faint bars; legs and feet bluish-white, covered with small scales. Immature birds are similar but have some white feather edges on back and buffy markings below.

IDENTIFICATION: A large hawk with striking black and white head markings, largely white below and plain dark brown above; wings very long. In flight the osprey characteristically holds its wings slightly bent at both elbow and wrist joints instead of extending them fully like most other hawks.

RANGE: Almost world-wide. In North America breeds throughout wherever suitable habitat is found. Winters from southern United States south to Peru and Chile.

NESTING: In tops of tall trees; occasionally on a pinnacle of a cliff. Nest, a large mass of sticks slightly depressed on top; increased in size as it is renovated and added to each year. Eggs, 2-4, buffy-white marked with chocolate brown; sometimes almost unmarked, sometimes so heavily marked that egg appears brown.

REMARKS: The osprey formerly nested at many of the larger lakes in central Alberta including Pine Lake, Pigeon Lake, Devil's Lake, Buck Lake, and Baptiste Lake. Today, as a breeding bird, it occurs in small numbers from Lesser Slave Lake north to Lake Athabasca, and in the Rocky Mountain regions. A pair nested for years in a large tree at the confluence of the Vermilion and the Bow within two hundred yards of Banff townsite until the old tree crashed in a high wind. Since then ospreys have nested in the Lake Minnewanka area. During migration ospreys have been reported from many parts of the province.

The osprey, or fish hawk, is rarely found far from lakes or rivers whose waters provide food and whose craggy or wooded margins provide nesting sites. When fishing it sails back and forth at medium height watching for movement in the water below. Then, plummeting downward with legs outstretched, it disappears entirely under the surface, reappearing in a moment amidst the spray to flap away with a fish held head-foremost in its claws. Fishermen are resentful of this competition but investigations show that most of the prey is coarse fish.

C. HAMPSON

MARSH HAWK
female

KAY HODGES

OSPREY

FALCONS — Subfamily Falconinae

Falcons fly with short rapid strokes of their pointed wings, holding them slightly bent and rarely raising them above the level of the back. Partly closing their wings they dive from a height upon their prey, killing it as they pass with a sharp blow of their feet. At rest the wing tips extend almost to the tip of the tail. A tooth-like projection near the tip of the upper mandible identifies the falcons.

GYRFALCON

Rare Winter Visitor.

Falco rusticolus subsp. (p. 489)

Length 21-24 in.

DESCRIPTION: Light adults may be almost pure white but most show some black spotting on crown, back and sides, and black bars on the wings, especially on the primaries. Dark adults are ashy-brown with some white streaking below and an obscure black moustache mark. There are many intermediate forms between these two extremes. Immature birds are similar to adults but more heavily marked with black.

IDENTIFICATION: In flight rapid wing strokes and pointed wing-tips separate the light gyrfalcon from the snowy owl. Dark birds are best identified in the field by their size. In the hand toothed bill and large size identify the gyrfalcon.

RANGE: Circumpolar. Breeds mainly in arctic regions. Winters throughout range but occasionally wanders south as far as northern states.

NESTING: On ledges of cliffs. Usually no nest is built. Eggs, 3-4, buffy heavily marked with reddish-brown.

REMARKS: This large falcon visits us only as a rare wanderer during the winter months. Its summer hunting grounds are the arctic tundras and its prey the lemming, the hare and the ptarmigan. In Alberta its hunting grounds are the frozen prairies and its prey the vole, the jackrabbit and the wintering game-birds. It does not eat carrion.

When falconry was a court pastime the gyrfalcon was reserved for the use of the King and his princes who flew it not only at grouse and ducks but at such larger game as herons and geese. More recently two young gyrfalcons taken from the same nest in Greenland for training made their first flights in Alberta. One was light, the other dark. Their dispositions differed as markedly as their colors. One was sulky and slow; the other was friendly, playful and quick. Both were ultimately lost and no doubt returned to the wild state.

Gyrfalcons have been shot during the winter months near Stavely, Calgary, Blackfalds and Camrose. There are a number of sight records, mainly from the prairies.

110

FALCONS — Subfamily Falconinae

PRAIRIE FALCON
Falco mexicanus

Scarce Resident or Summer Resident.
Length 17-20 in.

DESCRIPTION: Ads.—Above light brownish-gray, each feather edged with buffy; buffy bars on inside webs only of tail and flight feathers; light line extending over eye and across nape; black moustache mark edging white throat; underparts white or creamy streaked with black most heavily on sides. Im.—Similar but darker above, buffy below and more heavily streaked.

IDENTIFICATION: A falcon as large as a peregrine but grayer and showing in flight a dark streak on the side under the wing. Similar to the immature peregrine but lacking pure brown color. Long black feathers under wing at base will identify.

RANGE: Prairies of western North America. Winters throughout range but mainly in southern part.

NESTING: On a ledge or in a crevice of a cliff. No nest is made. Eggs, 3-6, cream or buff blotched with brown. (Rosebud, May 9.)

REMARKS: The high clay cliffs bordering prairie creeks and rivers provide suitable sites for the eyrie of the prairie falcon and are usually sufficiently remote from human habitation to provide it with a fair degree of immunity from persecution. Since the eyrie is inconspicuous and the adults do not attract attention to it, the brood is often successfully raised. As a result the prairie falcon seems to be holding its own better than many other species of hawk. Some prairie falcons winter in the vicinity of the eyrie and, even at this season, they will attack the golden eagles and other hawks which wander through their territory. Others scatter irregularly; young banded at Rosebud have been shot during the winter in southern Alberta, Saskatchewan, North Dakota and Kansas.

The prairie falcon lives largely on mice, gophers and rabbits, but insects and birds are also eaten. Propelled by short rapid strokes of its pointed wings the prairie falcon overtakes its prey with amazing ease and strikes or grasps it with its talons. During late summer families often give marvellous displays of aerial skill over the nesting cliffs, diving and swooping playfully at each other in a form of training which will stand the young birds in good stead when they must capture food for themselves. The family does not stay together very long. Each of the young birds goes its own way on a pre-migratory wandering which may take it several hundred miles in any direction. Early in October comes the urge to turn southward and, riding high on Indian Summer thermals, they move gradually along with other species of hawks. At such times they can be spotted only with binoculars often soaring in great circles like buteos.

111

GYRFALCON

PRAIRIE FALCON

C. HAMPSON

PEREGRINE FALCON
female and young

RAY SALT

PIGEON HAWK
male

PEREGRINE FALCON
Falco peregrinus subsp. (p. 489)

Scarce Summer Resident.
Length 16-20 in.

DESCRIPTION: Ads.—Crown, hindneck, face and a broad moustache mark black; back, wings and tail dark gray-blue, darkest on primaries and tail; throat and upper breast cream; lower breast and abdomen pinkish-buff with fine black marks; sides and legs light gray-blue with dark bars. Im.—Upperparts dark brown with buffy feather edges, darkest on crown; throat cream bordered by dark moustache mark; underparts buffy, heavily streaked with dark brown; tail very dark brown with light bars.

IDENTIFICATION: A large falcon almost black above with heavy black moustache mark. Immatures are browner than prairie falcons and do not show a dark streak on sides in flight.

RANGE: Northern Hemisphere and Australia. In North America breeds from Alaska to Baffin Island south to Mexico and Tennessee. Winters in southern part of range.

NESTING: On cliffs usually overlooking water. Nest, on a ledge sheltered by an overhang. The eggs are usually laid on the bare sand of the ledge but occasionally a few grasses and twigs represent a nest. Eggs, 3-6, reddish-brown marked with chocolate. (Rosebud, May 10.)

REMARKS: Our subspecies of the peregrine falcon is known locally as the duck hawk. Except for minor color differences it is the same falcon which was used for falconry by the nobles of Europe in mediaeval times. The sport is being revived today in America; this species, the prairie falcon, and the pigeon hawk are most commonly trained. The peregrine is the most spirited of the falcons. It kills its prey in the air, swooping upon it from above with a speed which is estimated at close to 200 miles per hour. Birds up to the size of pigeons form most of its food, but it can kill a mallard with ease. The prey is plucked before it is eaten. Some feathers, however, are swallowed with the flesh and later cast up with the undigested bones in the form of a pellet. Peregrine falcons will not eat carrion.

When hatched the young are covered with white down but at about 35 days of age they have acquired the brown juvenile plumage. They now spend considerable time vigorously exercising their wings and may suddenly find themselves lifted from the nesting ledge on their first flight. If they do not leave the nest, however, the adults refuse them food, bringing it instead to a nearby ledge until hunger forces them to try their wings.

The peregrine falcon is scarce throughout its range. It usually avoids settled areas and seldom comes into direct conflict with human interests. Despite its food habits it deserves the complete protection which is accorded to it in Alberta.

114

FALCONS — Subfamily Falconinae

PIGEON HAWK
Falco columbarius subsp. (p. 489)

Fairly Common Summer Resident.
Length 11-13 in.

DESCRIPTION: Ad. m.—Crown, back and wings light blue with black feather shafts; a buffy band across hind-neck; primaries black with large white spots on inner webs; throat creamy white; breast and abdomen cream, each feather with a medial streak of light brown; tail light blue with four black bars. (This is Richardson's pigeon hawk; the eastern is darker.) Ad. f.—Similar to male but blue replaced by yellowish-brown. Im. — Like female but dark chocolate brown.

IDENTIFICATION: A small dull-brown or bluish falcon. Differs from sharp-shinned hawk in having long pointed wings which extend, at rest, almost to tip of tail; from sparrow hawk by lack of black face markings and by much duller colors.

RANGE: North America. Breeds in Canada north to tree limit. Winters mainly in northern and central states, rarely in Alberta.

NESTING: In trees in old nests of other large birds; in Alberta, usually in a magpie's nest but occasionally in a crow's nest. Eggs, 4-6, reddish-brown with dark brown markings. (Beynon, May 16.)

REMARKS: In the south of the province during the nesting season the pigeon hawk is seldom found far from the wooded coulees; farther north it shows a preference for the mixed woods near rivers and lakes. Both adults vociferously protest any invasion of their territory, flying over the nesting tree on rapidly beating wings and helping the intruder to locate the nest rather than driving him away. If the approach is not too close pigeon hawks are not greatly concerned about human activity in their area. They often nest in shelter belts close to farm houses and one or more pairs usually may be found nesting along the river banks in our major cities. If they are not disturbed they will return year after year to the same spot.

In the fall pigeon hawks may be found on migration in any type of terrain, but many congregate around the shallow sloughs where waders abound. Families do not migrate as a group. Banding records show that some pigeon hawks raised in Alberta spend the winter in Arizona. Others, however, have been observed to remain here in winter.

Although it can take only the smaller species of birds, the pigeon hawk captures its prey with all the dash of the larger peregrine falcon. Its European counterpart, the merlin, was formerly carried by ladies in the sport of falconry. Large insects, such as grasshoppers and dragonflies, form a large part of the food. These are seized in flight and often eaten on the wing.

RAY SALT

SPARROW HAWK

S. D. MACDONALD

BLUE GROUSE

FALCONS — Subfamily Falconinae

SPARROW HAWK

Falco sparverius subsp. (p. 489)

Common Summer Resident.
Length 10-12 in.

DESCRIPTION: Ad. m.—Crown slate blue with large central patch of chestnut; hindneck and back orange-brown with black marks mainly on upper back; wings slate blue with black spots, flight feathers mainly black; tail orange-brown with broad black terminal bar; face and throat white; moustache mark and bar behind ear black; breast light orange shading to cream on abdomen, with round black spots mainly on sides. Ad. f.—Head and face similar to male; back, wings and tail reddish-brown with much black barring; primaries black; underparts buffy heavily streaked with brown. Im.—Immature birds are similar to adults of the same sex.

IDENTIFICATION: May be confused only with the pigeon hawk. The bright browns and the contrasting face markings of the sparrow hawk are distinctive.

RANGE: North America. Breeds throughout range. Winters in southern half of range.

NESTING: Most commonly in holes in trees. No nest is made. Eggs, 4-6, cream or buffy blotched with brown. (Rosebud, May 31.)

REMARKS: This pretty little falcon is the best known and the most widely distributed of all our hawks. In the fall sparrow hawks are everywhere, usually in family groups perched on telephone wires and fence posts. During the breeding season, while not so numerous, sparrow hawks may be found in the woodlands or on the prairies, in the wilderness or in the hearts of the cities. Where cavities in trees are not available as nesting sites they will accept any substitute, such as a crevice in a cliff, an old magpie's nest, or a nesting-box.

The sparrow hawk is poorly named; birds form only a small part of its diet. Insects and mice are staple foods. To capture these the sparrow hawk hovers on rapidly beating wings, watching for telltale movements in the grass which betray the presence of its prey. Insects are often picked out of the air in true falcon style. Like all the falcons the sparrow hawk will eat only freshly killed food.

During the second week of April the first sparrow hawks return to Alberta from the south. The earliest arrivals are almost invariably males; females arrive later in the month. The southward migration occurs mainly during the first two weeks of September although occasional laggards may be found in southern Alberta until early in October. Sparrow hawks do not winter in the province.

117

GROUSE — Family Tetraonidae

Grouse are plump, short-winged birds somewhat resembling the domestic fowl. Most species are gregarious except during the breeding season. They are largely terrestrial but are capable of strong, rapid flight. The nostrils, the legs and, in some species, the toes are covered with feathers. Grouse are classed as game birds. Their populations fluctuate periodically from causes at present unknown.

BLUE GROUSE
Dendragapus obsurus subsp. (p. 489)

Fairly Common Resident.
Length 18-21 in.

DESCRIPTION: M.—Overall color slate-gray, darkest on back, somewhat brownish on wings; much white on throat and abdomen; white tips on feathers of sides and under tail coverts; tail black with or without gray terminal band; small yellow comb over eye; on sides of neck a distensible sac of reddish-purple skin bounded by dark feathers with white bases. F.—Similar but feathers of upper parts and sides stippled with light brown; feathers of underparts have more white tips.

IDENTIFICATION: A large mountain grouse with no well-defined markings. Females may be confused with ruffed grouse but large size and plain black tail, sometimes gray-tipped, will identify them.

RANGE: Rocky Mountain regions from Yukon to New Mexico. Breeds throughout range.

NESTING: On the ground. Nest of grass, leaves and pine needles near fallen log or at foot of tree. Eggs, 5-10, buffy, finely spotted with light brown. (Canmore, May 29.)

REMARKS: During spring and summer blue grouse may be found in the scattered aspen groves of the foothills and on the lightly wooded slopes of mountain valleys. The male struts about on his territory occasionally pausing to fill his nuchal sacs with air and emit a guttural hoot with a peculiar ventriloquial quality. The female incubates closely trusting that her colors blending with the leaves and grasses of her surroundings will enable her to escape detection. Her chicks are equally well protected by color but their soft down will not protect them from chilling mountain rains and many of them perish if June is wet and cold. Late in August blue grouse move to higher altitudes feeding on berries and insects. As winter approaches they move to even higher wintering grounds often miles away from their summer territories. Here in the edges of a thick coniferous forest they spend the winter, remaining in the trees most of the time and feeding on needles and buds.

In our Rocky Mountain National Parks both adult and young blue grouse are usually quite tame. They will often allow close observation but any sudden movement startles them into precipitous flight down the mountainside.

GROUSE — Family Tetraonidae

SPRUCE GROUSE
Canachites canadensis subsp. (p. 489)

Fairly Common Resident.
Length 15 in.

DESCRIPTION: M.—Crown, hindneck, back and wings dusky brown to dusky blue, each feather finely barred with black; face black, a white line behind eye and a scarlet comb above it usually hidden by feathers; throat black, bounded, and sometimes marked with white; remainder of underparts black with much white barring; tail black (Franklin's grouse, a subspecies), or black tipped with cinnamon (spruce grouse). F.—Above finely barred with brown, gray-blue and black; below more coarsely barred with brown, white and black, darker colors predominating; tail feathers black sprinkled with fine cinnamon spots and sometimes with terminal cinnamon bar.

IDENTIFICATION: A small very dark grouse found in thick stands of spruce and pine; quite tame. The black tail, with or without cinnamon, is found on no other grouse except the much larger blue grouse.

RANGE: The coniferous forests of temperate North America. Breeds throughout its range.

NESTING: On the ground. Nest of leaves and grasses in the moss under low-hanging branches of a spruce tree. Eggs, 8-16, usually 10-12, light brown beautifully marked with darker browns. (Fawcett, May 14.)

REMARKS: The spruce grouse frequents the spruce woods and muskegs of the northern and western parts of the province. Franklin's grouse, until recently distinguished as a separate species, occurs in similar habitat in the mountains. When the snow is deep on the ground they spend much of their time in the coniferous trees upon whose needles they feed, but at other seasons they forage on the ground adding insects, leaves and berries to their diet. At the approach of an enemy they flutter into the branches of a conifer, relying on their protective coloration and immobility to make them inconspicuous. This habit, so effective in eluding all but human predators, has earned them the name fool hen. As the wilderness areas are opened up the spruce grouse is one of the first species to disappear. It withstands easily the assaults of goshawk, lynx, and weasel but is helpless against the axe and gun. The National Parks are the best hope for the survival of this species.

The male is a beautiful sight in the spring strutting about with red combs inflated and tail erect and spread. At the culmination of his display he flutters to the ground from a low bough producing a drumming sound somewhat similar to that of the ruffed grouse. The female with her family is as tame as a barnyard fowl, but at the first frightened peep from a chick she bravely attacks even a human marauder. Despite her boldness many chicks must be lost, for the fledged family rarely numbers more than half a dozen.

GROUSE — Family Tetraonidae

RUFFED GROUSE
Bonasa umbellus subsp. (p. 489)

Common Resident.
Length 17 in.

DESCRIPTION: Ads. and im.—Head crested; a ruff of glossy black feathers on each side of neck; upperparts gray mottled and streaked with soft browns, black and white; feathers of lower back with small 'eyes'; throat buffy; underparts whitish barred with dull brown and buff; tail gray finely speckled with black and with broad black sub-terminal band; legs feathered almost to base of toes. A 'red' phase also occurs. In this the markings are as above but the predominant color is reddish-brown on the back and tail.

IDENTIFICATION: Black ruffs on neck and fairly long tail with black band near tip are good distinguishing marks. Almost invariably found in the woods.

RANGE: Forested regions of temperate North America. Breeds across Canada except on prairies.

NESTING: On the ground. Nest of leaves and grass usually near or under a fallen log or root. Eggs, 8-14, buff, unspotted. (Ponoka, June 4.)

REMARKS: The ruffed grouse is a bird of the deciduous and mixed-wood forests, but it also thrives in the farm wood-lots and in the wooded coulees of the prairies if hunting pressure is not too great. It rises with a soft whirr from the leaves in which it crouched unseen and allows but a glimpse before it disappears behind a maze of tree-trunks. It is more solitary in its habits than any other species of grouse; small family groups may be found in early fall but these soon break up. In the spring the male displays upon a log, ruffs extended, wings trailing, and tail spread. From time to time he beats his wings against the air to produce a noise like the muffled roll of a drum. Occasionally he drums in the fall.

The two weeks after they hatch are the most critical period in the lives of the downy, precocious young. Predation is not the problem for they instinctively crouch motionless at their mother's danger call and their colors blend perfectly with the forest floor. Weather is the important factor; if June is rainy the chicks soon succumb from being constantly wet and chilled. Under favorable circumstances, however, they can fly short distances at ten days of age and shortly after, their down is replaced by more protective feathers.

The ruffed grouse is known locally by various names such as bush partridge, birch partridge, and even fool hen. Young birds may be so tame as to appear foolish but older birds become wise to the ways of the hunter. To the true sportsman who shoots only on the wing the ruffed grouse provides the finest of all upland bird hunting.

SPRUCE GROUSE
male

RUFFED GROUSE

GROUSE — Family Tetraonidae

WILLOW PTARMIGAN   Fairly Common Winter Resident.
Lagopus lagopus subsp. (p. 489)   Length 15 in.

DESCRIPTION: Legs and toes completely feathered; upper tail coverts completely cover tail when at rest. Summer m.—Head, neck, back and breast chestnut faintly barred with black; wings largely white; tail feathers black; abdomen white. Summer f.—Entirely yellowish-brown spotted and barred above with black and regularly barred below with black; wings mainly white; tail feathers black. Winter ads.—Pure white except black tail feathers, beak and eye.

IDENTIFICATION: Large amount of white on wings and black tail are the best field marks in summer. In winter all white except black tail which usually shows only in flight.

RANGE: Circumpolar. In Canada across the arctic regions. Moves south slightly in winter.

NESTING: On the ground. Nest of grass, leaves and feathers. Eggs, 7-10, yellowish or brownish spotted and blotched with rich reddish-browns.

REMARKS: In October flocks of willow ptarmigan arrive in northern Alberta from their breeding grounds on the tundra. At this time they prefer the frozen muskegs, the borders of lakes and streams, and similar openings in the woods. Normally willow ptarmigan winter only as far south as Calling Lake but stragglers have been reported during exceptional winters from Athabasca, Clyde, Fort Saskatchewan, Edmonton, Camrose and Sullivan Lake. In the northern part of Jasper National Park willow ptarmigan nest and are apparently locally resident in some areas as far south as the Tonquin Valley.

On the arctic tundra the male willow ptarmigan establishes a territory and while his mate does all the incubating, he shows off his beautiful chestnut and white plumage and does battle with any other male which, accidentally or deliberately, enters his domain. Like most grouse he is quite vocal at this time emitting a variety of booms and hoots. The downy young follow their mother from the nest a few hours after they hatch, their colors blending well with the moss. Many of them escape the keen eyes of jaegers and other predators for large flocks of adults and young, both now in white plumage, migrate southward in late fall. It is at this time that one may expect to find them in Alberta.

Ptarmigan are the only birds which assume a white plumage in winter. All species have an arctic or sub-arctic distribution except the white-tailed which finds arctic conditions at high altitudes in the mountains. The red grouse of the British Isles is a close relative of the North American ptarmigan; it does not turn white in winter.

GROUSE — Family Tetraonidae

WHITE-TAILED PTARMIGAN
Lagopus leucurus subsp. (p. 489)

Fairly Common Resident.
Length 13 in.

DESCRIPTION: Legs and toes completely feathered; upper tail coverts completely cover the tail when at rest. Summer ads.—Lower breast, abdomen, tail and much of wing white; remainder grayish-brown with fine markings of black and white. The over-all effect is a marvellous example of protective coloration allowing the bird to blend perfectly with the vegetation and rocks in which it lives. Winter ads.—Entirely pure white except beak and eye.

IDENTIFICATION: A small grouse, in summer mottled with browns, black and white and showing white wings and tail in flight; in winter entirely white. The white tail feathers are distinctive in any plumage.

RANGE: Mountains of western North America from Alaska to northern Mexico. Breeds throughout range.

NESTING: On the ground. Nest of grasses and feathers. Eggs, usually 6-8, buffy with fine spots of darker browns.

REMARKS: The white-tailed ptarmigan is found only in the mountains at high levels. In our Rocky Mountain National Parks the summer tourist must search the rocky slopes above tree-line to find a small group of cocks running about among the boulders, or a bantam-like hen escorting her downy chicks across an alpine meadow. They are very tame and the close study allowed is ample compensation for the effort required to reach their haunts.

Protective coloration is developed to a high degree in ptarmigan. Although they nest in the open, females blend so well with the short vegetation that it is almost impossible to pick them out even at close range. As though aware of this they sit very close and will not move until practically stepped upon. The chicks too seem to know that movement is more easily detected than color and, until their mother clucks an 'all clear', they crouch motionless among the grass and stones.

As the snow deepens on the peaks flocks of white-tailed ptarmigan, now in their white plumage, are forced to lower levels to find the buds which are their mainstay in the winter. At this season weed-seeds and grain may attract them to ranches and villages in the valleys, but with the approach of spring they leave again for higher altitudes.

123

WILLOW PTARMIGAN
winter

KAY HODGES

WHITE-TAILED PTARMIGAN

GREATER PRAIRIE CHICKEN

KAY HODGES

SHARP-TAILED GROUSE

C. HAMPSON

GROUSE — Family Tetraonidae

GREATER PRAIRIE CHICKEN
Tympanuchus cupido   subsp. (p. 490)

Rare Summer Resident.
Length 17 in.

DESCRIPTION: Ads.—Above indefinitely barred with black, buffy, and reddish-brown; throat buffy with a few brown spots at sides; rest of underparts distinctly barred with white and grayish-brown; short square tail, brownish-black narrowly tipped with white; a group of long feathers on each side of neck black edged with chestnut and buffy, 3-4 in. long in male, shorter in female; below these feathers is a bare patch of orange skin normally concealed but distensible to form a sac; small yellow comb over eye of male; legs buffy, feathered to base of toes.

IDENTIFICATION: A large brownish grouse strongly barred below, with short, square-tipped tail. The long feathers on sides of neck are positive identification.

RANGE: Formerly found from Atlantic states through Great Plains of North America. Now confined largely to Great Plains regions.

NESTING: On the ground. Nest of grass concealed in tall grass or low bushes. Eggs, 8-18, buffy-olive, sometimes finely marked with brown.

REMARKS: This is the bird to which, by precedence and by habit, rightfully belongs the name prairie chicken. From the long feathers on its neck it has also received another name, pinnated grouse. It should be watched for on grassy prairies and cultivated fields especially in the eastern part of the province. Early in the spring pinnated grouse gather in a chosen spot to perform a courtship dance in which the males are the only active participants. This performance, repeated each morning for several weeks, is similar to that of the sharp-tailed grouse.

In the northern part of its range this species is migratory. Until about 1930 pinnated grouse bred regularly in small numbers near Buffalo Lake, Beaverhill Lake, and in other parts of southeastern Alberta. Many hunters will remember shooting them during the fall hunting season. The grouse left the province during the winter and probably spent this season in the Dakotas where the species is still reasonably common. During the past 25 years there have been no reports of pinnated grouse nesting in Alberta and few records of its occurrence at other seasons. Several birds were seen near Tofield in the spring of 1934 and it is probable that this was the last time they nested in that area. Unfortunately some confusion exists, perhaps through the use of locally popular names, in separating this species from the sharp-tailed grouse and even the ruffed grouse. Sportsmen occasionally report that they have shot greater prairie chicken in mistake for other upland birds; it would be helpful if the tails of these specimens were preserved and sent to an ornithologist for examination. Cooperation of this kind might show that prairie chicken still occur in the province on occasion.

GROUSE — Family Tetraonidae

SHARP-TAILED GROUSE
Pedioecetes phasianellus subsp. (p. 490)

Common Resident.
Length 18 in.

DESCRIPTION: Ads. and im.—Upperparts a mixture of buff, brown, black and white, giving a light brown effect vaguely barred with light and dark; light line over eye and dark line below it spreading out on ear; male with orange comb over eye usually hidden by feathers; throat cream or buffy; remainder of underparts white, each feather of breast and sides with a V of blackish and the sides with some brown; tail feathers graded in length, outer ones short and white, middle two longest and mottled with brown, black and white; legs feathered to base of toes.

IDENTIFICATION: A large brownish grouse mainly white below with V marks on breast and a pointed tail. In flight the white sides of the tail make a good field mark.

RANGE: Northern Quebec to Alaska south to Minnesota and New Mexico, but scarce west of the Rockies.

NESTING: On the ground. Nest of grasses concealed in grass or low brush. Eggs, 10-14, olive-brown finely dotted with reddish-brown. (Craigmyle, May 26.)

REMARKS: This is the bird which is known throughout Alberta as the prairie chicken although it is rarely found on the open prairies. It prefers the brushy parklands and the edges of the forest clearings. Grain fields adjacent to these areas are favorite feeding spots in the fall and winter, and the flocks that congregate here provide excellent sport for the upland game hunter. When disturbed the birds usually fly for a mile or more and the hunter who travels on foot must earn his bag.

Each spring the sharp-tailed grouse gather on the ancestral dancing ground where, at dawn, the males perform a courting dance with much strutting and fighting. Large purple sacs on their necks are inflated with air. When this is released through the mouth a booming sound is produced which carries with ventriloquial effect for several hundred yards. The hens play a passive role in this performance; they take no part in the dance but mating occurs here. In winter sharp-tails often burrow under the loose snow to spend the night in a cosy room at the end of a short tunnel. At this season they feed on grain, berries and tree-buds, but when spring arrives they add insects, green leaves and even blossoms to their diet.

Sharp-tailed grouse occur in the wooded areas of northern Alberta and the foothills in fluctuating but ever-decreasing numbers. Until a few years ago the species was found throughout the parklands, in the irrigation districts and even occasionally in brushy coulees extending into the prairies; today sharp-tailed grouse are rarely seen in these cultivated areas where introduced exotics abound.

C. HAMPSON

SAGE GROUSE
female — male displaying

H. SIVYER

RING-NECKED PHEASANT
male

GROUSE — Family Tetraonidae

SAGE GROUSE   Scarce Resident.
Centrocercus urophasianus   subsp. (p. 490)   Length 22-30 in.

DESCRIPTION: M.—Crown and hindneck gray finely marked with black; back and wings gray, many feathers with white shafts and all except primaries finely barred or splotched with buff and black; face, throat and foreneck black with small white marks; upper breast and sides of neck covered with stiff white feathers, underlying these are large sacs which are inflated during the spring dance; thin, long black plumes on sides of neck; lower breast and abdomen black; sides a mixture of black, buff and white; tail of long pointed feathers finely barred with black, buff and white; legs gray feathered to base of toes. F.— Similar but more buffy above, throat white, foreneck and upper breast mostly gray with fine black marks; lacks distensible nuchal sacs; smaller than male.

IDENTIFICATION: A very large grouse; males weigh 5-7 lbs., females 3-4½ lbs. The large black abdominal patch is distinctive.

RANGE: The sage-brush plains of central North America. Resident throughout its range.

NESTING: On the ground. Nest of grass and leaves usually in shelter of sage bush. Eggs, 7-15, olive-buff with fine spots of dark brown.

REMARKS: As the spruce grouse is confined by its food habits to the coniferous forests, so by its diet the sage grouse is restricted to the sage-bush plains. Birds of this type which are constitutionally unable to change their food habits are so dependent upon one kind of habitat that its destruction means their extermination. Sage grouse will be found in Alberta only as long as the sage-bush plains remain intact. It is doubtful if they will ever be sufficiently numerous to permit their use as a gamebird. At present the species is confined to the extreme southeastern part of the province which is drained by the Milk River.

Sage hens form large flocks during fall and winter. Sage leaves and buds form most of their food at this time and their flesh becomes so strongly impregnated with the taste and odor of this plant that it is quite inedible. In the spring the males gather at dawn to perform a peculiar type of dance. The nuchal sacs are inflated until the stiff feathers covering them scrape upon the ground; as the air is released through the mouth a guttural grunt is produced. The females are largely ignored during this performance. Shortly after sunrise the birds fly off to disperse over the prairies where they feed and sun themselves during the long day then sleep through the short night until dawn calls them again to the dance. By early May the females are attending to nesting duties and the males, gradually losing the urge to display, take no further interest in family matters.

129

PHEASANTS, PARTRIDGES — Family Phasianidae

The members of this family have unfeathered legs, short wings, and a scale over the nostril at the base of the beak. Although largely terrestrial in habit they also fly well, but usually for only short distances. Several species have been domesticated; from this family came our domestic chicken. No members of the family are native to Alberta but three species have been successfully introduced as game birds.

RING-NECKED PHEASANT
Phasianus colchicus subsp. (p. 90)

Common Resident.
Length 21-36 in.

DESCRIPTION: Ad. m.—A large bird with a very long tail, brilliantly colored in iridescent purple on the head and neck and iridescent bronze and black on the body; usually a white ring around neck; legs not feathered. Ad. f.—Much smaller. Upperparts buffy, each feather marked with black and brown; throat cream; underparts buff, indistinctly marked with brown and black on sides; tail not as long as in male, buffy-brown barred with black, central feathers much longer than outer ones. Immature birds moult into plumage similar to adults during first fall.

IDENTIFICATION: The male is unmistakable. The female resembles the sharp-tailed grouse but is more buffy, lacking any patches of pure white; the legs are unfeathered.

RANGE: Originally southern China and Japan. The origins of the first introductions of pheasants into Europe are unknown. In Canada introduced into the southern parts of most provinces.

NESTING: On the ground. Nest of grasses, leaves and weeds, concealed in tall grass or low bushes. Eggs, 6-12, olive or buffy. (Brooks, May 6.)

REMARKS: The earliest attempts at introduction of the pheasant into Alberta were failures, and it was not until birds were released in the irrigated lands around Brooks that the species became established. Since then ring-necked pheasants have been liberated in many parts of the province with varying success. They do best in those regions where there is plenty of tight cover close to cultivated fields; tangles of willow, rosebush, and clover bordering streams and irrigation ditches are ideal. This is the habitat formerly occupied by our native grouse. Pheasants will eat almost anything. Grain is a staple food but green sprouts are relished; in truck farming areas considerable damage may be done to vegetable and root crops.

The ring-neck is polygamous; from six to eight females are usually found in company with one cock in the spring. The hens are notoriously poor mothers and mortality among the chicks is often quite high. Hatchery raised chicks apparently fare little better; according to Alberta banding records only about 6% of the cocks released at the age of eight weeks are later shot by hunters.

130

PHEASANTS, TURKEYS, PARTRIDGES — Family Phasianidae

CHUKAR
Alectoris graeca subsp. (p. 490)

Recently Introduced.
Length 14 in.

DESCRIPTION: Ads.—Upperparts bluish-grey, lightest on crown and washed with rusty over back and wings; flight feathers brownish-gray, many with buff outer webs; middle tail feathers like back, outer ones reddish-brown; cheeks and throat creamy-buff; black line across forehead through eye and over ear, becoming very broad down side of neck and across upper breast; breast bluish-gray; abdomen cinnamon-buff; sides creamy-buff strongly barred with black and chestnut; beak orange; legs reddish.

IDENTIFICATION: Somewhat similar to Hungarian partridge but much grayer, unmarked on back, and with black gorget around throat and across breast.

RANGE: Eurasia; introduced into North America.

NESTING: On the ground. Nest of grass and leaves lining a shallow depression usually well hidden in vegetation. Eggs, 10-13, yellowish-white speckled with brown.

REMARKS: The chukar partridge was first liberated in Alberta in the Calgary district in September, 1937, but this implantation and others in immediately succeeding years were unsuccessful. In 1954 and 1955 the Game Branch of the Government of Alberta released 2,345 adult and young chukars along the Milk River in the Avalon-Comrey districts. By the spring of 1955 some of the birds had crossed the border into Montana, but many remained and nested not far from the points of release. In 1962 biologists were unable to find chukars in Alberta although the birds were still present in cultivated areas immediately south of the border. It was felt that the chukars were showing preference for grainfields over uncultivated grazing lands.

WILD TURKEY
Meleagris gallopavo subsp. (p. 490)

Recently Introduced.
Length 45-50 in.

DESCRIPTION: The Mexican variety of this bird was the ancestor of the domesticated turkey. The wild turkey is a large bronze-brown bird with naked, wattled head and long brown tail barred with black; tail and coverts tipped with rusty. Males have a tuft of coarse black bristles hanging from the breast.

IDENTIFICATION: Similar to the domesticated turkey but browner; tail and tail coverts tipped with white in domesticated turkeys, rusty in wild turkey.

RANGE: Wooded areas of North America north originally to southern Ontario but not Alberta. Introduced into Cypress Hills of Alberta.

NESTING: On the ground. Nest of grass and leaves, well hidden. Eggs, 10-18, light buffy speckled with brown.

REMARKS: On March 6 and 26, 1962, a total of sixteen wild turkeys which had been wild-trapped in South Dakota were released near Reesor Lake in Cypress Hills. Five were males and eleven females; nearly all were young birds hatched the previous year. They found suitable habitat immediately and by late summer of 1963 their numbers had increased to over seventy. In 1965, despite the previous severe winter, there were at least two hundred wild turkeys spread throughout the Cypress Hills in Alberta and Saskatchewan. In the light of this success it is proposed to introduce wild turkeys into other suitable parts of the province.

PHEASANTS, PARTRIDGES — Family Phasianidae

GRAY (HUNGARIAN) PARTRIDGE
Perdix perdix subsp. (p. 490)

Common Resident.
Length 12 in.

DESCRIPTION: Ads.—Face and throat pale cinnamon; crown brown streaked with buff; back bluish-gray, most feathers tipped with chestnut; breast and sides blue-gray, several broad bars of chestnut on sides and a broad chestnut horseshoe-shaped mark on lower breast; abdomen white; central four tail feathers marked like back, remainder chestnut. In immature birds the chestnut horseshoe may be replaced by white.

IDENTIFICATION: A small brownish partridge with light brown face and throat; usually some evidence of chestnut horseshoe on lower breast. In flight the chestnut tail feathers are obvious and distinctive.

RANGE: Europe and western Asia. Introduced into various parts of North America. Resident throughout range.

NESTING: ·On the ground. Nest of grass concealed in grass or low bushes. Eggs, 10-22, olive or olive-buff, unmarked. (Calgary, June 6, 19 eggs.)

REMARKS: In 1908 seventy pairs of gray partridge were imported from Hungary and liberated at Midnapore. From this importation came the name Hungarian partridge. In 1909 another ninety-five pairs were released. The Huns increased so rapidly that a shooting season was allowed in 1913. Since then they have spread throughout the southern half of the province. They have recently been introduced into the Peace River district.

Although normally the Hungarian partridge is a bird of the brushy plains, it has adapted itself in Alberta to all types of habitat except the deep woods. In the fall coveys of ten to twenty birds provide excellent sport for the gamebird hunter. Huns run and fly fast, hide well, and rise with a disconcerting racket which unnerves the tyro. A fat bird weighs only a pound but the flesh is highly prized by the connoisseur.

Flocks of Hungarian partridge spend the winter in a territory rarely more than 600 acres in area. When snows are deep they dig their way to the ground upon alighting and there, sheltered from the wind, they sit and absorb the warmth of the winter sun or dig a pathway through the stubble eating as they go. Only a head peeking over the snow now and then gives them away. They never tunnel under the snow like sharp-tailed grouse nor do they crowd together for warmth like quail yet these "yards" are undoubtedly an important factor in winter survival. Often flocks of partridge resort to farmsteads at this season seeking the protection of the farm shelterbelt and an easy meal of spilled grain. In February partridge are often found in pairs during the middle of the day but they flock again in the evening. By April only mated pairs are seen and they remain together until incubation commences late in May.

CHUKAR

VALERIE J. MAY

GRAY (HUNGARIAN) PARTRIDGE

C. HAMPSON

CRANES — Family Gruidae

Cranes are very large birds with long legs, long necks, and stout pointed beaks. Part of the face and much of the crown is devoid of feathers, the rough skin having only a sparse hair-like covering. Unlike herons, cranes fly with neck and legs fully extended. They migrate in flocks stopping periodically to feed, like geese, in cultivated fields.

WHOOPING CRANE
Grus americana

Rare Migrant and Summer Resident.
Length 50-56 in.

DESCRIPTION: Ads.—Pure white except a bare patch of red skin from beak over crown and under eye; wing tips (primaries and coverts) black; beak yellowish; iris yellow; legs black. Im.—Similar but many feathers washed with rusty or cinnamon; area on head which will later become bare covered with short gray feathers.

IDENTIFICATION: Unmistakable on the ground; a large white bird standing four feet high. In flight black wing tips distinguish it from pure white swan; very long neck and long legs extended behind distinguish it from snow goose and pelican.

RANGE: Formerly most of North American. Today the only known breeding ground is in extreme northern Alberta and adjacent territories. Winters on Aransas Refuge in Texas.

NESTING: On the ground in a marsh. Nest, a bulky mass of grasses and reeds with a depression on top. Eggs, 2, olive or buffy blotched with brown.

REMARKS: The whooping crane, closer to extinction than any other species of American bird, is known by name across the continent yet few people have seen any of the twenty-odd survivors of a once populous race. These migrate across Alberta and Saskatchewan twice a year offering an opportunity to bird students of these provinces which cannot be duplicated elsewhere in Canada. Lone birds or small groups are occasionally seen, more often in the fall, beside ponds and sloughs in grain fields. Here they rest and feed before continuing their long journey.

Unfortunately such large white birds are conspicuous, and despite legal protection, a few are killed or wounded by ignorant or irresponsible people each year. The number of young reared in recent years has not replaced these losses. Obviously, unless this situation can be rectified the species is doomed. To afford complete protection for the surviving whooping cranes over a migration route of several thousand miles is almost impossible. It would appear then that attempts to raise young in captivity, although they have not yet been too successful, offer the best hope for the survival of this species.

CRANES — Family Gruidae

SANDHILL CRANE
Grus canadensis subsp. (p. 490)

Migrant and Summer Resident.
Length 40-48 in.

DESCRIPTION: Ads.—Reddish bare patch confined to forehead and crown; overall color brownish-gray slightly paler on cheeks and throat, only a little darker on wings; feathers of head and neck may be stained with rusty; beak and legs black. Im.—Similar but head feathered and plumage browner.

IDENTIFICATION: A large brownish-slate bird standing over three feet high. Often confused with great blue heron but lacking any distinct markings and head plumes and with bare red crown; in flight the crane extends neck to full length whereas the heron folds it over the back. Flocks of cranes in flight can often be distinguished from geese by their habit of circling in a thermal updraft.

RANGE: North America. Breeds from Alaska to Baffin Island south to California and Michigan; a subspecies breeds in Georgia and Florida. Winters in southern states and Mexico.

NESTING: On the ground in marshes. Nest, a depression in a dry spot in muskeg or on a muskrat house, lined with grass and reeds. Eggs, 2, olive-buff lightly spotted with brown. (Fawcett, May 16.)

REMARKS: On migration sandhill cranes are found throughout Alberta. As breeding birds they occur mainly in the area lying north of the Athabasca river although the former breeding range extended well down into the parklands. There are reports of a pair nesting near Sedgewick in 1936 and near Camrose in 1943.

During the spring migration small flocks of sandhill cranes alight in the fields of southern Alberta to rest and feed. Often they leap high in the air or jump about with partially spread wings in a series of antics which are part of the mating display. A few weeks later each pair selects a nesting territory in some inaccessible marsh or muskeg and until the young have been reared they are never found far from this area. Roots, insects, crustaceans, frogs and mice form much of their food at this time but berries and grain are staple foods at other seasons. Late in summer the scattered families congregate in flocks and in September they wing southward again. Strung out in orderly skeins high against the sky they are often mistaken for geese, but as they descend in great circles towards a grain field below their long legs become noticeable and their rolling calls, which have earned for them the name wild turkey, identify them readily. A sandhill crane flying within range of a hunter could not possibly be mistaken for any game bird.

EUROPEAN COMMON CRANE, *Grus grus*   See page 501

C. HAMPSON

WHOOPING CRANE
immature

C. HAMPSON

SANDHILL CRANE

VIRGINIA RAIL

ALLAN BROOKS

SORA
immature — adult

RAILS, COOTS — Family Rallidae

Rails are marsh birds with long legs, large feet, and small weak wings. Noisy yet secretive they are more often heard than seen. They run and skulk among the reeds and rushes taking flight only as a last recourse when hard pressed. Coots, or mudhens, are similar in build to rails but larger. The toes of the former have scalloped webs on the sides and the base of the beak extends up onto the forehead. Because they spend a great deal of time on open water they are often confused with ducks.

VIRGINIA RAIL
Rallus limicola   subsp. (p. 490)

Status Unknown.
Length 9 in.

DESCRIPTION: Ads.—Upperparts black, the feathers of lower neck and back with broad edges of brown, giving streaked appearance; face slate-blue; throat white; foreneck, breast, and wing chestnut; abdomen dull white; sides dark brown barred with white; dark brown under tail; iris, beak, and legs reddish-brown; beak over one inch long, curved downward. Im.—Upperparts black streaked with dark brown; throat white; rest of underparts black with gray feather edgings; wings chestnut.

IDENTIFICATION: Like a very dark wader; heavy beak and very long toes distinguish from sandpipers of similar size. In any plumage separated from sora rail by slightly larger size, chestnut on wings, and long, down-curved reddish beak.

RANGE: North America. Breeds in southern Canada, United States, and Mexico. Winters from southern states to Central America.

NESTING: In marshes or sloughs. Nest of grass and reeds attached to grass or rushes several inches above water. Eggs, 7-12, white or buffy speckled with brown.

REMARKS: Through the cooperation of many observers considerable information has been gathered about the status and range of the Virginia rail in Alberta since the first edition of this book appeared. It is now established that the species breeds not uncommonly in the Edmonton area, probably as far north as Glenevis and Athabasca, south to Millet and east to Czar, Wainwright and Vermilion. Several nests have been found in this area and specimens have been collected. An unsuccessful nesting attempt was previously reported from Brooks and a specimen was taken near Ft. Chipewyan. It is likely that, as ornithological interest increases and further records are obtained, the breeding range of the Virginia rail may be found to be even more extensive.

The Virginia rail spends all its time in marshes well hidden in thick grass or reed beds. It is not likely to be seen by a casual observer since it rarely comes into the open and flies only when very hard pressed. Recognition of its call, a series of loud metallic notes, is the best identification.

RAILS, COOTS — Family Rallidae

SORA
Porzana carolina

Common Summer Resident.
Length 8 in.

DESCRIPTION: Ads.—Crown and upperparts olive-brown with a black stripe in crown and back streaked with black and light gray; black band extends from forehead around base of beak to throat and down fore-neck to middle of breast; remainder of face, sides of neck, and upper breast light bluish-gray; rest of under-parts white, the sides heavily barred with dark brown and the abdomen tinged with cinnamon; beak short, stout, yellow; legs yellowish-green. Im.—Upperparts dark olive-brown marked as in adult; throat white; face, sides of neck, and band across breast light brownish; rest of underparts as in adult; lacks black on face, neck and breast.

IDENTIFICATION: Identified as a rail by heavy beak, short wings, and very long toes. Distinguished from Virginia rail by short, yellow beak, black markings of head and neck, and large areas of slate-gray on neck; from yellow rail by larger size, olive back with light streaks instead of bars.

RANGE: North and South America. Breeds from southern Mackenzie and eastern Quebec to California and Maryland. Winters from southern states to northern South America.

NESTING: In marshes or sloughs. Nest of grass and reeds attached to reeds or rushes a few inches over water. Eggs, 7-13, buffy spotted with reddish-brown. (Edmonton, June 4.)

REMARKS: Any extensive bed of reeds or sedges, whether it be in a prairie slough or bordering a woodland lake, is likely to have its complement of sora rails, for the species is found throughout Alberta even in the mountains. The first indication of their presence is likely to be a strident maniacal call, a series of piercing notes gradually decreasing in tone and intensity.

The sora rail frequents grassy tangles or reed beds bordering sloughs and lakes but it leaves their shelter more commonly than other rails and may sometimes be seen among the bushes bordering woodland pools or wading in shallow open water. Walking with mincing steps, short tail pertly erect, it is an amusing figure resembling somewhat a little bantam cock. At the first sign of danger it retreats into nearby cover. When pursued the sora rail often takes to flight; long legs dangling and wings beating feebly it just skims the tops of the reeds and soon drops again into the sanctuary of the marsh.

139

YELLOW RAIL

C. HAMPSON

COOT

RAILS, COOTS — Family Rallidae

YELLOW RAIL   Scarce Summer Resident.
Coturnicops noveboracensis subsp. (p. 490)   Length 7 in.

DESCRIPTION: Ads.—Upperparts brownish-black becoming very dark on rump and tail, each feather narrowly barred with white and, on back, edged with buffy; the feather edges form several buffy streaks down back and wings; throat white; dark line through eye; underparts buffy barred with black and white on sides and under tail; beak and legs yellowish. Im.—Similar to adult but darker above and below and with no definite markings on head.

IDENTIFICATION: A small rail of buffy-yellow color, with short beak. May be confused with sora rail but lacks black and slate-blue colors on head and neck of adult; distinguished from sora rails of any age by large amount of fine white cross barring on back and wings. Looks something like a small chicken.

RANGE: North America. Breeds from southern Mackenzie region to Quebec south to California and Massachusetts. Winters in southern states.

NESTING: On the ground in or near grassy marshes. Nest, a depression lined with grass. Eggs, 6-10, buffy spotted with reddish-brown.

REMARKS: During the early part of the century the yellow rail nested in certain large marshes southeast of Red Deer and at Dried Meat Lake near Camrose. With the drought of the late 1920s it disappeared from these areas and has not since returned. More recently the yellow rail has been reported from several places within about one hundred miles north and west of Edmonton. A specimen was collected on the delta of the Athabasca river in 1945. The only records from the mountains are of two specimens taken in the Jasper Park area in the first few years of this century.

The yellow rail frequents the edges of woodland marshes or muskegs where the water is only an inch or so deep and where thick grass replaces tall reeds and rushes. In such surroundings it is almost impossible to see small birds unless they can be flushed. The yellow rail is extremely shy; it hides among the grass clumps and cannot be forced to fly. If it were not for its notes it would go undetected. The distinctive call, *tik — tik — tik —*, can be easily imitated by tapping a piece of metal with a small stone.

RAILS, COOTS — Family Rallidae

COOT
Fulica americana

Common Summer Resident.
Length 15 in.

DESCRIPTION: Ads.—Head and neck black; rest of body slaty-black, paler below and with some feathers lightly tipped with white; tips of secondaries white forming narrow white line on wing; under tail coverts white; bill white extending up onto forehead and with brownish band near tip; iris red; legs green, the toes with large scalloped webs on each side. Im.—Similar to adults but paler, the beak flesh color and not extending onto forehead, and iris brown.

IDENTIFICATION: When swimming often confused with ducks but short beak and bobbing motion of neck will identify the coot; it can rarely be forced to fly and must patter along the water for some distance before taking to the air. On land its long legs and more upright stance distinguish it from ducks.

RANGE: North and South America. Breeds in Central and North America except in arctic. Winters from southern British Columbia south to northern South America.

NESTING: In vegetation over water. Nest, a mass of reeds and rushes, attached to vegetation but floating on shallow water. Eggs, 8-12, cream, finely spotted with dark brown. (Balzac, June 1.)

REMARKS: Wherever there is enough cover in shallow water to hide their nests coots will be found. They breed in suitable ponds, sloughs and lakes all over the province even in the mountain valleys. Old-timers say that they are more abundant today than they were sixty years ago.

Coots are more commonly known as mudhens in Alberta. They prefer reedy sloughs or extensive reed-beds on the margins of lakes where they have to dive two or three feet to reach the leaves and roots of succulent pond weeds. Omnivorous in taste they also scavenge along the shore picking up insects, snails, and dead animal matter. When alarmed coots dive beneath the water or else patter along the surface using both wings and feet to get them to the safety of the reeds. So rarely do they take to the air that many people believe them incapable of flight. Their unwillingness to fly makes them poor game birds but occasionally in the fall the hunter waiting for scaups or canvasbacks, sees flights of dark gray birds with feet extending beyond their tails flying low over his point. These are coots setting out on a southward journey. If they fall to his gun he hasn't much of a prize for their flesh is too strong for the average palate.

142

PLOVERS, TURNSTONES — Family Charadriidae

Plovers are compactly built wading birds with relatively short stout beaks. Most species have only 3 toes on each foot. Gregarious in habit, except during the breeding season, they usually occur in small flocks which frequent the shoreline or the adjacent meadows and cultivated fields. Turnstones are similar in build to plovers but their stout pointed beaks turn up slightly at the tip, enabling them to turn over pebbles in their search for food along the shores.

SEMIPALMATED PLOVER
Charadrius semipalmatus

Fairly Common Migrant.
Length 7 in.

DESCRIPTION: Forehead, face and ears black except a white band over beak from eye to eye; crown plain grayish-brown; throat, foreneck, and a broad band around neck white; bordering this, a black band across breast extends around neck; rest of upperparts plain grayish-brown, wings darkest and with thin light bar; rest of underparts white; base of beak orange, tip black; legs yellow-orange; toes partially webbed. Sexes alike. Immatures and fall adults similar but black replaced by dark grayish-brown.

IDENTIFICATION: Like a small killdeer but with only one black breast band and lacking orange rump. Similar to piping plover but much darker and with black instead of light face. Does not nest in Alberta.

RANGE: North and South America. Breeds from Alaska and northern B.C. to Greenland and occasionally Nova Scotia. Winters in southern United States, Central and South America, south to Argentina.

NESTING: On the ground. Nest a depression in the sand usually unlined. Eggs, 4, buffy, blotched with black and brown.

REMARKS: While migrating through Alberta semipalmated plover occur in small flocks which frequent the mudflats and sandy beaches of the larger lakes. Unlike sandpipers which tend to remain close together with heads down, probing the mud for food, they spread out over the shore when they alight, running about with heads up or pecking occasionally at some morsel on the sand. But when alarmed the scattered birds rise together and fly off rapidly in a compact flock like their larger relatives the golden and black-bellied plovers. Individuals, or small groups of semipalmated plover, often associate with various species of sandpiper.

The semipalmated plover has not been reported from the mountains but elsewhere in Alberta it is a regular migrant. In spring it appears at some of its favorite stopping-over places such as Miquelon and Beaverhill lakes with remarkable regularity about the third week of May. It is less regular on the return journey, the earliest migrants sometimes appearing about the end of July.

143

PIPING PLOVER
Charadrius melodus subsp. (p. 490)

Scarce Summer Resident.
Length 7 in.

DESCRIPTION: Spring ads.—Head white except a band of black above forehead from eye to eye and remainder of crown pale grayish-brown; throat and a band extending around neck white; a narrow black band borders this on the hindneck and becomes broader as it extends onto upper breast where it may or may not be complete; remainder of upperparts pale grayish-brown except flight feathers which are dull black; underparts white; beak orange tipped with black; legs orange. In females the black markings are duller and less extensive. Fall ads. and im.— Similar to above but black on crown lacking and the dark markings reduced to brownish.

IDENTIFICATION: Like a very pale semipalmated plover. The only small plover known to nest in Alberta or likely to occur during the nesting season.

RANGE: Eastern North America. Breeds in southern Canada west to Alberta and in the eastern and central states. Winters along the coasts of the southern states bordering the Atlantic and the Gulf of Mexico and in the West Indies.

NESTING: On the ground on the sandy or rocky shore of a lake. Nest, a depression in the sand, sometimes lined with pebbles or bits of shell. Eggs, 4, light buff evenly but lightly marked with black. (Bittern Lake, June 8.)

REMARKS: Piping plover have been recorded at very few places in Alberta but since they are unobtrusive in habits it is possible that they have been overlooked elsewhere. One or two pairs nest regularly at the second Miquelon Lake. They have also been found nesting at Buffalo, Bittern, Gull, Baxter, and Beaverhill lakes.

Piping plover frequent the sandy and pebbly shores of large lakes and occasionally forage in the short grass well back from the water. In Alberta it is unlikely that more than half-a-dozen, a family group, would be seen together. They have the characteristic plover way of feeding, running a short distance then pausing for a few moments to search the surroundings for the movement of an insect or a worm. Motionless they are almost invisible, their colors blend so well with the sand which is an essential part of their habitat. As though aware of their protective coloration they usually remain still at the appearance of danger but if it comes nearer they run swiftly along the beach taking flight only when hard pressed. Their notes are melodious whistles quite unlike the harsh cries of killdeer which may nest in the same area.

SEMIPALMATED PLOVER   C. HAMPSON

PIPING   PLOVER   C. HAMPSON

KILLDEER
Charadrius vociferus subsp. (p. 490)

Common Summer Resident.
Length 10 in.

DESCRIPTION: Ads.—Crown and sides of head grayish-brown except a white band across forehead extending back over eyes and a black band above this from eye to eye; throat white extending around neck in a complete band; underparts white except two black bands, one completely encircling neck, the other across upper breast; upper back and wings plain grayish-brown with much white on flight feathers; lower back pale orange-brown; tail pale orange-brown becoming dark brown toward tip and tipped with white. Immatures are similar to adults.

IDENTIFICATION: The killdeer usually identifies itself by voice. White underparts with two black bands across upper breast and orange rump conspicuous in flight are best field marks.

RANGE: North and Central America. Breeds over most of United States and Canada except the arctic. Winters from southern Canada south to West Indies and Central America.

NESTING: On the ground in meadows, cultivated fields, or gravel bars, often some distance from water. Nest, a depression containing a few pebbles or bits of dry weed stalks.. Eggs, 4, buffy, blotched and scrawled with dark brown and black. (Calgary, May 19.)

REMARKS: The killdeer is the commonest plover in the settled parts of Alberta and the most widespread in distribution. It breeds throughout the province but in the mountains and in the northern wastelands it is not abundant.

The killdeer is equally at home on the gravel bars of a river, on the sandy shore of a lake, at the muddy margin of a slough, or in a damp meadow. It usually announces its presence with shrill notes *kill-dee, kill-dee-dee,* repeated with monotonous regularity. Lacking the wariness of other species of plover, the killdeer often nests close to farm buildings and even enters towns and villages. Broods have been raised on the University campus in the heart of Edmonton. Shortly after they break from the egg the fluffy long-legged young run about like their parents, stopping occasionally to pick at an insect or small crustacean. When approached, they crouch on the ground, their colors blending well with gravel, sand, or mud, while the adults attempt to lure the intruder away by feigning a badly broken wing.

Early in April the first killdeers arrive from the south; they come singly or in twos and threes. In the fall larger groups of up to a dozen may be loosely associated as they move southward, but they never form compact migrating flocks like other plovers. In recent years a few killdeers have remained over winter on the banks of the Bow River near Calgary.

PLOVERS, TURNSTONES — Family Charadriidae

MOUNTAIN PLOVER
Eupoda montana

Scarce Summer Visitor.
Length 8½ in.

DESCRIPTION: Line from beak to eye, and bar across fore crown from eye to eye black; rest of upperparts uniform grayish-brown; central tail feathers grayish-brown, outer ones paler, all tipped with white; entire underparts white, occasionally lightly shaded with rusty-gray on breast.

IDENTIFICATION: Like a large semipalmated plover but lacking black and white rings around neck. To be expected only in extreme south of province.

RANGE: Rocky Mountain plateaus of North America and Mexico. Breeds from Montana and North Dakota south to New Mexico, Texas and Oklahoma. Winters mainly west of breeding range in California, Texas and Mexico.

NESTING: On the ground. Nest, a depression on the prairie sparsely lined with bits of dry vegetation. Eggs, 3, olive buff spotted and scrawled with black.

REMARKS: The name of this species is misleading. It does not inhabit the mountain regions; it is a bird of the dry uplands of western North America—of the prairies and arid plains from which rise the Rocky Mountains. Like the upland plover the mountain plover is rarely found near water unless it be one of the small muddy puddles which provide water for all the desert creatures. Instead it frequents the short-grass uplands where one would least expect to find a wading bird. Here it walks about like other prairie birds or chases the grasshoppers and other insects which thrive on the hot dry prairie. When enemies approach it crouches motionless trusting that it will blend with the surroundings and not be noticed but if the enemy be man it flies off, keeping a good distance ahead of him. The mountain plover is one of several species of birds which were unable to cope with the advance of settlement and the consequent destruction of their habitat. As a result it has been forced into the more remote plains regions and its numbers are greatly reduced.

There is but one record of the species in Alberta. On June 22, 1941, four mountain plover were observed about five miles north of the 49th parallel near Wildhorse. From their actions it was believed that the birds might have nested in this area but no young were found. Two of these birds were collected; both proved to be males.

147

KILLDEER

MOUNTAIN PLOVER

GOLDEN PLOVER

C. HAMPSON

BLACK-BELLIED PLOVER
adult   *immature*

ALLAN BROOKS

149

AMERICAN GOLDEN PLOVER
Pluvialis dominica   subsp. (p. 490)

Fairly Common Migrant.
Length 10½ in.

DESCRIPTION: Spring ads.—Upperparts dark grayish-black spotted and barred with yellow-orange and white; a strong white line running across forehead and eyes and down sides of neck to end on sides of breast; underparts jet black; tail brownish-black barred with light gray; Fall ads. and im.—Upperparts similar to spring adult but duller; underparts grayish-white heavily streaked on face, neck and across breast with pale gray.

IDENTIFICATION: Adults in breeding plumage might be confused only with black-bellied plover but the 'golden' tinge on the upperparts is evident at quite a distance. Fall birds are similar to many gray sandpipers but the heavy plover beak is distinctive; in flight golden plover do not show a black streak under the wing and the tail is dark.

RANGE: The breeding range is circumpolar. In the Americas breeds from Alaska to Baffin Island; winters chiefly in Argentina and Uruguay.

NESTING: On the ground on the tundra. Eggs, 4, buff heavily marked with dark browns and black.

REMARKS: During May golden plover migrate through most of Alberta except the mountainous regions on their way to their arctic nesting grounds. In small flocks of from six to thirty birds they frequent cultivated fields or grassy meadows, often some distance from large bodies of water. When disturbed they fly off swiftly in close formation uttering a melodious liquid whistle. In August, after the young have been reared on the tundra, the adult golden plover, accompanied by some of their young, migrate eastward through the arctic and thence to Labrador and Nova Scotia. From here they make an uninterrupted flight across the eastern Atlantic to Brazil. They then move southward, arriving on their wintering grounds on the pampas early in September. Many young golden plover, however, migrate directly south from their birthplace and, unaccompanied by adults, pass through Alberta and the interior states in September and October. At this time they commonly frequent the shore line, often in company with other species of waders. These birds then fly south over Central and northern South America to join their parents in Argentina several weeks later. What instinct or sense guides these birds, three or four months of age, over an unknown route and brings them to the ancestral wintering grounds thousands of miles away?

PLOVERS, TURNSTONES — Family Charadriidae

BLACK-BELLIED PLOVER
Squatarola squatarola

Fairly Common Migrant.
Length 11 in.

DESCRIPTION: Breeding ads.—Upperparts brownish-gray spotted and barred with white; forehead, and a streak down sides of neck and breast largely white; throat, foreneck, and breast black; abdomen white; tail white barred with gray; foot with 4 toes, the hind one very small. Fall ads. and im.—Upperparts similar to spring adults but lacking white forehead and sides of neck, sometimes with few flecks of yellow; underparts white streaked with gray on face, neck and across breast. In all plumages the axillars (long feathers under the wing, at its base) are dull black.

IDENTIFICATION: Light gray upperparts lacking yellow, and white abdomen distinguish this plover from the golden in spring plumage. In the fall the dark axillars of the black-bellied plover, which show well in flight, are distinctive. Specimens in the hand may be identified by presence of 4 toes.

RANGE: Breeding range circumpolar. In the Americas breeds from Alaska to Greenland; winters on coasts of North America as far north as Virginia on the Atlantic and Washington on the Pacific, also on coasts of Central America and northern South America.

NESTING: On the ground on the tundra. Eggs, 4, pale green or buff spotted with browns and black.

REMARKS: This species passes northward through Alberta at the same time as the golden plover. Black-bellied plover are less likely to be found in the fields, however, and are more commonly found along sandy and muddy shorelines. Erect posture and contrasting colors cause them to stand out among the multitude of less distinctly marked waders; but their numbers are not great today, even though they may no longer be shot legally in North America. Black-bellied plover may occur anywhere in the province. There are only a few records from the mountains mainly during the fall migration. Spring migrants pass through Alberta during May; the first southbound migrants, still in the black-breasted breeding plumage, are back in the Edmonton area again by late July.

In the fall adult and immature black-bellied plover, both now clad in less distinctive plumage, are often called gray plover. As they probe the shallows or search the shore for insects and crustaceans it is more difficult to distinguish them from other species of waders with which they commonly associate. Some stay in the province until October and the duck hunter, well hidden in a blind, may have an excellent opportunity to study them as he waits for ducks to cross his sandy spit.

151

KAY HODGES

RUDDY TURNSTONE

C. HAMPSON

COMMON SNIPE

RUDDY TURNSTONE　　　　　　　　　　　　　Scarce Migrant.
Arenaria interpres　subsp. (p. 490)　　　　　　　　Length 9 in.

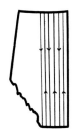

DESCRIPTION: Ad. m.—Head, neck, and breast black except for large white patches on throat, across forehead and under eye, bordering crown and extending down across ears, and forming band on hindneck; rest of upperparts reddish-brown except broad black V between wings; flight feathers black with two white stripes conspicuous in flight; lower back white; tail white with terminal black band; beak black, pointed; legs orange, rather short for a wader. Female similar but reddish largely replaced by gray-brown. In autumn young and adults are similar to female but black pattern is largely mixed with white.

IDENTIFICATION: Boldly marked in black, white, and rufous the ruddy turnstone cannot be confused with any other species. In flight it shows five white stripes along the upperparts.

RANGE: Almost cosmopolitan. In North America breeds across arctic from Alaska to Greenland. Winters in southern United States, Central America and northern South America.

NESTING: On the ground. Nest, a depression poorly lined with grass and leaves. Eggs, 4, olive-buff spotted with brown.

REMARKS: The ruddy turnstone is a true shore bird rarely seen far from the water's edge. It usually occurs in small flocks, sometimes in company with black-bellied plover but singles and pairs are often seen. Using its beak as a pry the turnstone flips over stones and pieces of driftwood to get at the insects hidden beneath, or else roots about in the wet sand to unearth tiny molluscs and crustaceans.

The main migration route of the ruddy turnstone is along the Atlantic and Pacific coasts and only small numbers pass through the interior of the continent. The species has been recorded at scattered points in Alberta including Newell, Miquelon, Beaverhill, and Cooking lakes, Lac Ste. Anne, and Lake Athabasca. It appears fairly regularly in small numbers at the second Miquelon lake towards the end of May. It has not been seen in the mountains. A few ruddy turnstones also follow the inland route on the return migration. These birds pass through central Alberta early in August at which time they are still wearing their badly worn breeding plumage. As in the spring, they often associate with black-bellied plover feeding along the sandy shore line rather than on the mudflats.

SNIPES, CURLEWS, SANDPIPERS — Family Scolopacidae

Twenty-four species of shore birds from this large family occur in Alberta. With few exceptions they are plain-colored birds of medium size with long beaks and legs. They are most commonly found in flocks on sandy shores or mud flats, or in the grassy margins of sloughs. Some species nest close to water, others choose dry upland meadows, and a few nest in the woods.

COMMON (WILSON'S) SNIPE Fairly Common Summer Resident.
Capella gallinago subsp. (p. 490) Length 11 in.

DESCRIPTION: Beak straight, very long (2½ in.) and slender; crown brownish-black with white median stripe; pale buff stripe over eye and black stripe from beak to eye; hindneck, back and wings brownish-black streaked and spotted with white and buff, the scapulars edged with buff forming four light lines down back; throat buffy; neck, breast and sides buffy barred and streaked with grayish-brown; remainder of underparts white; tail reddish-brown barred with black.

IDENTIFICATION: Length of beak will distinguish from all waders of similar size except the dowitchers. Lacks reddish underparts of spring dowitcher and shows no white on back in flight; light streak on crown and light lines down back identify Wilson's snipe at rest.

RANGE: North and South America. Breeds across northern United States and Canada north to tree limit. Winters in southern states, Central America, West Indies, and northern South America.

NESTING: On a hummock in marshes and muskegs. Nest, a depression lined with grass and leaves. Eggs, 4, olive-buff or brownish heavily marked with dark brown. (Winterburn, June 6.)

REMARKS: Marshes, muskegs, and grassy margins of sloughs and creeks are the favorite habitat of Wilson's snipe at all seasons. If a few alders and willows stand in the wet ground so much the better. Here the snipe probes deep into the mud, its long sensitive beak, flexible at the tip, searching for worms, a staple item in the diet. It stands motionless when approached, its colors blending well with the surroundings. Then rising suddenly and noisily it is off in erratic flight. In the spring while the female is incubating on a dry hummock, the male rises high overhead to perform a courtship flight. On fluttering wings he spirals in great circles, his spread tail producing a winnowing *who — who — who — who —*, as the air passes through the stiff feathers.

Wilson's snipe is found in suitable habitat throughout Alberta even in the mountains. It is nowhere abundant. It is not a gregarious species; usually single birds rise from the marsh grass with a harsh *scape* and dart away in zig-zag flight. At a few places including Canmore and Calgary, where warm springs keep shallow waters unfrozen, snipe occasionally remain over winter.

SNIPES, CURLEWS, SANDPIPERS — Family Scolopacidae

LONG-BILLED CURLEW   Fairly Common Summer Resident.
Numenius americanus   subsp. (p. 490)   Length 22-26 in.

DESCRIPTION: Ads.—Large waders with very long beaks (5-7 in.) curved down toward the tip. Throat white; remainder of head and neck buff streaked with brownish-black; back and wings buffy-cinnamon spotted and barred with brownish-black; tail pale cinnamon barred with brownish-black; underparts pale cinnamon with buffy feather margins, a few brownish-black marks on upper breast and sides. The female is larger and has a longer beak than the male. Immatures are similar to adults.

IDENTIFICATION: Large size, long legs, long decurved beak, and buffy color are distinctive. The hudsonian curlew is smaller and grayer.

RANGE: North and Central America. Breeds in southern parts of four western provinces and in United States west of Mississippi river. Winters in Central America and southwestern United States.

NESTING: On the ground. Nest, a depression poorly lined with grass, weeds or straw, on open prairie or in stubble not necessarily near water. Eggs, 4, olive-buff marked with shades of brown and olive; as large as a hen's egg but pointed at one end. (Rosebud, May 23.)

REMARKS: On the prairies of southern and eastern Alberta the long-billed curlew nests regularly but in small numbers. This is the northern limit of its breeding range for, although it has been seen at Tofield and Belvedere, there are no nesting records from north of Castor and Botha.

Towards the end of April long-billed curlews arrive in Alberta, alone or in twos and threes. Upon alighting they pause to fold their wings carefully before moving off over the uplands with slow and stately tread. They feed in cultivated fields, on grass lands, or along the edge of sloughs, picking up insects and berries with long beaks which seem better fitted for probing the mud than for searching the grass. By the end of May the females are incubating four handsome eggs in some exposed location. They sit very close, relying on their color for concealment, and will sometimes allow themselves to be touched before fluttering from the nest. Like most waders they feign lameness to lure away the intruder. The young are led away across the fields a few hours after they hatch and now any intrusion by man, beast, or bird is met with vociferous aerial attack from the parents. Later in the summer families of curlews, the young now strong on the wing, may be seen flying in loose association. By the end of August all but a few stragglers have left the province.

WHIMBREL   Scarce Migrant.
Numenius phaeopus   subsp. (p. 490)   Length 17 in.

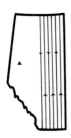

DESCRIPTION: Crown dark grayish-brown bordered with a white line over eye and with a faint median stripe; remainder of upperparts grayish-brown, the feathers with narrow light margins; underparts dull grayish-buff marked on neck, breast and sides with grayish-brown; beak 3-4 in. long, curved down.

IDENTIFICATION: The decurved beak will identify as a curlew; smaller size, grayer color, and shorter beak will distinguish this species from the long-billed curlew.

RANGE: North and South America. Breeds in arctic from Alaska to Hudson Bay; winters on coasts of southern North America and South America.

NESTING: On the ground on the tundra. Eggs, 4, olive-buff marked with browns and lavender.

REMARKS: The main migration routes of the whimbrel, or hudsonian curlew, are along the east and west coasts of North America; only small numbers of these birds pass through the interior. A few migrate through Alberta in the spring but there are no records of occurrence during the fall migration period. The species. has been observed or collected at Buffalo, Beaverhill, and Miquelon lakes, Lac La Nonne, and Rosebud.

On their breeding grounds in the arctic hudsonian curlews are noisy birds but on migration they are quiet and timid. In Alberta they may be expected in pairs or in small groups on the shores of large bodies of water; occasionally they are found feeding on insects in cultivated fields in the manner of long-billed curlews.

Many species of wading birds were shot for table or market until early in this century. Curlews and plover, which occurred in large flocks on migration and were easily decoyed, were favorite targets of the market gunner. All species of shore birds were greatly reduced in numbers and one, the eskimo curlew, a small replica of the hudsonian, was completely exterminated. Under protection many species of shorebirds have gradually rebuilt their populations to safe numbers, but with the advance of civilization into arctic regions such northern-nesting species as the whimbrel are now threatened with disturbances on their nesting grounds. It remains to be seen how each species will respond to the advance of settlement. Certainly any plans for opening northern Canada to settlement should be moulded in the light of modern concepts of wildlife management.

LONG-BILLED CURLEW

B. & J. MORGAN

WHIMBREL

C. HAMPSON

SNIPES, CURLEWS, SANDPIPERS — Family Scolopacidae

UPLAND PLOVER Scarce Summer Resident.
Bartramia longicauda Length 11½ in.

DESCRIPTION: A sandpiper, not a plover. Crown and back dull black, each feather with buffy margin, and a light median stripe on crown; wings buffy-brown barred with brownish-black; tail long for a sandpiper, buffy-cinnamon barred with black; face and throat white streaked with dusky under eyes; foreneck and breast buffy with well defined brownish-black streaks on neck changing to V's on breast and bars on sides; remainder of underparts white; slender beak about 1¼ in. long; legs grayish-yellow. Sexes alike.

IDENTIFICATION: A dark sandpiper with slender neck, rounded head, and dark Vs on breast. Usually found on prairies and therefore not likely to be confused with other sandpipers; slender beak will distinguish it from plover which may occur in similar habitat.

RANGE: North and South America. Breeds irregularly from Alaska across Canada and South to Colorado and Virginia. Winters in southern half of South America.

NESTING: On the ground. Nest, a depression lined with grass, usually in a clump of grass which arches over nest. Eggs, 4, creamy-buff spotted with shades of brown. (Calgary, June 6.)

REMARKS: Despite its habits and its wild, melodious cry, the upland plover is not a plover but a true sandpiper — the bartramian sandpiper. Until the early 1900's upland plover were as numerous as meadowlarks on the short-grass prairies and were commonly used for food. But even as the Migratory Birds Convention Act put a stop to market gunning, the plough was destroying more and more grassland, the natural habitat of the species. It has never been able to adapt to agricultural development; today small numbers occur mainly on marginal wasteland or on the grasslands used as cattle range.

During the nesting season upland plover are not gregarious; only one or two pairs may occupy a large stretch of virgin prairie. They walk about in the grass, feeding on the abundant insect life, or fly low over the prairie uttering a mellow whistle, *kway-a-lee*. Frequently they perch upon a prominence such as a rock or a post; when alighting they hold the wings extended high over the back for a few seconds before folding them into place.

In Alberta upland plover breed irregularly and locally throughout the prairie regions west to the base of the foothills. There is one record from the mountains — a pair was observed near Banff during the nesting season.

158

SNIPES, CURLEWS, SANDPIPERS — Family Scolopacidae

SPOTTED SANDPIPER Common Summer Resident.
Actitis macularia Length 7½ in.

DESCRIPTION: Breeding ads.—Upperparts dark greenish-gray streaked on crown and neck, and barred on back and wings with dull black; wings have white bar visible only in flight; face greenish-gray except white line over eye and white eyelids; underparts white with small dusky spots on throat and large black spots elsewhere, most numerous on upper breast. Im. and fall ads.— Similar to above but dark markings of upperparts indistinct or lacking; underparts white with no spots, but grayish on sides of breast.

IDENTIFICATION: A small greenish-gray sandpiper with distinct spots on underparts in spring; in flight shows white streak along wing. Teetering habit and peculiar flight are distinctive. The only small sandpiper which nests commonly in southern Alberta.

RANGE: North and South America. Breeds throughout most of United States and Canada north to Arctic ocean. Winters from southern states to Argentina, rarely in southern B.C.

NESTING: On the ground or on banks always near water. Nest, a depression lined with grass, moss, or other handy material. Eggs, 4, creamy-buff blotched with brown. (Rocky Mountain House, June 1.)

REMARKS: While immense flocks of small gray sandpipers are passing through Alberta on their way to northern nesting grounds two non-gregarious species, the solitary and the spotted sandpipers, arrive in less spectacular manner and remain to nest. Of these the spotted sandpiper is the most widely distributed and the best known. It arrives in southern Alberta towards the end of April and soon spreads throughout the province even into the mountains. It rarely remains beyond the first week of September.

The spotted sandpiper frequents the banks of rivers and streams and the shores of deep-water lakes especially those where bushes grow to within a few feet of the water's edge. Pausing every few moments in its search among the sand and stones it flexes its legs and dips its body forward then back with peculiar teetering motion which is characteristic of the species. It is not wary but when hard pressed it teeters nervously a few times then takes off low over the water in a wide arc which brings it back to shore some distance away. A series of rapid wing strokes followed by a period of sailing with quivering wings held downward, their tips almost touching the water, produces a flight pattern which identifies the spotted sandpiper more accurately than voice or color.

159

UPLAND PLOVER

SPOTTED SANDPIPER
female and young

SOLITARY SANDPIPER

S. D. MACDONALD

WANDERING TATTLER

SNIPES, CURLEWS, SANDPIPERS — Family Scolopacidae

SOLITARY SANDPIPER

Tringa solitaria subsp. (p. 491)

Scarce Summer Resident.
Length 8 in.

DESCRIPTION: Ads.—Upperparts dark olive-brown streaked on crown and hindneck with white, and lightly spotted on back and wings with white or buffy; white ring around eye; underparts white streaked on face, neck, and upper breast with olive-brown, and barred on sides with same color; tail with broad bars of white and dull black; legs olive-green. Im.—Similar but lacking white streaks on crown and pattern of upperparts faint; markings of underparts faint, mostly confined to lower neck and upper breast; white eye-ring present.

IDENTIFICATION: A medium-sized sandpiper, dark brown above, usually seen around woodland pools during summer. The white eye-ring is distinctive.

RANGE: North and South America. Breeds across the wooded parts of Canada and the northeastern states. Winters in Central and South America, rarely in southern states.

NESTING: In trees near a stream or small slough. Nest: no nest is built; the eggs are laid in an old nest of other birds such as the robin, blackbird, waxwing, or jay. Eggs, 4, greenish-white, spotted and blotched with reddish-brown. (Winterburn, June 10.)

REMARKS: The solitary sandpiper is aptly named. Even on migration it is usually seen alone or in twos and threes. During the summer muskeg ponds, shallow woodland pools, and the narrow margins of woodland lakes are the favorite haunts of the solitary sandpiper. In such spots it leads a secluded life while its mate is incubating in an old discarded nest in the woods. Only a few hours after the young hatch the mother flies to the ground and encourages the long-legged balls of fluff to tumble after her. From that time until they are able to fly their only defence is their coloration and their ability to crouch motionless in the thick vegetation. Keen-eyed crows and magpies discover them too often.

The solitary sandpiper is found throughout Alberta on migration. It nests in the northern and western parts of the province but it is quite local in distribution. Owing to its peculiar nesting habits the nest and eggs were unknown for many years; to E. Thomson who homesteaded near Bowden goes credit for discovering the first set of eggs in an old robin's nest on June 6, 1903. For many years the species nested along the North Saskatchewan river within the city of Edmonton but in recent years as human activity has increased in the valley it has moved farther afield. A surprising number and variety of birds are attracted to areas of natural habitat even though they are surrounded by human developments. The preservation of such areas is too often overlooked by planners who lack biological insight.

SNIPES, CURLEWS, SANDPIPERS — Family Scolopacidae

WANDERING TATTLER   Rare Wanderer.
Heteroscelus incanum   Length 10½ in.

DESCRIPTION: Ads.—Upperparts plain dark slate-gray with no pattern; light line over eye; dark line through eye over ear; rest of face white streaked with gray; underparts white with streaks on neck and many irregular bars of slate elsewhere. Im.—Similar but streaks and bars on underparts replaced by a wash of pale gray on foreneck, breast, and flanks.

IDENTIFICATION: The heavy barring below distinguishes the wandering tattler from all other waders in the spring except the stilt sandpiper which is brown above and much smaller. In fall plumage young tattlers look something like yellowlegs; absence of white on rump and tail distinguishes them.

RANGE: North and South America, Asia, Australia. In North America breeds in mountains of Alaska and Yukon. Winters along Pacific coast south to Ecuador.

NESTING: On the ground. There is no nest; the eggs are laid in the gravel near a river. Eggs, 4, greenish spotted with brown.

REMARKS: The wandering tattler is a maritime species which in spring follows the Pacific Coast north to Alaska. It frequents rocky shores rather than sand or mud flats, finding among the shellfish attached to the rocks the crustaceans and worms which comprise most of its food. Although most commonly seen alone or at most in very small groups, the wandering tattler is occasionally found in company with black turnstones. It has the habit of tipping-up or teetering on its long legs like the spotted sandpiper and when disturbed it flies off like the spotted sandiper, alternately flapping and sailing on arced wings. On the southward migration some wandering tattlers make a long overseas journey from Alaska to the Hawaiian Islands; others move gradually down the coastline up which they travelled in the spring.

On May 30, 1938, a wandering tattler was collected on the east shore of Swan Lake near the Alberta-B.C. boundary west of Grande Prairie. It had been seen two days previously on Tupper Creek. Strong westerly gales had been blowing for several days prior to its appearance and are believed to be responsible for blowing this straggler so far east of its usual course. This is the only specimen secured in Alberta but there are two sight records of the species. A wandering tattler was seen at Patricia Lake in Jasper National Park in July, 1961, and one was seen at a lake a few miles northwest of Edmonton in June, 1965.

ALLAN BROOKS

WILLET

ALLAN BROOKS

GREATER YELLOWLEGS

SNIPES, CURLEWS, SANDPIPERS — Family Scolopacidae

WILLET   Fairly Common Summer Resident.
Catoptrophorus semipalmatus subsp. (p. 491)   Length 15 in.

DESCRIPTION: Spring ads.—Upperparts light brownish-gray lightly streaked on crown and back with black; when folded, wings colored like back but opened they show much white on secondaries, and primaries are white at base, black toward tip; rump white; tail pale brownish-gray; underparts white except face and foreneck spotted with dusky-brown, the breast with U's and the sides with bars of same color; legs grayish; beak 2½ in., black. Im. and fall ads.—Plain brownish-gray above; plain white below except a grayish wash on foreneck; wings as in spring adult.

IDENTIFICATION: A large gray sandpiper with long, rather stout beak, showing no distinctive markings when at rest. In flight broad white band along wing and black wing tips are very noticeable and distinctive.

RANGE: North and South America. Breeds in southern Canada and northern United States. Winters in southern States south to Peru.

NESTING: On the ground, usually within a hundred yards or so of water. Nest, a depression lined with grasses and weeds. Eggs, 4, olive-buff spotted and blotched with dark browns. (Miquelon Lake, June 18.)

REMARKS: The willet was formerly a very common breeding bird around the sloughs of our prairies and parklands, but did not occur north of the North Saskatchewan river. Today its numbers are considerably reduced and while it still occupies much of its former range its distribution, especially in the parklands, is local. The willet has not been recorded in the mountains.

Wet meadows and grassy margins of prairie sloughs are the favorite haunts of the willet during the summer. Here, often in company with long-billed curlews and marbled godwits, it finds the water insects, small crustaceans, and worms, which comprise its food. Unlike its larger associates it rarely strays far from water. Incubating birds do not allow close approach; while the intruder is still at some distance from the nest they join their mates in aerial attacks with harsh cries of *kerwek — kerwek*. When undisturbed the note is a rather musical *pill-will-willet*.

Willets arrive in southern Alberta about the end of April. They are not gregarious birds and are most commonly found alone or in small groups of up to half a dozen. They migrate southward early; most have left the province before the end of August but occasionally the duck hunter may hear the willet's call or see its well marked gray and white wings in early September.

SNIPES, CURLEWS, SANDPIPERS — Family Scolopacidae

GREATER YELLOWLEGS   Scarce Summer Resident.
Totanus melanoleucus   Length 14 in.

DESCRIPTION: Spring ads.—Crown and hindneck black streaked with white; back and wings a mixture of black and grayish-brown, the feathers spotted and edged with white; rump and tail white barred with light grayish-brown; eyelids white; underparts white, the face and neck with streaks and the upper breast and sides with V's and bars of dark grayish-brown; legs long, yellow; beak over 2 in., black, very slightly upcurved. Im. and fall ads. —Uniform gray above spotted with dusky and white on back; wings and tail as in spring adult; underparts white except washed with gray on neck, breast and sides.

IDENTIFICATION: A large gray sandpiper with long yellow legs showing a great deal of white on tail in flight. Easily confused with lesser yellowlegs but larger and with longer, slightly upturned beak.

RANGE: North and South America. Breeds in the northern forested regions of Canada and Alaska. Winters in southern states south to Argentina and Peru.

NESTING: On the ground in dry, lightly wooded areas not necessarily close to water. Nest, a depression lined with grass and leaves. Eggs, 4, buffy spotted and blotched with dark browns. (Fawcett, May 11.)

REMARKS: Little was known of the nesting habits of the greater yellowlegs until 1930 when it was found breeding in numbers near Fawcett. Since that time it has been found nesting locally in various heavily forested parts of north-central and western Alberta including Lac la Biche, Athabasca, Entrance, Nordegg, Rocky Mt. House, and Sundre. It probably breeds also in parts of extreme northern Alberta but its status there is not definitely known. It is scarce in the mountains; one was seen at Banff and there is a breeding record from Jasper. On migration it occurs throughout southern Alberta.

During the nesting season the greater yellowlegs frequent sand ridges and muskeg areas of heavily wooded regions. Once the family is grown all repair to the muddy shores and shallow margins of lakes. They probe the mud for worms or wade sedately into the water to pick up insect larvae and crustaceans. In September they gradually move southward stopping at prairie sloughs to feed on the way. Their flight is not as swift as that of the smaller sandpipers nor do they form compact flocks yet the group keeps together as it migrates and stragglers are few.

SNIPES, CURLEWS, SANDPIPERS — Family Scolopacidae

LESSER YELLOWLEGS
Totanus flavipes

Common Summer Resident.
Length 10½ in.

DESCRIPTION: Spring ads.—Crown and hindneck dull black streaked with white; back and wings spotted and barred with grayish-brown, black, and white; rump and tail white barred with light grayish-brown; eye-lids and line from beak over eye white; line from beak to eye dusky; throat white; underparts white, the neck with streaks, and the upper breast and sides with V's and bars of grayish-brown; legs long, yellow; beak about 1½ in., black. Im. and fall ads.—Uniform gray above, spotted, mainly on back, with dusky and white; wings and tail as in spring adult; throat and line over eye white; underparts white but heavily marked on neck, breast and sides with pale gray.

IDENTIFICATION: A gray sandpiper with long, yellow legs; larger than the peeps and showing, in flight, a great deal of white in the tail. Most likely to be confused with the greater yellowlegs but smaller and the beak straight and shorter.

RANGE: North and South America. Breeds throughout the forested regions of northern Canada and Alaska. Winters from the Gulf states south to Argentina and Chile.

NESTING: On the ground in dry, lightly wooded areas not far from water. Nest, a depression lined with dry leaves and grass. Eggs, 4, creamy-buff, spotted and blotched with rich browns. (Winterburn, May 24.)

REMARKS: As a migrant the lesser yellowlegs is found in suitable habitat throughout the province except in the mountains where it is reported only from Jasper. As a breeding bird it occurs in the wooded regions from near Edmonton to the northern boundary. Occasionally it nests in the parklands as far south as Buffalo Lake.

On their nesting grounds lesser yellowlegs perch incongruously on the topmost branches of bushes and trees, a feat for which their long legs are obviously not adapted. Fretting on this perch or flying about with yellow legs dangling, they protest vociferously any intrusion into their nesting territory. Although the antics of the parents often assist the naturalist in discovery of the nest, there is no doubt that they usually divert animal predators from the well concealed eggs or young. On migration lesser yellow-legs are found in small, rather loosely associated groups on the shores or in the shallow waters of sloughs and lakes. Here they find the insects and small crustaceans which form most of their food. When resting or feeding they are usually quiet but in flight they utter melodious calls. Yellowlegs were legally shot as game in Alberta as late as 1926.

KNOT   Scarce Migrant.
Calidris canutus subsp. (p. 491)   Length 10½ in.

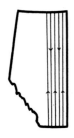

DESCRIPTION: Spring ads.—Crown streaked with black and light gray; hindneck similar but lighter; feathers of back and wings gray with black centers and buffy margins, the latter mainly on back; flight feathers black; rump and upper tail coverts barred black and white; tail gray; face and underparts cinnamon shading to white on sides and abdomen; some dusky barring on sides and sometimes on breast; beak black, about as long as head; legs black. Fall ads. and im.—Plain light gray above, the feathers with faint dusky centers; face and underparts white streaked or barred except on abdomen with gray; wings, lower back, and tail as in spring adults.

IDENTIFICATION: In spring reddish underparts separate the knot from all waders but dowitchers; the knot has a larger body, very much shorter beak, and in flight shows much less white on the back. In fall similar to black-bellied plover but smaller with shorter legs, and lacking thick plover beak.

RANGE: World wide. In western hemisphere breeds on arctic islands across North America; winters in South America.

NESTING: On the ground. Nest a depression among vegetation on dry arctic uplands. Eggs, 4, olive-buff spotted with brown.

REMARKS: The knot is a regular migrant through Alberta but it apparently passes over the southern prairies without stopping, for it has rarely been recorded there. Occasionally a few knots are seen on migration at the larger lakes east of Calgary. At Beaverhill and Bittern Lakes knots occur regularly, sometimes in large flocks, about the end of May or the beginning of June. They return from the north towards the end of September, usually in smaller numbers.

Most knots follow the coasts on migration, stopping to feed on the tidal flats, but a few migrate through the interior of the continent. Those that pass through Alberta are most likely to be found on those broad sandy edges of large lakes which most resemble the seashore. They stay close to the water gleaning small marine animals cast up by the waves or wading in the shallows if the water is still. Knots often associate with black-bellied plover and, more rarely, with other waders; their plump build and relatively short legs identify them at some distance along the shore in these mixed flocks. As the flock takes wing the knots come together and swing out over the lake in a compact group before alighting on the flats again some distance away.

LESSER YELLOWLEGS

KNOT

169

PECTORAL SANDPIPER Common Migrant.
Erolia melanotos Length 8½ in.

DESCRIPTION: Feathers of upperparts buff, light brown or gray with black centers giving pattern of brownish-gray streaked with black; lower back and central tail feathers black; outer tail feathers pale gray; throat white; foreneck and breast buffy-gray with numerous fine streaks of brownish-black; rest of underparts white; beak 1 in. long, curved down slightly; legs yellow-olive.

IDENTIFICATION: A brownish-gray sandpiper much larger than least and semipalmated sandpipers which are similar in color. Most likely to be confused with Baird's sandpiper but browner, especially on crown and face, and with yellowish legs instead of black. In flight all of these four species show a wide black mark extending down lower back into central tail feathers.

RANGE: North America, northeastern Siberia, and South America. Breeds in arctic from Hudson Bay to Alaska and across to Siberia. Winters in southern half of South America.

NESTING: On the ground. Nest, a depression in dry ground lined with grass. Eggs, 4, buffy with large blotches of dark browns.

REMARKS: This is the largest of several species of gray sandpipers, quite similar in appearance, which differ mainly in size. Others of this group are the semipalmated, the least, and Baird's sandpipers. The pectoral sandpiper shows a much greater preference for grassy shores and wet meadows than any of the others. It is a common migrant throughout most of Alberta except the mountains where it has been recorded only from Waterton Lakes and Banff.

Early in May flocks of pectoral sandpipers alight in the fresh green grass at the edge of prairie sloughs to feed on small crustaceans and aquatic insects. Their movements are slow and deliberate. When approached they stand motionless and the observer may get his first glimpse of them as they dart off in zig-zag flight uttering a harsh *skreek*. Often a few individuals remain behind; these may be approached more closely if caution is used. On its breeding ground in the arctic the male pectoral sandpiper has a peculiar mating display in which the oesophagus is inflated with air, forming a pendant pouch on the breast. A grunting note is produced as the sac is deflated. Once mating and nesting duties are over, however, the adults lose little time in starting their southward journey. Early migrants may reach central Alberta in the first week of August.

SNIPES, CURLEWS, SANDPIPERS — Family Scolopacidae

WHITE-RUMPED SANDPIPER
Erolia fuscicollis

Scarce Migrant.
Length 7½ in.

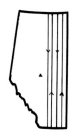

DESCRIPTION: Feathers of upperparts brownish-black edged with buff, gray, and brown, giving overall effect of grayish-brown streaked with black; upper tail coverts white; central tail feathers black, rest gray; light line over eye and ear; dusky brown stripe from beak under eye to ear; underparts white but foreneck and upper breast spotted and streaked with dull black and sides with few black bars; beak black; legs greenish-black. Sexes alike.

IDENTIFICATION: With wings folded very similar to Baird's and other small gray sandpipers but markings on breast more distinct; in flight the white tail coverts form a white band at base of dark tail which is distinctive.

RANGE: North and South America. Breeds on arctic islands and arctic coast from Alaska to Baffin Island. Winters in southern South America and Falkland Islands.

NESTING: On the ground. Nest, a depression lined with grass and leaves. Eggs, 4, olive-buff marked with brown.

REMARKS: The white-rumped sandpiper is rarely seen in Alberta and never occurs in numbers, for the main migration route of the species lies farther east. The first record for the province is four specimens collected at Ft. Chipewyan early in June, 1893. Since then it has been seen and collected infrequently near Camrose and at Beaverhill Lake. It has also been seen at lakes near Calgary.

In the large flocks of least and semipalmated sandpipers which congregate along the sandy and muddy shores of some of our large lakes, one or two white-rumped sandpipers may occasionally be found. There is nothing about their behavior which distinguishes them from their more common relatives and it is usually not until the flock takes flight that the white rump mark identifies the rarer members.

Several species of small gray sandpipers form a group which are difficult to identify in the field, the more so since they commonly associate with each other. Many observers call them all 'peeps' a name derived from their call notes. To separate them in the field requires careful observation of small differences in size, leg color, and breast markings, a task which can rarely be accomplished successfully without the aid of field-glasses. Baird's, the least, the semipalmated, and the white-rumped sandpipers are included in this group.

PECTORAL SANDPIPER

WHITE-RUMPED SANDPIPER

BAIRD'S SANDPIPER

VALERIE J. MAY

LEAST SANDPIPER   SEMIPALMATED SANDPIPER

autumn plumage

ALLAN BROOKS

173

BAIRD'S SANDPIPER Common Migrant.
Erolia bairdii Length 7 in.

DESCRIPTION: Feathers of upperparts dull black with edges of gray or buffy giving effect of gray heavily streaked and spotted with black; lower back and central tail feathers black; outer tail feathers gray; throat white; neck and breast buffy-gray with many fine streaks of brownish-black; rest of underparts white; beak (less than 1 in.) and legs black.

IDENTIFICATION: Smaller than pectoral sandpiper but larger than least and semipalmated. Grayer than pectoral and least; feathers of back having scaly appearance. Like all of these species shows black streak down back and tail in flight. Black legs and beak distinguish from all but semipalmated; Baird's is larger and has darker face.

RANGE: North and South America, northeastern Asia. Breeds in arctic from Greenland to Alaska and Siberia. Winters in Chile and Argentina.

NESTING: On the ground. Nest, a depression in dry ground lined with grass. Eggs, 4, buff splotched with shades of brown.

REMARKS: Baird's sandpiper is a common migrant through most of Alberta except the mountains and the foothills, but it is not usually as abundant as the pectoral, semipalmated, and least. It frequents the bare margins of alkaline prairie sloughs and the mudflats of large lakes, associating commonly with least and semipalmated sandpipers and sometimes with pectorals. Baird's sandpiper moves northward through Alberta in May; the earliest fall migrants are back in the central part of the province early in August.

The sandy or muddy shores of some of our large shallow lakes are popular resting places for migrating sandpipers. Here flocks of many thousands congregate at the height of the spring migration period late in May. It is in these mixed flocks that Baird's sandpipers are most easily identified by comparisons of size and color. Their numbers are not likely to be great whether they be in mixed company or alone. In the fall the first migrating groups are even smaller, often consisting of less than half a dozen individuals, all males, spread out along the muddy shore of a prairie slough. Several weeks later the females and young come through in larger numbers. Baird's sandpipers are not as active and restless as many of the sandpipers. At rest they often stand with their heads drawn down towards their shoulders giving them a rather plump appearance which is dispelled when they move. Unlike pectoral sandpipers Baird's are rarely found in wet grasslands and marshes.

174

SNIPES, CURLEWS, SANDPIPERS — Family Scolopacidae

LEAST SANDPIPER
Erolia minutilla

Common Migrant.
Length 6 in.

DESCRIPTION: Feathers of upperparts black edged with brown, buff, or white, giving overall striped grayish-brown appearance; lower back and central tail feathers black; outer tail feathers pale gray; throat white with few dusky marks; foreneck and breast buffy with many small dull black streaks; rest of underparts white; beak black; legs yellowish-olive. Sexes similar. In autumn adults and young are browner.

IDENTIFICATION: Similar to Baird's, white-rumped, and semipalmated sandpipers; smaller than Baird's and white-rumped, lacks white rump of latter and is browner than former. Most likely to be confused with semipalmated but browner, especially on face and back, and has olive instead of black legs.

RANGE: North and South America. Breeds in arctic and sub-arctic from Alaska to Labrador south to northern Manitoba, and occasionally Nova Scotia. Winters in southern United States, Central America, and the northern half of South America.

NESTING: On the ground. Nest, a depression in the moss of the tundra lined with grass and leaves. Eggs, 4, olive-buff spotted with brown.

REMARKS: This diminutive sandpiper occurs as a migrant, usually in large flocks, over all of Alberta except the mountains. Extensive mudflats or sandy shores of large lakes are its favorite haunts, but it is often found with pectoral sandpipers near grassy pools or with Baird's probing the alkaline margins of prairie sloughs.

As a flock of least sandpipers alights its members scatter along the water's edge foraging busily with quick nervous movements. They run before an intruder but, when pressed too closely, rise and form a compact flock in flight. At Beaverhill Lake east of Edmonton about the 24th of May, immense flocks of sandpipers, many of them least, may be seen in flight far out over the water, appearing in the distance like swarms of gnats. White underparts flash in the sun as they twist and turn in close formation, all wheeling swiftly in the same direction at the same instant, as though aware through some sixth sense of the intentions of their fellows. This intuition must be possessed by many species of shore birds for mixed flocks perform similar miracles of precision flying with never an error.

When they take flight least sandpipers show a very dark stripe down the middle of the rump and tail bordered with white on both sides. These markings are found also on the semipalmated, pectoral and Baird's sandpipers and serve to separate these four species from all others.

175

DUNLIN

S. D. MACDONALD

DOWITCHER

B. & J. MORGAN

DUNLIN   Scarce Migrant.
Erolia alpina   subsp. (p. 491)   Length 8½ in.

DESCRIPTION: Spring ads.—Crown and back reddish brown with black streaks; wings gray, primaries darkest; rump and central tail feathers black, outer tail feathers light gray; throat and foreneck white heavily streaked with dark gray; large black patch on breast; rest of underparts white; beak black, slightly decurved at tip; legs dark olive. Im. and fall ads.—Plain brownish-gray above indistinctly streaked with dusky on head and neck; brownish patch on ear; underparts white lightly streaked with grayish-brown on lower neck and upper breast; no black patch.

IDENTIFICATION: Black patch on breast identifies in spring. At any time the beak, fairly stout at base, tapering and curved down toward tip, is distinctive.

RANGE: North America, Europe, Asia. In North America breeds in arctic from Hudson Bay to Alaska. Winters mainly on coasts of southern United States.

NESTING: On the ground near water. Nest, a depression lined with grass and leaves. Eggs, 4, buffy or greenish marked with brown.

REMARKS: The European race of this sandpiper is known as the dunlin in the British Isles but the American race is often called the red-backed sandpiper. The species is a common migrant along the Pacific coast to and from the western arctic regions and through the Atlantic coast — Great Lakes route to the northern shores of Hudson Bay. Smaller numbers follow an inland route which is mainly east of Alberta. Dunlins migrate a little later in the spring and the fall than most other species of sandpipers. In Alberta there are a few sight records, mostly during the fall migration period, from Brooks, Red Deer Lake and Beaverhills Lake. The only Alberta specimens were collected on October 31, 1924, from a small flock at Beaverhills Lake. It is unusual to find any shorebirds in the province so late in the year.

The red-backed sandpiper frequents extensive mudflats and the broad sandy shores of large lakes. The Alberta records indicate that small numbers of red-backed sandpipers occasionally pass through the province as late spring and fall migrants. They are most likely to be in small flocks, perhaps associated with other species of sandpipers. During the fall migration, they are not easy to identify.

SNIPES, CURLEWS, SANDPIPERS — Family Scolopacidae

DOWITCHER   Length 11 in.

Limnodromus griseus subsp. (p. 491) Fairly Common Summer Resident.
Limnodromus scolopaceus   Common Migrant.

DESCRIPTION: Breeding ads. — Beak straight, long (over 2 in.) and slender; crown brownish-black flecked with buffy; a dark line from beak to eye and buffy line over eye; hindneck, back and wings brownish-black streaked and barred with buff and brown; large white patch on back is covered by wings when at rest; lower back and tail barred with black and white; entire underparts reddish-cinnamon, the neck and breast spotted and the sides barred with brownish-black. Im. and fall ads. —Above brownish-gray, the feathers of back edged with brown; white mark on back and barred lower back and tail as in breeding adults; throat, breast and sides gray, lightest on chin; rest of underparts white.

IDENTIFICATION: Length of beak distinguishes from all waders but Wilson's snipe. Reddish underparts in spring are distinctive; in flight white patch on back, and barred rump and tail are excellent field marks at any season.

RANGE: North and South America. Breeds from south of Yukon across to Hudson Bay south to northern parts of adjacent provinces. Winters in southern states, Central and northwestern South America.

NESTING: On a dry hummock in muskegs. Nest, a depression lined with grass and leaves. Eggs, 4, olive-green heavily marked with brown. (Winterburn, June 1.)

REMARKS: The inland dowitcher which nests in Alberta and the long-billed dowitcher which migrates through the province to northern nesting grounds were, until recently, considered to be variants of the same species. They are now classed as two distinct species but since their habits are similar and the color differences minute they are here treated together. The inland dowitcher is known to breed from Edmonton north to Lesser Slave Lake; its status in the more northerly parts of the province is unknown. The long-billed dowitcher occurs throughout the province as a migrant but has been recorded in the mountains only from Banff.

Shortly after the middle of May flocks of dowitchers may be seen feeding in shallow sloughs or along the margins of lakes. Probing the mud with their long beaks they move along slowly in compact groups. They are not at all wary but when alarmed they rise together and fly off rapidly in a tight flock. Dowitchers nest near Edmonton in muskeg areas which may also be inhabited by Wilson's snipe. Downy young dowitchers leave the nest shortly after hatching; in the comparative security of the muskeg their chances of survival are good.

178

SNIPES, CURLEWS, SANDPIPERS — Family Scolopacidae

STILT SANDPIPER Fairly Common Migrant.
Micropalama himantopus Length 8½ in.

DESCRIPTION: Spring ads.—Upperparts black, the feathers edged with light gray or buffy, giving an overall dark gray effect; rump white barred with brownish-gray; tail pale gray; crown bordered with chestnut; light line over eye; cinnamon line from beak through eye and over ear; underparts dull white heavily streaked with brownish-gray on throat and neck and elsewhere heavily barred with same color; beak black, 1½ in., slightly decurved; legs long, yellowish-green. Im. and fall ads.—Upperparts plain brownish-gray; light line over eye; buffy line through eye and over ear; underparts white or buffy streaked, not barred, with gray.

IDENTIFICATION: A dark gray sandpiper of medium size with relatively long legs. The barred underparts are distinctive in spring. Sometimes confused with lesser yellowlegs but has relatively longer beak and greenish legs. In all plumages light line over eye is pronounced.

RANGE: North and South America. Breeds in arctic from Hudson Bay to Alaska. Winters from southwestern states south to central Chile and Peru.

NESTING: On the ground. Nest, a depression in the tundra lined with grass and leaves. Eggs, 4, buffy blotched with brown.

REMARKS: The stilt sandpiper is a regular and, at times, abundant migrant in the central and northern parts of the province. It apparently by-passes the southern parts for it is rarely seen at prairie lakes and sloughs. It has been recorded only at Jasper in the mountains.

Stilt sandpipers are often overlooked among the swarms of similarly-colored waders which frequent the shores of our larger lakes but they have certain characteristic habits which identify them. The members of the flock stay close together usually wading as far into the water as their long legs will allow. This keeps them apart from most other species of small shore birds. It also necessitates that, in feeding, they immerse the whole head and often the neck in water in order to probe the mud, a habit which is distinctive.

Spring migrants arrive in central Alberta about the last week in May; southbound migrants may be seen from the middle of July until early in September.

179

SNIPES, CURLEWS, SANDPIPERS — Family Scolopacidae

SEMIPALMATED SANDPIPER Common Migrant.
Ereunetes pusillus Length 6 in.

DESCRIPTION: Feathers of upperparts black with buffy margins giving overall striped brownish-gray appearance; light line over eye; lower back black extending onto central tail feathers; outer tail feathers pale gray; underparts white except a band of grayish marks extending across foreneck and upper breast; beak and legs black; toes slightly webbed at base. Sexes similar. Fall birds are lighter and dark breast band may be almost lacking.

IDENTIFICATION: Similar in color pattern to several species of sandpipers but, because of size, most likely to be confused with least, Baird's, and white-rumped. Smaller than Baird's and not as buffy; lacks white rump of white-rumped; same size as least but grayer especially on face, ears, and back, and has black instead of olive legs.

RANGE: Northeastern Siberia, North and South America. Breeds across arctic from Siberia to Labrador. Winters in southern United States, Central America and northern South America.

NESTING: On the ground. Nest, a depression lined with grass, moss, and leaves. Eggs, 4, dull white spotted with reddish-brown.

REMARKS: On migration the semipalmated sandpiper is found throughout Alberta around those lakes and sloughs whose shores extend into sandy or muddy flatlands. In the mountains it has been seen only near Banff. The species passes northward through the province during May reaching a peak of abundance about May 20th in central Alberta. Southbound migrants reappear late in July becoming more abundant in August and early September.

Among the multitudes of migrating waders which stop for a few days rest at some of our large shallow lakes, flocks of semipalmated sandpipers occur commonly. Like many species of sandpipers they migrate at night appearing in numbers in the morning where there were none the evening before. Spread out along the shoreline they run about picking up small insects from the wet sand or from the froth thrown up by the waves. From time to time flocks rise into the air and perform remarkable aerial manoeuvres, appearing in the distance like clouds of insects far out over the water. In the air or on the shore they mingle freely with other sandpipers especially least and Baird's which they resemble closely in habits as well as appearance.

STILT SANDPIPER

S. D. MACDONALD

SEMIPALMATED SANDPIPER
(see also p. 173)

181

BUFF-BREASTED SANDPIPER
Scarce Migrant.
Tryngites subruficollis
Length 8 in.

DESCRIPTION: Ads.—Feathers of upperparts black centrally with broad buffy margins producing a scaly appearance; line over eye, face, and underparts pinkish-buff; sides of breast spotted with brownish-black; tail dull black, most feathers edged with buffy; beak black, short (¾ in.) and slender; legs greenish-yellow. On their pale gray under surfaces the primaries are beautifully mottled with black. Fall adults and young are similar but darker above, with grayish rather than buffy effect on back.

IDENTIFICATION: A buffy sandpiper more commonly found in the grass back from the water than along the shoreline. In flight pale bases of flight feathers form a light area along wing which is distinctive; in the hand the marbling on the under surface of primaries is distinctive.

RANGE: North and South America. Breeds along arctic coast from Alaska to Hudson Bay. Winters in Argentina and Uruguay.

NESTING: On the ground. Nest, a depression lined with leaves and grass. Eggs, 4, buffy heavily marked with brown.

REMARKS: Very little is known of the distribution of the buff-breasted sandpiper in Alberta. It occurs regularly on migration in central Alberta, but there are few records from other regions. It should be watched for in fields adjacent to the larger lakes.

Although it is rarely seen in other parts of the province the buff-breasted sandpiper appears regularly shortly after the middle of May on fields near Beaverhill Lake. The flocks alight in meadows or in cultivated fields well back from the lake and the birds scatter to feed. As they run about in the sparse vegetation, or stop from time to time with rounded heads held erect on thin necks, they resemble miniature upland plovers. They are not particularly wary; when feeding with golden plover they usually remain behind long after their cautious associates have left in alarm. Buff-breasted sandpipers disappear from the fields as suddenly as they appeared, apparently migrating at night. The southward migration in August is less regular for records are few.

While in Alberta in May buff-breasted sandpipers may be seen performing their courtship display. Raising one wing vertically one male approaches another which assumes a similar posture. A chase follows until one suddenly puts down his wing whereupon the two resume feeding as though nothing had happened. There are many variations: either wing, or both, may be raised, the birds may face each other and stamp their feet. A partner is not essential but when one starts a chain reaction usually sets in until most males in the flock are displaying. It is a beautiful sight yet the females show no evidence of either appreciation or participation.

SNIPES, CURLEWS, SANDPIPERS — Family Scolopacidae

MARBLED GODWIT
Limosa fedoa

Common Summer Resident.
Length 17-19 in.

DESCRIPTION: A large buffy wader with long (4 in.) upturned beak. Head and neck dull white to buffy streaked, except on throat, with gray-brown; back mottled and barred with buff and brownish-black; wings and tail pale cinnamon barred with brownish-black; underparts pinkish-cinnamon barred on breast and sides with wavy lines of brown. In autumn much of the barring of the underparts is lacking.

IDENTIFICATION: Large size, buffy color and long beak distinguish the marbled godwit from all waders except the curlews. The upturned instead of downcurved beak separates it from the curlews.

RANGE: North and South America. Breeds throughout the prairie regions of western Canada and northwestern United States. Winters from southern states south to Peru.

NESTING: On dry grassy flats bordering lakes and large sloughs. Nest, a depression in the ground, sparsely lined with grass. Eggs, 4, creamy-buff heavily marked with browns. (Beaverhill Lake, May 18.)

REMARKS: The marbled godwit is a common breeding bird near the alkaline lakes of the prairies and parklands. It has not been recorded north of the village of Rochester.

Marbled godwits and long-billed curlews, similar in habits as well as in appearance, are often seen together on the shores of sloughs or on adjacent grasslands. Godwits, however, are rarely seen far from water. They are noisy birds; harsh cries of, *kerect — kerect,* or, *eradica — radica — radica,* the latter generally given in flight, announce their presence when they might otherwise be overlooked.

Well back from the water, incubating birds, sitting close with necks stretched along the ground, blend well with their surroundings. Crows and hawks which wander into their territory are met by their mates with vicious swooping attacks which soon put them to rout. Human beings, although never struck, receive similar treatment with added vocal abuse from all the godwits in the vicinity. Leaving the nest shortly after hatching, young godwits survive the perils of early life fairly well and are ready to join their parents on the southward migration early in September. Unfortunately many of them do not survive the unrestricted hunting permitted on some of their wintering grounds.

R. GEHLERT

BUFF-BREASTED SANDPIPER

C. HAMPSON

MARBLED GODWIT

KAY HODGES

HUDSONIAN GODWITS

S. D. MACDONALD

SANDERLING

SNIPES, CURLEWS, SANDPIPERS — Family Scolopacidae

HUDSONIAN GODWIT
Limosa haemastica

Scarce Migrant.
Length 15 in.

DESCRIPTION: Spring—Crown brownish-black lightly streaked with buff; face and throat dull white lightly streaked with black; back and wings black, the feathers tipped or barred with buff and brown; rump white; tail black the outermost feathers white at base; underparts deep chestnut streaked on neck, barred elsewhere, with fine lines of brownish-black; beak about 3 in. long, upturned toward tip. Fall — Above brownish-gray paler on head and neck; white rump; black tail; underparts dull white with faint dusky markings.

IDENTIFICATION: Size, upturned beak, and dark brown color distinguish the hudsonian godwit from other waders in spring; at any season white rump and black tail are distinctive.

RANGE: North America east of Rocky Mountains and South America. Breeds in northern Canada from Mackenzie valley to Hudson Bay. Winters in southern South America.

NESTING: On the ground. Nest, a depression in the tundra sparsely lined with grass. Eggs, 4, olive-buff sparsely marked with browns.

REMARKS: In late April or early May the hudsonian godwit appears regularly but in small numbers at Bittern, Miquelon, Beaverhill, and other central Alberta lakes. As many as twenty-one birds have been seen together but usually the flocks are much smaller. Records indicate that the fall migration through Alberta is less regular.

Hudsonian godwits are found along the shoreline or wading in the shallow waters of large lakes. Their habits are similar to those of the marbled godwit but they are less noisy. On the verge of extinction only a few years ago the hudsonian godwit now appears to be slowly increasing in numbers although it is still not past the danger point. Complete protection provided by law in North America has undoubtedly stopped the depletion of various species of waders but those which, like the hudsonian godwit, migrate to South America have to withstand the effect of virtually uncontrolled shooting on their wintering grounds. Whether the hudsonian godwit and other migrant species whose numbers are at low ebb can be saved without all-year-round protection remains to be seen.

Hudsonian godwits are most likely to be seen in small flocks not far from water. They work through the shoreline debris looking for small crustaceans, molluscs, worms and insects. When this is not profitable their long legs allow them to wade well out from shore where they can probe the bottom for similar food. Unlike marbled godwits they are usually silent; their occasional calls have a soft sandpiper-like quality.

186

SNIPES, CURLEWS, SANDPIPERS — Family Scolopacidae

SANDERLING
Crocethia alba

Common Migrant.
Length 8 in.

DESCRIPTION: Feathers of head, neck and upperparts streaked with black and brown but all with white edges giving pale whitish appearance; wings with one white bar and white at base of primaries; central tail feathers dull black, rest pale gray; throat and foreneck like head but more brownish; rest of underparts white; beak and legs black; only 3 toes on foot. Sexes alike. Fall birds similar but paler with less brown and more white.

IDENTIFICATION: A plump little sandpiper whose plumage is suffused with white. Pale upperparts and dark throat distinguish it from other small gray sandpipers; in flight white on wings is distinctive.

RANGE: Almost cosmopolitan. In North America breeds on arctic islands across continent; winters from southern United States south to Central and South America.

NESTING: On the ground. Nest, a depression lined with grass and leaves. Eggs, 4, pale yellowish spotted with brown and black.

REMARKS: The sanderling occurs on migration throughout Alberta except in the mountains. While passing through the province in the spring sanderlings may show considerable variation in color. Some still retain much of the winter plumage and appear almost white at a distance; others, well into the breeding plumage, are a decided reddish-brown. But regardless of color their habits will identify them. They are very active birds scurrying about on such rapidly moving legs that their bodies seem to glide along. Only the sandy shores of large lakes attract sanderlings. On windy days when waves are washing the shore sanderlings run after each retreating wave, picking up particles of food which it has left behind and hurrying back as the next one threatens to overtake them.

Most sanderlings migrate along the sea coasts but fair numbers travel inland. They move north a little later in the spring than most waders, the main body passing through central Alberta about the first week in June. At some of the larger lakes sanderlings may outnumber all other waders at this time. In the fall, still in large numbers, they pass southward through the province during the last half of September. The intervening months have been spent in the arctic building a nest and raising the young. The illustration is a photograph of a sanderling incubating its eggs on the tundra, a sight which few people are privileged to see for the sanderling is one of our most northerly nesting birds.

AMERICAN AVOCET

RED PHALAROPE

AVOCETS — Family Recurvirostridae

AMERICAN AVOCET Fairly Common Summer Resident.
Recurvirostra americana Length 16-19 in.

DESCRIPTION: Breeding ads.—Head and neck cinnamon except a white ring around eye and base of beak; beak long (3½ in.), narrow, flattened, and upturned; upper back white with broad central V of brownish-black; wings black with a large white patch on secondaries; rest of body white; tail pale gray; legs long, light grayish-blue. Fall ads. and im.—Similar to above but cinnamon lacking; instead head, neck, and breast are washed with pale gray.

IDENTIFICATION: A large black and white wader with reddish head and neck, pale blue legs, and long, pointed, upturned beak; can be mistaken for no other species even in fall when reddish color is lacking.

RANGE: North America. Breeds from prairies of western Canada to California, Texas and Iowa. Winters from southwestern states to Guatemala.

NESTING: On the ground near water, sometimes in small colonies. Nest, a depression in the sand lined with a few weed stems. Eggs, 3-5, deep olive-buff, spotted and blotched with black and brown. (Calgary, June 11.)

REMARKS: The avocet is found throughout southern Alberta, except in the mountains, north to Edmonton and Tofield, but it is rather local in distribution. Earlier in the century it ranged more widely for specimens were taken at Lesser Slave Lake, Peace River, and Ft. Chipewyan.

The avocet frequents the alkaline sloughs and lakes of the prairies and parklands where its long legs allow it to wade far out into the shallow water. Often a dozen birds or more will move parallel to the shore sweeping their sickle beaks from side to side across the surface of the water as they gather insects and crustaceans. At other times they probe the mud for food. Avocets are quiet, shy birds with a preference for the company of their own species. Even during the nesting period they are often found in groups, several pairs nesting in close proximity on a sand bar or island. Two females sometimes lay in the same nest and probably share incubation duties. The young, clothed in buffy gray down, leave the nest shortly after hatching and are cared for solicitously by the parents. Not all survive the perils of early life and migration, however, for avocets are not now as abundant as they were a few decades ago.

Avocets reach central Alberta early in May congregating in flocks of up to one hundred birds. At this time, as a result of courtship activities and squabbles they may be rather noisy, their shrill cries reaching a crescendo as the flock takes flight or swims out onto the water. By the end of the month, however, the flocks have broken up into smaller, more amicable nesting groups.

PHALAROPES — Family Phalaropidae

Phalaropes are small wading birds which spend as much time on the water as along the shore. When swimming they move about with a whirligig motion as though propelled by only one foot. Phalaropes show a remarkable reversal of the usual activities of the two sexes: the female has bright colors and takes the initiative in courting but, of course, lays the eggs; the male, in duller plumage, incubates the eggs and cares for the young. The toes have narrow flattened lobes on the sides.

RED PHALAROPE
Phalaropus fulicarius

Scarce Migrant.
Length 8 in.

DESCRIPTION: Spring f.—Upperparts brownish-black, many feathers edged with yellowish-brown; face white; wings dark gray with broad white bar; underparts rich reddish-brown. Spring m.—Similar but more streaked above and paler red below. Im. and fall ads.—Head, neck, and underparts white, except gray mark under and behind eye, and gray mark over eye extending down back of neck to back; back gray; wings dark gray with broad white wing bar; legs and base of beak yellow.

IDENTIFICATION: In spring plumage the red phalarope is distinctive but not likely to be seen in Alberta. In fall similar to northern and Wilson's phalaropes, larger and paler than former; white wing bars separate from latter; yellow legs are distinctive.

RANGE: World wide. Breeds in North America on arctic coasts and islands. Migrates down both coasts and probably spends the winter on the Atlantic and Pacific oceans from near the southern states to the Falkland Islands.

NESTING: On the ground on the tundra. Nest, a depression lined by the male with grasses and leaves. Eggs, 4, olive-buff boldly marked with brown.

REMARKS: The red phalarope is a maritime species which rarely appears in the interior of the continent. There are few definite records of its occurrence in Alberta: a specimen was taken near Didsbury in September, 1903; one was collected at Beaverhill Lake in September, 1925; and a female was collected on Pigeon Lake on July 13, 1960. There are also sight records from Banff and Beaverhill Lake.

Red phalaropes in their normal range regularly alight on the ocean to rest and feed, acting more like aquatic birds than shore-birds. It is not surprising therefore, to find that most inland records of this species come from large bodies of water. Since red phalaropes spend so much time on open water far from shore they easily escape detection and it is possible that our few records are not a true indication of the numbers which pass through the province.

190

PHALAROPES — Family Phalaropidae

WILSON'S PHALAROPE
Steganopus tricolor

Fairly Common Summer Resident.
Length 9 in.

DESCRIPTION: Spring f.—Crown pearly gray becoming white on hindneck; white line over eye; heavy black line through eye and down sides of neck where bordered by chestnut which continues in long V on back; back and wings brownish-gray becoming white near tail; tail pale gray and white; underparts white except tinged with chestnut on neck and gray on sides; legs black; toes with long narrow web on each side. Spring m.—Upperparts brownish-gray flecked with dusky on crown and back; underparts white except tinged with gray on neck; sides of neck indistinctly washed with rusty. Im. and fall ads.— Upperparts light brownish-gray with many light feather edgings, lightest on head; underparts white except grayish on sides of neck and breast; tail as in spring.

IDENTIFICATION: The largest and lightest colored of the phalaropes and the only species nesting in Alberta. Heavy black and chestnut streak on side of neck is distinctive in spring female.

RANGE: North and South America. Breeds in four western provinces south to California and Indiana. Winters from Mexico south to Argentina.

NESTING: On the ground in wet or dry meadows. Nest, a depression lined with grass. Eggs, 4, creamy-buff spotted and blotched with dark brown and purple. (Ensign, June 8.)

REMARKS: Wilson's phalarope has been recorded from all parts of the province as far north as Lake Athabasca and west into the mountains at Jasper and Waterton Lakes, but only in the southern prairies and parklands is it at all common. Even here its distribution is quite local and its occurrence from year to year rather erratic.

Wilson's phalarope acts more like a sandpiper than either the red or the northern phalarope. It commonly probes along the muddy or grassy margins of prairie sloughs or wades in their shallow waters but like its smaller relatives it swims readily. On the water it moves erratically in small circles as though propelled by only one foot, its round head bobbing back and forth as it picks insects from the surface.

In spring several females may pester a male with their attentions interrupting him in the important occupation of food gathering. When he attempts to avoid them in flight they pursue him relentlessly until he alights again. Sooner or later conflict among the competing females is unavoidable, and unladylike brawls ensue involving a great deal of feather-pulling but no great harm to the combatants. Although he appears unconcerned the male usually succumbs to the wiles of the winner and soon becomes the most henpecked husband of the bird world, saddled with the entire responsibility of nest building, incubation, and care of the young. Sic transit gloria viri!

PHALAROPES — Family Phalaropidae

NORTHERN PHALAROPE
Lobipes lobatus

Common Migrant.
Length 7 in.

DESCRIPTION: Spring f.—Face and all upperparts blackish-slate except white eyelids and wing-bar and narrow cinnamon V extending along back; throat white; band of blackish-slate extends across lower neck and upper breast; in front of this a band of chestnut across lower neck is continuous with patch of chestnut on sides of neck; rest of underparts white; beak black, needle-like; legs bluish-gray; toes with narrow scalloped webs. Spring m.—Similar but duller and with less chestnut on neck. Im. and fall ads.—Upperparts dull black, many feathers edged with white especially on crown; white wing-bar; face and underparts white except dark patch under eye and faint gray band across lower neck; few rusty feathers on sides of neck.

IDENTIFICATION: Distinctively marked in spring; a small dark bluish-black wader with reddish-brown on sides of neck. In fall white-frosted dark back and white underparts help to identify. At any season white wing-bar is distinctive; often seen swimming.

RANGE: North and South America. Eurasia. In North America breeds across continent in arctic regions. Winters at sea off the coasts of South America.

NESTING: On the ground near water. Nest, a depression in a dry mound lined with grass. Eggs, 4, olive-buff blotched with brown.

REMARKS: The northern phalarope is found throughout Alberta on migration but is scarce in the mountains. The spring migration of northern phalaropes, like that of many waders, is a spectacular affair; thousands of individuals hurry northward together passing through a particular locality in a period of only two or three weeks. The return journey is more leisurely; small widely dispersed groups move gradually southward from late in July to early September.

During the last two weeks of May large flocks of northern phalaropes mill and wheel like sandpipers over their feeding grounds at some of our large shallow lakes or run about on the sandy shores. Unlike sandpipers, however, they often alight on the water, swimming in little circles, first one way then the other, as though propelled by only one foot at a time. In August small groups may be seen even on prairie sloughs whirling about in this manner, their round heads bobbing back and forth as they pick up morsels of food. Northern phalaropes spend more time on the water than along the shore; in fact it is probable that during the winter months they do not come to land at all, remaining on the open ocean along the coasts of South America.

WILSON'S PHALAROPE
female

NORTHERN PHALAROPE
male

JAEGERS — Family Stercorariidae

Jaegers are gull-like in general appearance but the central tail feathers are elongated and the beak has a distinct nail at the end forming a strong hook. The wing stroke is rapid and the flight resembles that of a falcon. Two color phases occur regardless of age and sex. Jaegers are predaceous birds which eat the eggs and young of other birds or harry gulls and terns to rob them of their food.

PARASITIC JAEGER *Stercorarius parasiticus*	Scarce Wanderer. Length 21 in.
LONG-TAILED JAEGER *Stercorarius longicaudus*	Scarce Wanderer. Length 23 in.

DESCRIPTION: Middle two tail feathers tapering and extending beyond remainder about three inches in parasitic jaeger and six to eight inches in long-tailed. Ads.—both species. Upperparts brownish-black darkest on crown, wings and tail; face yellowish; throat and underparts white shading to grayish on abdomen. Females are duller, more gray below and the yellow may be obscure. A dark phase, more commonly found in first species is entirely brownish-black, slightly paler below and usually with yellow tinge behind eye.

IDENTIFICATION: No reliable color differences separate the two species; the length of the middle tail feathers is the only reliable field mark. Young, and moulting adults, are difficult to identify even in the hand. If the shafts of the outer three primaries are white the bird is probably a parasitic jaeger; if the outer two are white and the third dark it is probably a long-tailed.

RANGE: Both species: Northern parts of northern hemisphere. Breed in North America on arctic coasts and islands. Winter on Atlantic and Pacific coasts.

NESTING: Both species nest on the ground. Nest, a depression lined with grass and moss. Eggs, 2-3.

REMARKS: The parasitic jaeger usually migrates along the coasts to reach its arctic nesting grounds but occasionally individuals wander inland. The species has been seen in Alberta at Lake Newell, Sylvan Lake, Camrose, and Edmonton, and a specimen was collected at Beaverhill Lake. A parasitic jaeger was seen on several occasions during July and August, 1953, at Spray Lake near Banff. In June, 1952, one was seen at Lake Athabasca chasing the nesting terns and forcing them to drop the minnows they had captured.

There are few records of the long-tailed jaeger in Alberta. The species was observed at Baptiste Lake on three occasions between 1932 and 1934, and at Lake Athabasca on June 13, 1933. On June 3, 1965, two long-tailed jaegers were seen in flight near Edmonton. The long-tailed jaeger migrates mainly along the sea coasts and rarely wanders inland. It might be expected only near our larger lakes, especially those in the northern part of the province.

GULLS — Family Laridae

Gulls are large birds usually white with a grayish-blue mantle over their backs, with black wing tips, and sometimes with black heads. Seasonal and age differences in plumage make sight identification difficult.. Their beaks are strong and slightly hooked and their feet are webbed. They are strong swimmers and fliers. In flight they move gracefully with slow short wing strokes or soar on motionless wings. Gulls are usually found near water but being omnivorous some species often feed in the fields or scavenge on refuse heaps.

GLAUCOUS GULL
Larus hyperboreus subsp. (p. 491)

Scarce Migrant.
Length 28 in.

DESCRIPTION: Ads.—Pure white except a mantle of pale bluish-gray over back and wings; beak yellow with red spot near tip; legs dull yellowish or flesh color; iris pale yellow. Im.—Pale grayish-brown mottled and streaked with darker grayish-brown; quite variable but never has dark primaries.

IDENTIFICATION: A very large gull almost entirely white; the only Alberta gull with pure white primaries.

RANGE: Circumpolar. Breeds in North America on coasts and islands of arctic from Alaska to Greenland. Winters along east and west coasts south to New Jersey and California.

NESTING: On rocky cliffs. Nest of soft grasses and moss. Eggs, 3, buffy-brown blotched with dark brown.

REMARKS: Gulls are noted for their endurance in flight but many species normally exercise these powers only over water. Occasionally however, perhaps affected by prolonged gales, migrating individuals of these maritime species are seen well inland. Appearances of the glaucous gull in Alberta are of this nature. There are only two records of the occurrence of this arctic species in the province. An immature glaucous gull was shot west of Lacombe in 1915 and is now preserved in the Provincial Museum at Edmonton. Another was caught in a coyote trap near Youngstown in November, 1940. This specimen is also preserved.

Gulls with white heads are popularly known as 'sea gulls' in Alberta. It is not commonly recognized that six species of white-headed gulls occur in the province, three of which are reasonably abundant. All are quite similar in color. The glaucous gull is the largest of this group and the one most easily distinguished since it lacks any black on its wings. Immature birds of these species all have large amounts of gray or brown in the plumage and form a confusing group which challenges the skill of even the best field men.

PARASITIC JAEGER

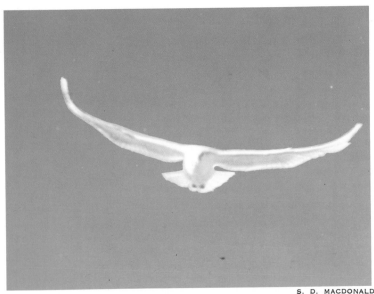

GLAUCOUS GULL

GLAUCOUS-WINGED GULL

HERRING GULL
adult   *immature*

GULLS, TERNS — Family Laridae

GLAUCOUS-WINGED GULL
Larus glaucescens

Status Uncertain.
Length 25 in.

DESCRIPTION: Ads.—All white except for a mantle of light bluish-gray over back and wings; primaries gray or pale gray with white scallops at tips; iris brown; beak yellow with red spot near tip of upper mandible; legs pink. Im.—Brownish-gray spotted and streaked with grayish-white and buffy-white over the entire body. Second and third year plumages are generally similar but the underparts become paler and the upperparts show patches of pale bluish-gray as the bird becomes older.

IDENTIFICATION: A large gull similar to herring and California gulls but primaries gray instead of black. Primaries of immature glaucous-winged gulls may be dark gray but are never black.

RANGE: Pacific coasts of North America and Asia south to California and Japan and north to Aleutians. In North America breeds along coast from Alaska to Washington. Winters from Alaska to Gulf of California.

NESTING: On the ground usually in colonies on small islands and rocky coasts. Nest of sticks, grass and seaweed. Eggs, 2-3, brownish-olive spotted with brown.

REMARKS: The glaucous-winged gull has only recently been found in Alberta and records have come from only two areas, both in the northern half of the province. A specimen was obtained at Bear Lake northwest of Grande Prairie in mid-September, 1958. In the summer and fall of 1959 several glaucous-winged gulls were seen in the same area and on Aug. 11, 1959, a specimen was secured. None of these birds was in adult plumage. On June 2, 1960, a banded gull was found wounded on the shores of Therien Lake north of St. Paul. It was thought that the bird would survive so it was released. Banding records showed that this was a glaucous-winged gull which had hatched on Christie Island in the Strait of Georgia in early June, 1959. These records indicate that immature glaucous-winged gulls may occur regularly around some of the lakes of north-central Alberta.

Glaucous-winged gulls do not breed until they are four years old. During the first three years of their lives they are not bound, therefore, to any particular territory although apparently the majority of these immature birds stay close to the Pacific Coast. Some, however, cross the Rocky Mountains and spend part of the year in Alberta. Peculiarly the species has not been recorded from the interior of B.C.

This is the common gull of the west coast. Glaucous-winged gulls follow the ferries back and forth across the Strait of Georgia, accepting the bounty thrown from the galley or riding the air-currents set up by the moving ship. They are equally at home along the shoreline where they follow the receding tide picking up crabs and shellfish from the shallowing pools and breaking them open with their strong beaks. In Alberta glaucous-winged gulls have been found only at a few large lakes whose shores resemble their normal maritime habitat. They bear the dark immature plumage although the older ones may show a strong admixture of pale blue.

GULLS, TERNS — Family Laridae

HERRING GULL
Larus argentatus   subsp. (p. 491)

Fairly Common Summer Resident.
Length 24 in.

DESCRIPTION: Ads.—A mantle of pale bluish-gray over back and wings; first two primaries largely black tipped with white and with sub-terminal white spots; next four primaries with reduced amount of black but all tipped with white; rest of plumage white; beak yellow with red spot near tip of lower mandible; legs flesh-pink. Im.—Dark brownish-gray all over but streaked with white on head and neck and with white barring at base of tail. The change from immature to adult plumage requires more than three years and many color variations are produced.

IDENTIFICATION: Adults are similar to California and ring-billed gulls but are larger than the latter. They are difficult to separate from California gulls in flight but at rest the pink instead of yellowish legs and the lack of black on the beak are distinctive. Young herring gulls are darker than any other young gulls.

RANGE: The northern hemisphere. In North America breeds from New York and Alberta north to the Arctic coast. Winters on Great Lakes and Pacific and Atlantic coasts south to Central America.

NESTING: On the ground usually on an isolated rock in water; occasionally in colonies. Nest of seaweed and sticks. Eggs, 2-3, pale grayish-brown blotched with dark brown.

REMARKS: Numbers of herring gulls spend the summer at various lakes in central Alberta but these appear to be non-breeding birds for no nests have been found south of Lake Athabasca. From Lake Athabasca northward herring gulls breed fairly commonly. On migration they may occur throughout the province although there is only one record from the mountains; that was at Jasper.

On Canada's eastern and western coasts herring gulls regularly follow ocean liners far out to sea to feed on the refuse thrown from the ships. It is only natural, therefore, that in Alberta they usually frequent large lakes. Herring gulls wing slowly along the shore-line watching for dead fish and other carrion. They are mainly scavengers but their diet includes crustaceans and insects and even eggs and young birds when opportunity is presented. In mixed company the large pugnacious herring gulls might be expected to get all the delicacies thrown up by the waves but the greater agility of the smaller gulls assures them of their fair share.

199

C. HAMPSON

CALIFORNIA GULL

C. HAMPSON

RING-BILLED GULL

GULLS, TERNS — Family Laridae

CALIFORNIA GULL
Larus californicus

Common Summer Resident.
Length 20-23 in.

DESCRIPTION: Ads.—White except grayish-blue mantle over back and wings; first six primaries largely black with white tips, the amount of black gradually decreasing from first to sixth primary; iris dark brown; beak yellow with spot, half black and half red, near tip of lower mandible, and small dark spot on upper; legs greenish-yellow. Im.— Dull white heavily streaked with brownish and bluish-gray. In its second year the immature becomes lighter but does not show adult plumage until fully two years of age.

IDENTIFICATION: Intermediate in size between herring and ring-billed gulls; greenish-yellow legs and black as well as red spot on beak distinguish from former; red spot and lack of complete dark ring around end of beak from latter. The terminal two inches of the first primary of the California gull is white sometimes with a narrow black bar half an inch from the tip.

RANGE: Western North America. Breeds from Great Slave Lake south to California and North Dakota. Winters from southern B.C. to Mexico.

NESTING: On the ground in colonies. Nest of sticks and grass. Eggs, 3 bluish-white to buffy-brown blotched with brown and black. (Camrose, May 26.)

REMARKS: Early in the century California gulls nested at various large lakes in south-central Alberta but after the drought of the late 1920's few of these breeding colonies remained. The southernmost colony today is at Lake Newell near Brooks. Known colonies in the more northerly parts of the province are at Lake Winnifred, Lac la Biche, and Lake Athabasca. There are probably other breeding colonies at some of the inaccessible lakes of the northern forested region. On migration California gulls may be found throughout the province.

California gulls are early spring migrants appearing at our larger lakes and rivers early in April before the ice is entirely gone. They have omnivorous appetites. If there is insufficient food along the shore they visit the fields to eat vegetation and insects. Some may follow the plough like the smaller Franklin's gulls. Others scavenge around city dumps in company with ring-billed gulls or tear at small animals killed on the roads. On their nesting grounds they eat the eggs and young of other birds which nest in the vicinity and are not above cannibalism on occasion. In the fall well after ice has formed on the lakes California gulls may still be seen slowly winging their way along the edges of the open water looking for dead ducks which the hunter has been unable to retrieve.

GULLS, TERNS — Family Laridae

RING-BILLED GULL
Larus delawarensis

Common Summer Resident.
Length 19 in.

DESCRIPTION: Ads. — Plumage white except a mantle of pale bluish-gray over back and wings; first two primaries mainly black with white patch near tips, next four with diminishing amounts of black but with white tips; beak yellow with black band encircling it near tip; legs greenish-yellow. Im.—Dull white mottled and barred with brown; tail dull white with dark brownish-gray tip.

IDENTIFICATION: Color pattern same as herring and California gulls but with complete dark ring near end of beak. Smaller size is useful field mark only when other species are present. Plumage of immature is lighter than that of other two species.

RANGE: North America. Breeds throughout Canada except the arctic and in northern states. Winters from southern Canada to Mexico.

NESTING: On the ground in colonies usually on islands. Nest of coarse grass and reeds in a slight depression. Eggs, 2-4, variable in color, pale blue to light brown blotched with brown and lavender. (Ministik Lake, May 31.)

REMARKS: Until the drought of the 1920s colonies of ring-billed gulls nested at many lakes in southern and central Alberta; today few colonies remain. The largest are at Lake Newell, Buffalo Lake, and Lac la Biche. Farther north the species nests at Lake Athabasca and will probably be found at many other inaccessible northern lakes. Ring-billed gulls and California gulls often nest on the same island one colony usually being separated from the other by a short distance. When the young are hatched, however, all flock together and even an expert taxonomist would have difficulty in separating them. The two species also associate away from the nesting grounds. Both may be found on rivers, especially near the outlets of city sewers, and both commonly resort to city dumps to feed on the garbage. It is in mixed flocks of this sort that size is most helpful in identification. Ring-billed gulls often travel miles to a good feeding spot; each evening in loose flocks they wing slowly back to the safety of a lake or river passing over the center of a city with as little concern as over a grain field.

Gulls are scavengers for a great part of the year but, particularly when they have ravenous young to feed, the larger species prey heavily upon any living creatures which they can capture and kill. Families of waterfowl hatched in the vicinity of a ring-bill colony are particularly vulnerable to their depredations and very few of the ducklings survive. Outside the breeding season however, the food habits of the gulls cannot be criticized.

202

GULLS, TERNS — Family Laridae

MEW GULL
Larus canus subsp. (p. 491)

Scarce Migrant.
Length 17½ in.

DESCRIPTION: Ads.—Mantle of pale grayish-blue over back and wings; black tips on primaries similar to those on herring gull but small black spot on seventh primary also; rest of plumage white; beak short, clear yellow with no black or red spots; legs yellowish-green. Im.—Dark brownish-gray; beak dark horn, flesh-colored at base; legs brownish-pink.

IDENTIFICATION: The smallest of the white-headed gulls. Adults are similar to ring-billed gulls but lack black mark on beak. Immature birds are much darker than young ring-bills.

RANGE: Western North America. Breeds from Alaska to Lake Athabasca and central B.C. Winters along Pacific coast south to California.

NESTING: On the ground, on rocky or marshy shores of lakes; sometimes in trees. Nest of sticks and coarse rushes in a shallow depression. Eggs, 2-3, olive-buff blotched with browns.

REMARKS: On its regular migrations to and from its wintering grounds on the Pacific coast and its nesting grounds in the north the mew, or short-billed, gull cuts across the Rocky Mountains and over northern Alberta, by-passing the southern part of the province. There are nesting colonies just outside the Alberta boundary near Ft. Smith in the N.W.T. and at the east end of Lake Athabasca in Saskatchewan but so far there are no records of nesting within the boundaries of Alberta. Records of casual occurrence of the species have been made at Brooks, Camrose, Tofield, Belvedere and Jasper.

The white-headed gulls offer a definite challenge to anyone who prides himself on his ability at field identification. The adults are closely alike in plumage and the immature plumages are so variable for each species that one can hardly rely at all on the plumage for identification. There are no distinctive peculiarities of behavior to separate one species from another. Size, voice, and color of legs and beak are therefore the most reliable means of identification. Gulls will often permit fairly close approach making possible a careful examination of their distinguishing features but even at a distance the short bill of the mew gull gives it a round-headed appearance which helps to separate it from other species. Although the main migration route is farther north mew gulls should be watched for in southern Alberta where they will likely occur around large lakes and rivers, probably in company with other gulls.

GULLS, TERNS — Family Laridae

FRANKLIN'S GULL
Larus pipixcan

Common Summer Resident.
Length 15 in.

DESCRIPTION: Spring ads.—Head entirely black; bluish-gray mantle over back and wings; primaries gray becoming black towards end but tipped with white; rest of plumage white beautifully tinted with pink on underparts; beak and legs dark red. Fall ads.—Head white except a dark gray band around nape from eye to eye; rest same as in spring. Im.—Similar to fall adults but mantle tinged with brown; outer tail feathers white, rest with terminal black band; dark gray on head more extensive.

IDENTIFICATION: Adult Franklin's and Bonaparte's gulls may be distinguished either in spring or fall by amount of white on wings (see Bonaparte's gull). Immature birds are often difficult to separate; Franklin's gull has more extensive gray area on head usually including all of rear of crown and continuing over ears and completely around eye; Bonaparte's has only thin crescent in front of eye and patch behind; Franklin's has white outer tail feather, Bonaparte's barred.

RANGE: Interior of North America. Breeds in prairie regions of U.S. and Canada. Winters from Texas and Louisiana south to Chile and Patagonia.

NESTING: In colonies over shallow water. Nest, a large mass of reeds floating among reeds or rushes on water one or two feet deep. Eggs, 3, greenish-blue or greenish-brown marked with brown and lilac. (Hay Lakes, May 30.)

REMARKS: Nesting colonies of Franklin's gulls are scattered throughout Alberta from Many Island Lake in the south to Lake Athabasca in the north but the species occurs only rarely in the mountains and then only as a migrant.

In southern Alberta Franklin's gull is the best known and the best liked member of the gull family. To the farmer tiresomely working his fields in the spring the pretty black-headed gulls which follow the plough to pick up cutworms and wireworms from the freshly turned furrow are both friends and companions. All day long they help him and then in the evening slowly wing their way back to the marsh perhaps thirty miles or more away. Later in the season thousands of Franklin's gulls alight in his fields to feast on grasshoppers infesting the grain.

The nesting marsh is usually some extensive shallows at the edge of a lake overgrown with cat-tails and reeds. The colony returns to it year after year. Most colonies are not diminishing in numbers thanks to wide-spread recognition of the value of this highly beneficial species.

204

B. & J. MORGAN

MEW GULL

C. HAMPSON

FRANKLIN'S GULL

GULLS, TERNS — Family Laridae

BONAPARTE'S GULL
Larus philadelphia

Fairly Common Summer Resident.
Length 14 in.

DESCRIPTION: Spring ads.—Head entirely black; bluish-gray mantle over back and wings; front edge of wing from bend outward, and including first three primaries, white except narrow black tips in primaries; rest of plumage white; beak black; legs reddish-orange. Fall ads.—Head white except gray patch on nape and dark gray spot behind and below eye; rest same as spring plumage. Im.—Similar to fall adults but mantle tinged with brown; tail with black terminal band and outer feathers barred.

IDENTIFICATION: Only Franklin's and Bonaparte's gulls have black heads in spring; Sabine's gull has a dark gray head. In flight Bonaparte's gull shows a large strip of white from bend of wing outward; this area in Franklin's is gray. The primaries are tipped with black in Bonaparte's and white in Franklin's. The beak of Bonaparte's gull is black, of Franklin's red. In fall Bonaparte's gull has three dark spots on head; Franklin's has complete band around nape.

RANGE: North America. Breeds from Alaska and Mackenzie south to central B.C. and Alberta. Winters on Pacific coast from Alaska to Mexico and coasts of southern Atlantic and Gulf of Mexico.

NESTING: In trees, usually high in evergreens. Nest of twigs lined with grass. Eggs, 3, olive-gray marked with brown and lavender. (Winterburn, May 24.)

REMARKS: One hardly expects to see gulls sitting in trees but in the muskegs of northern Alberta the sight is not all unusual. While his mate covers her eggs in a tree nearby the male Bonaparte's gull stands guard on top of an old jack-pine or spruce, a conspicuous figure against the blue of the sky. Three or four pairs often nest in the vicinity of a small muskeg lake and the male birds fraternize on and around its waters. Like terns they are fond of resting on stumps or posts projecting above the surface. On migration Bonaparte's gull is most often seen near large lakes. It never occurs in large flocks like Franklin's gull but the two species are occasionally associated. In such cases the very harsh note of Bonaparte's gull is helpful in identifying it.

Bonaparte's gull is widely but quite locally distributed as a breeding bird in the heavily forested areas of northern Alberta from near Edmonton to the northern boundary. On migration it occurs throughout southern Alberta and has been seen at Jasper and Banff in the mountains. It is a late fall migrant; while most Bonaparte's gulls leave central Alberta lakes about the end of September some usually remain until after the middle of October.

GULLS, TERNS — Family Laridae

SABINE'S GULL
Xema sabini

Scarce Wanderer.
Length 13½ in.

DESCRIPTION: Ads.—Head dark slate-gray bordered behind with black; grayish-blue mantle over back and wings; outer five primaries black with small white tips; rest of plumage white; tail forked about one inch; legs black; beak black with yellow tip. Im.—Upperparts barred with slate-gray and white; underparts white; wrist and outer five primaries mainly black; tail forked as in adult, white with black bar on middle feathers.

IDENTIFICATION: Gray instead of black head and forked tail distinguish Sabine's gull from Franklin's and Bonaparte's; black wrist and primaries can be seen at a distance.

RANGE: Arctic regions of Asia and North America. The only known wintering grounds is off the coast of Peru.

NESTING: On the ground. Nest, a depression lined with grass. Eggs, 2-3, olive-brown blotched with brown.

REMARKS: Sabine's gull is an arctic species which nests in colonies on islands in small tundra lakes and ponds often in company with arctic terns. On migration they follow the coastlines closely, rarely appearing inland in the southern parts of Canada. There are few records of the occurrence of Sabine's gull in Alberta. On September 15, 1929, three were seen at Beaverhill Lake and one was collected. On June 9, 1959, the remains of two Sabine's gulls were found on the shores of Cold Lake. There are also sight records from Baptiste Lake, Sullivan Lake, Muriel Lake and Calgary. Sabine's gull may be expected to occur in Alberta only as a rare erratic wanderer near large bodies of water.

It is noteworthy that all records of Sabine's gull have so far come from central or southern Alberta whereas one might expect that wandering individuals of this arctic-nesting species would more commonly occur in the extreme northern part of the province. Most of our knowledge of the birds of northern Alberta has been obtained during brief visits made by ornithologists to a few accessible areas. Residents of these regions with sufficient interest and enthusiasm for bird study could render great service by developing their ability to identify birds and by keeping records of their observations. As the number and skill of resident observers increases it may be found that such birds as Sabine's gull have a wider distribution in the north than is at present suspected.

ALLAN BROOKS

BONAPARTE'S GULL
adult   immature

FRANKLIN'S GULL
adult   immature

DAVID F. PARMELEE

SABINE'S GULL

ALLAN BROOKS

FORSTER'S TERN
adult *immature*

C. HAMPSON

COMMON TERN
on nest

GULLS, TERNS — Family Laridae

Terns are dainty gull-like birds with narrow wings, forked tails, pointed beaks, and webbed feet. Most species are white with black caps but our commonest species, the black tern, is dark slate-gray. Graceful as swallows in flight, terns wheel about over the water ready to plunge beneath the surface after minnows, frogs, or large insects. When flying they point the beak downward in an attitude which distinguishes them from the gulls.

FORSTER'S TERN   Scarce Summer Resident.
Sterna forsteri   Length 15 in.

DESCRIPTION: Spring ads.—Top of head and nape black; mantle of pale bluish-gray over back and wings; rest of plumage white, washed on underparts with pale silvery-gray; tail forked about 3½ in. silvery-gray; inner webs of outer tail feathers gray; legs and beak orange-red, beak with black tip. Fall ads.—Similar but black confined to a streak through eye and a few feathers on crown and nape. Im.—Similar to fall adults but many feathers are tipped with brown.

IDENTIFICATION: Difficult to separate in the field from common tern. Outer vanes of outermost wing and tail feathers light; these are dark in the common tern. Tail mostly silvery-gray; tail of common tern mainly white. Call note of Forster's tern is a low-pitched *churrr*, not as harsh as the *tee-arrrr* of the common tern.

RANGE: North America. Breeds in southern parts of prairie provinces south to Illinois and California. Winters in countries bordering the Gulf of Mexico.

NESTING: On floating rushes, muskrat houses, or occasionally on islands; sometimes in loose colonies. Eggs, 3-4, pale buffy to greenish-brown heavily marked with dark brown. (Lake Wabamun, June 5.)

REMARKS: Perhaps because of its close resemblance to the common tern there are few records of Forster's tern in Alberta. The species has been seen at Many Island Lake, Lac la Nonne, and Fawcett and has been found nesting at Buffalo Lake, Dried Meat Lake, and Lake Wabamun. Forster's terns nest in reedy shallows which are often found along the borders of lakes in central Alberta. It is reported that Forster's and common terns form a small mixed colony in habitat of this type at Lake Wabamun, their floating nests attached to sparse reed growth. Apart from its preference for marshy nesting sites there is nothing peculiar about the habits of Forster's tern which distinguish it from other similar species of tern.

GULLS, TERNS — Family Laridae

COMMON TERN Fairly Common Summer Resident.
Sterna hirundo subsp. (p. 492) Length 15 in.

DESCRIPTION: Spring ads.—Top of head and hind-neck black; mantle of pale bluish-gray over back and wings; outer web of first primary black; rest of plumage white; tail forked about 3 in., outer web of outer two pairs of tail feathers gray; legs and beak orange-red, beak with black tip. Fall ads.—Similar but black on head duller and confined to a streak behind eye and across nape. Im.—Similar to fall adults but with some brownish edges on feathers of back and front edge of wing very dark.

IDENTIFICATION: In all plumages much like Forster's tern but distinguished by dark instead of light outer webs of tail feathers and by black instead of gray outer web of first primary. In fall plumage black band across nape distinguishes from Forster's.

RANGE: Nearly world-wide. Breeds in most of the interior of North America. Winters along coasts of Mexico and South America south to Straits of Magellan.

NESTING: In colonies on the ground usually on an island in a lake. Nest, a depression lined with a few bits of grass and reeds. Eggs, 2-4, light greenish to olive-brown blotched with brown. (Miquelon Lake, June 9.)

REMARKS: In leisurely flight common terns patrol the waters of many of our lakes as far north as Lake Athabasca and west to the foothills and the Peace River District. When small fish are sighted they hover momentarily with beak and tail pointed downward then dive beneath the surface to reappear with squirming prey in their beaks. This may be carried to a small island nearby where dozens of females have scraped shallow depressions in the sand or among the rocks. The precocious young terns are not long confined to these nests. They soon seek company and shade in the grass. Just how each parent returning with food finds its own family in the resultant crowd is a mystery which may never be solved but it is probable that filial ties are of less importance to young terns than a full stomach. All is noise and bustle in the vicinity of the island at this time but later in the summer both adults and fledged young sit about more quietly on the rocks spending a few weeks in relaxation before they start their southward journey.

Although a few common terns arrive in Alberta late in April when only a narrow strip of ice-free water borders the lakes they do not appear in numbers until the ice has broken up. The fall migration occurs late in September with a few stragglers remaining into October.

ARCTIC TERN
on nest

CASPIAN TERN

GULLS, TERNS — Family Laridae

ARCTIC TERN
Sterna paradisaea

Scarce Wanderer.
Length 15½ in.

DESCRIPTION: Ads.—Top of head and nape black; mantle of pale bluish-gray over back and wings; tail forked about 4½ in. white, outer web of outer feather gray; underparts pale bluish-gray much lighter than mantle; beak red; legs red, very short. Fall ads. and im.— Similar but black on head reduced to streak through eye and band across nape.

IDENTIFICATION: So much like common tern that field identification is often unreliable where ranges overlap. Arctic tern has all-red beak and shorter legs than common tern.

RANGE: Almost world-wide but rarely inland. In North America breeds mainly in arctic regions but south on Atlantic coast to Massachussets. Winters in southern hemisphere south to antarctic.

NESTING: On the ground in colonies. The nest and eggs are indistinguishable from those of the common tern.

REMARKS: There are few records of the arctic tern in Alberta. It is a maritime species which rarely appears inland and any occurrence in the southern half of the province must be considered highly unusual. A specimen was taken at Lac La Nonne in 1938 and there are several records from Lake Athabasca.

Arctic terns born in northeastern North America migrate eastward to the Atlantic coast. They cross the North Atlantic, fly slowly south along the coasts of Europe and Africa, and finally cross the South Atlantic to arrive at a region near the southern tip of South America. They have now travelled over ten thousand miles. Here they meet other arctic terns from northwestern North America which have travelled, at a similar pace, a more direct route south along the Pacific coast of the Americas. This southern journey has taken them about four months and it is now time for them to start back. Following either the Atlantic or the Pacific coast they fly leisurely northward, arriving at their ancestral breeding grounds in time to prepare for parental duties. Those which nest in the eastern arctic have travelled a distance of over twenty thousand miles, the longest annual migration known to science.

CASPIAN TERN
Hydroprogne caspia

Scarce Summer Resident.
Length 21 in.

DESCRIPTION: Ads.—Feathers of crown extend back in short crest; top of head extending to below eye and including crest black; mantle over back and wings pale bluish-gray; primaries darker gray; tail pale gray, forked about 1/3rd of its length; rest of plumage white; beak large, red; legs black. Fall ads. and im.—Similar but forehead white and back of crown often mixed with white; young birds may have dark spots in gray mantle.

IDENTIFICATION: Black cap and forked tail identify it as a tern; large size, crest, and heavy beak distinguish it from other terns.

RANGE: Nearly cosmopolitan. In North America breeds locally from Gulf of Mexico to Great Slave Lake. Winters mainly on southern coasts.

NESTING: On the ground in colonies on islands or beaches. Nest, a scantily lined depression. Eggs, 2-3, pale gray or buff lightly spotted with brown. (Lake Athabasca, June 15.)

REMARKS: This large tern with an almost world-wide distribution has become relatively scarce in recent years, especially in Canada. In Alberta Caspian terns have been recorded at Brooks, Sullivan Lake, and Athabasca, but the only known breeding area in the province today is the west end of Lake Athabasca. Here, on ·an islet near Ft. Chipewyan, some twenty pairs of Caspian terns nested in 1952 in close association with a colony of California and herring gulls.

Caspian terns frequent large lakes well stocked with small fish. They behave in typical tern fashion, winging back and forth over the lake until prey is sighted and causing quite a splash when they dive head-first into the water. They rest for hours at a stretch sunning themselves on a sand bar or standing head into the wind on the shore of their island. At such times their short legs give them a squat appearance which readily distinguishes them from gulls. In the air at a distance Caspian terns may be mistaken for gulls but now and again they identify themselves by hovering with beaks pointed downward. Their flight is effortless and graceful; their form, though not so swallow-like as the smaller terns, is sleek and stream-lined; their white bodies and black caps flash in the sun; but only harsh discordant notes issue from their throats spoiling somewhat the impression of beauty which they have created.

GULLS, TERNS — Family Laridae

BLACK TERN
Chlidonias niger subsp. (p. 492)

Common Summer Resident.
Length 10 in.

DESCRIPTION: Spring ads.—Head, neck, and underparts black; under tail coverts white; rest of plumage dark slate-gray; tail slightly forked; beak black; legs dark red. Fall ads.—Head and all underparts white except black ring around eye joining black patch behind eye and dark gray cap over back of head; rest of plumage as in spring. Im.—Similar to fall adults but gray of upperparts washed with brown and brownish-gray tinge on sides.

IDENTIFICATION: Distinctive in spring plumage; adults during summer gradually become mottled with white as the fall plumage grows in. Fall adults and young are small light-colored terns with only slightly forked tail; wings extend well beyond tail tip when sitting.

RANGE: North and South America. Breeds from Great Slave Lake, southern B.C., and California east to Great Lakes and Tennessee. Winters from Gulf of Mexico to Peru and Chile.

NESTING: In marshes or sloughs. Nest, a raft of reeds and grasses floating in reeds in shallow water, or on wet hummocks in marsh. Eggs, 2-4, olive-brown blotched with brown and black. (Calgary, June 12.)

REMARKS: The black tern is found throughout the province but is more common in the eastern half. It is scarce in the foothills and has been recorded only rarely in the mountains.

A sedge-covered pond in the parklands, a grassy slough on the prairies, a cat-tail marsh on the margin of a northern lake, each supports its colony of black terns. Red-winged blackbirds nest there also and, if the marsh is large enough, perhaps a pair of bitterns. It is a noisy place even when undisturbed for the terns keep up strident calls of *kip — kep* as they patrol the marsh, but when an intruder wades into the shallows pandemonium breaks out and he is dive-bombed by vociferous terns each vying with the others to see which can come closest to his head without actually hitting. Later in the summer things quieten down a little. Parents and fledged young perch in rows on fences and poles protruding from the water or else wing back and forth over the slough swooping now and again to pick up insects from the surface. Their food is almost entirely aquatic insects; unlike their larger relatives they rarely catch fish. Black terns are fairly early migrants for when the hunter visits the marshes in the fall they have all gone south.

PIGEONS, DOVES — Family Columbidae

The terms pigeon and dove are synonymous although many people call the larger members of the family pigeons and the smaller ones doves. They are medium-sized birds with small heads, short necks, and short legs. The beak is narrow and hard at the tip with a soft swelling at the base. The young are fed a secretion from the crop popularly known as "pigeons' milk". Of several hundred species in this family most are found in the eastern hemisphere. Only three species are native to Canada and one of these, the passenger pigeon, is now extinct; one species has been introduced.

DOMESTIC PIGEON (ROCK DOVE)
Columbia livia

Common Resident.
Length 14 in.

DESCRIPTION: The rock dove from which our domestic pigeons originated is grayish-blue with white on the lower back and dark barring on the wings; there is a light purplish iridescence on the sides of the neck; the legs are red. Pigeon fanciers have produced a great many color variations from this original stock. In the wild state these varieties interbreed forming numerous color combinations.

RANGE: Europe, Asia, Africa; introduced into North America. Resident wherever found.

NESTING: On ledges inside or outside buildings; in crevices on cliffs. Nest of twigs and coarse grass, poorly constructed. Eggs, 2, white. Several broods may be raised in one year.

REMARKS: Pigeons were considered to be farm poultry until a few years ago. With the disappearance of the horse-barn pigeons became unwelcome guests around the farmstead and were persecuted to such an extent that many sought safer places to live in the wilds. Granaries in the fields, grain elevators in towns, and bridges over streams became popular nesting sites. On the high clay banks of the Rosebud River pigeons were found nesting in crevices of the cliff only a few inches from a cluster of cliff swallows' nests, several of which were occupied by house sparrows. Today it is probable that there are more pigeons living in the wild than in domesticated semi-captivity in Alberta. It will be interesting to note, as the different color varieties mingle year after year, whether the original species characteristics of the rock dove will reappear.

Pigeons best withstand the rigors of the Alberta climate if they can find a granary or similar building in which to shelter during the winter and to build their nests in the summer. They rarely stray far from these abodes. Under the circumstances it is surprising that their numbers have not increased markedly. Possibly the very buildings which provide shelter also allow ready access for feral cats and other enemies including people who relish a pigeon pie.

216

BLACK TERN

C. HAMPSON

ROCK DOVE   (DOMESTIC PIGEON)

C. HAMPSON

PIGEONS, DOVES — Family Columbidae

MOURNING DOVE

Zenaidura macroura subsp. (p. 492)

Fairly Common Summer Resident.
Length 12 in.

DESCRIPTION: Ad. m.—Forehead and line over eye light brown; crown and hindneck bluish-gray, the sides of neck with purplish iridescence; rest of upperparts light grayish-brown; wings lightly tinged with pale slate-blue, the tertiaries with a few large black spots; tail pointed, about 6 in. long, middle feathers dark grayish-brown, rest pale slate-blue with black bar and broad white tip; sides of head and underparts pale brown shading to cream on throat and abdomen; narrow black streak below ear; flanks slate-blue. Ad. f.—Like male but paler and with more black on wings. Im.—Like adults.

IDENTIFICATION: A trim, long-tailed bird showing much white on shorter outer tail feathers in flight. The wings squeak as though in need of oiling as the dove alights or takes flight.

RANGE: North America. Breeds across southern Canada south through the United States to Mexico. Winters from the middle states to Central America.

NESTING: In trees and bushes or on the ground. Nest, a flat structure made of twigs so loosely put together that the eggs can be seen through the bottom. Eggs, 2, white. (Rosebud, June 5.)

REMARKS: In Alberta the mourning dove breeds mainly in the wooded river valleys and coulees of the prairies and in the lightly wooded parklands. It has been seen in all of our mountain National Parks and occurs rarely in northern Alberta at least as far as Ft. Vermilion and Ft. Chipewyan.

The mourning dove is not a woodland bird but an inhabitant of the fringes where fields and bushes meet. It gets its name from its call, a mournful, *ah — hooo — hooo — hooo*, somewhat reminiscent of the hoot of the horned owl but not as deep in tone. The first note is on a higher pitch than the rest and sounds as though the breath were being drawn in. Mourning doves feed commonly on the ground picking up grain and seeds like domestic pigeons but they also alight readily in trees and bushes to feed on fruits and berries. Unlike the extinct passenger pigeon mourning doves never congregate in large flocks, nor do they nest in colonies. These habits probably saved them from the fate of their larger relative and undoubtedly contribute to the increase in their numbers in recent years. Strong, swift, and direct in flight, mourning doves make a very sporting target in those states where they are classed as game birds. In Alberta they are protected.

218

CUCKOOS — Family Cuculidae

Cuckoos are long-tailed birds with thin, decurved beaks. Two toes point forward and two back. The plumage is soft in texture and color. Most species are arboreal and solitary in nature. Unlike the European species American cuckoos are not parasitic but raise their own young. Only one species occurs in Alberta.

BLACK-BILLED CUCKOO
Coccyzus erythropthalmus

Scarce Summer Resident.
Length 12 in.

DESCRIPTION: Ads.—Upperparts plain olive-brown lightly washed with rufous on head and wings; underparts white tinged with gray on throat and flanks; tail 6 in. long, olive brown, all but middle pair of feathers tipped with white, outer feathers graduated in length; red ring of bare skin around eye; iris brown; beak black, lower mandible yellow at base. Im.—Similar but many feathers above tipped with white; underparts washed with pale buff.

IDENTIFICATION: Similar in size and form to brown thrasher but olive-brown instead of reddish-brown above and unstreaked below.

RANGE: North and South America. Breeds in southern Canada east of the Rockies, south to Kansas and Georgia. Winters in South America.

NESTING: In shrubs and bushes. Nest, a loose flat platform of twigs and dead leaves. Eggs, 3-6, pale bluish-green. (Duhamel, June 23.)

REMARKS: Nearly all nesting records of the black-billed cuckoo in Alberta are from the south of the province although it has been found nesting at Camrose and Athabasca. It is extremely local in distribution and never abundant.

The black-billed cuckoo inhabits dense brush in prairie coulees and willow thickets along roads and streams. Occasionally it builds its nest in garden hedges if the surrounding shrubbery provides adequate protection. It is rather secretive and rarely appears in the open but its presence is revealed by various peculiar vocal efforts. These noises, not at all bird-like in quality, consist of a long series of guttural notes which sound like rapid repetitions of the syllables *ca, cow,* and *coo.* The black-billed cuckoo feeds almost entirely on insects and their larvae. It is one of the few birds which will eat hairy caterpillars; tent caterpillars are a favorite food.

The black-billed cuckoo starts incubating with the laying of the first egg and since as much as three days may elapse between layings, eggs and young of vastly different ages may be found in a nest. Doubtless mortality among members of the family is great for the eldest have left the nest long before the youngest are fledged and it must be difficult for the parents to provide food and protection for both groups.

KAY HODGES

MOURNING DOVE
with young

ALLAN BROOKS

YELLOW-BILLED CUCKOO
(not found in Alberta)

BLACK-BILLED CUCKOO

SCREECH OWL
gray phase — red phase

GREAT HORNED OWL

OWLS — Family Strigidae

Owls are carnivorous birds with large heads and eyes, strong hooked beaks, sharp talons, and thick soft plumage which covers them completely. Both eyes are immovably fixed in the front of the head necessitating that the head be turned completely around to look behind. Most species are nocturnal but some also hunt by day. Their flight is noiseless and their hearing acute, enabling them to capture prey by sound rather than by sight. Indigestible parts of the food, such as fur, feathers, and large bones, are regurgitated in pellets.

SCREECH OWL Status Unknown.
Otus asio subsp. (p. 492) Length 8-10 in.

DESCRIPTION: A small owl with ear-tufts. Two color phases occur independent of age or sex. Red phase.—Upperparts bright reddish-brown with narrow black streaks; row of white streaks on each side of back; facial disk pale reddish-brown margined with black; white stripe over eye; underparts white splotched with pale reddish-brown and streaked with black; tail reddish-brown barred with dusky; iris yellow. Gray phase.—Upperparts grayish-brown, delicately mottled and barred with white and streaked with black; row of white streaks on sides of back; facial disk grayish margined with black; white stripe over eye; underparts white streaked and barred with black; tail grayish-brown barred with buffy.

IDENTIFICATION: A small owl under a foot in length with long ear-tufts on its head.

RANGE: Southern Canada and most of United States. Largely resident wherever found.

NESTING: In cavities in trees, in buildings, or in nest-boxes. Eggs, 3-7, white.

REMARKS: There are few records of the screech owl in Alberta. A screech owl was captured by hand near Flatbush in 1954 and kept in Edmonton for a short time until its death. Another was picked up dead on a road near Kinuso south of **Lesser** Slave Lake in 1955. Both of these specimens, one in the gray phase, the other in the red, have been preserved. On December 21, 1959, a screech owl was captured by hand near Cardston. It was released apparently in good health about a week later. There is also a sight record of this species from Belvedere.

The screech owl is a friendly, harmless little owl which has taken kindly to man's invasion of its territory and is often found in towns and villages and in the vicinity of farm dwellings. Despite its name, its call is not a screech, but a rather musical series of notes suggestive of the whinny of a horse. It is largely nocturnal, rarely leaving its daytime hiding place before dusk when mice become active.

OWLS — Family Strigidae

GREAT HORNED OWL
Bubo virginianus subsp. (p. 492)

Common Resident.
Length 20-24 in.

DESCRIPTION: A large owl with long ear-tufts on its head. Upperparts buffy or brownish speckled, streaked, and barred with white and black; facial disk grayish or buffy bordered with black, throat white; underparts white or buffy, wavy-barred with black especially on sides; iris yellow. There is great variation in the relative amounts of brown, white, and black; some birds are extremely dark with black and brown predominating; others are mostly gray and white.

IDENTIFICATION: The great horned owl is the only very large owl with prominent ear-tufts. Ear-tufts are towards sides of head rather than towards middle as in long-eared owl.

RANGE: North and South America. Breeds north to tree limit. Resident wherever found.

NESTING: In the old nest of hawk or crow; in hollow trees. Eggs, 2-3, white; laid very early in year. (Midnapore, March 19.)

REMARKS: The great horned owl occurs throughout Alberta but on the prairies it is confined during the nesting season to the wooded coulees and river valleys. There is no true migration; in the fall the young disperse widely in all directions ensuring an intermingling of the families.

During daylight hours the horned owl sits motionless and quiet on a branch close to the trunk of a tree. When disturbed his big eyes solemnly survey the situation before he flaps silently through the maze of branches deeper into the woods. But at dusk when other birds are hidden for the night he rouses himself, hungry and alert. Each sound has significance, the scurry of a squirrel, the thump of a rabbit. Upon his ability to hear and locate these depends his evening meal.

Early in the spring deep-throated calls, *uh-hoo — hoo — hoo*, indicate that a pair of horned owls has selected a nesting territory. Both parents defend the young ferociously, attacking human marauders from unexpected angles and ripping back and scalp with razor-sharp claws. With such protection it is not surprising that young are sometimes successfully raised despite widespread persecution. Because it occasionally kills birds and mammals whose slaughter is reserved for human beings the horned owl has gained a bad reputation. To some sportsmen, who otherwise profess devotion to free enterprise, this constitutes unfair competition.

RAY SALT

SNOWY OWL

ALLAN BROOKS

HAWK OWL

SNOWY OWL
Nyctea scandiaca

Irregular Winter Visitor.
Length 21-26 in.

DESCRIPTION: Ad. m.—Pure white, sometimes almost immaculate but usually with blackish or brownish-black markings; these take the form of spots on the crown and breast and bars on wings, tail and flanks; completely feathered, only tip of black beak and black claws exposed; iris yellow, Ad. f.—Similar to male but larger and more heavily marked; usually only face, throat, and legs are immaculate. Im.—Immature birds resemble the female in being heavily marked.

IDENTIFICATION: A large white owl with round head lacking ear-tufts. Some horned owls may be as light as heavily marked snowy owls; round white face and lack of ear-tufts identifies the latter.

RANGE: Northern parts of northern hemisphere. In North America breeds in arctic from Alaska to Greenland. Winters occasionally as far south as middle United States.

NESTING: On the ground on the tundra. Nest, a depression lined with grass and feathers. Eggs, 5-7, creamy white.

REMARKS: From November through March snowy owls may usually be seen in the settled regions of Alberta. In some winters they are quite numerous, while in others they are scarce or absent. Their abundance here is said to reflect a scarcity of food in more northerly regions. Since they appear about the time the snow flies there is a popular belief that snowy owls are resident birds which have turned white for the winter. This is not so.

Each snowy owl has a territory of several square miles of open country and if food is plentiful it will remain in that territory all winter. Banding records show that it returns to the same winter territory year after year. A haystack or granary in the middle of a field is its favorite perch although it often sits on fenceposts, telephone poles and even treetops. Often too it is seen on the ground standing out whiter than the snow in the winter sunlight. The snowy owl is mainly diurnal in nature and uses its eyes as much as its ears for daytime hunting. It flies low over the stubble with slow measured wing beats ready at an instant to pounce on any vole or rabbit which is so incautious as to move or squeak. Game birds are occasionally captured, but the number is insufficient to class the snowy owl as a serious predator of upland game. Since its food habits are mainly beneficial and since it is nowhere abundant the snowy owl is legally protected in Alberta.

HAWK OWL

Surnia ulula subsp. (p. 492)

Scarce Resident.
Length 13-15 in.

DESCRIPTION: Crown and hindneck brownish-black thickly spotted on crown and streaked on neck with white; back and wings dark grayish-brown with large spots of white on wings; tail grayish-brown with six or seven narrow whitish bars, face and sides of neck gray with two vertical black bars on neck; chin black; underparts white with a large patch of black on each side of upper breast and many narrow bars of brownish-black elsewhere, iris yellow.

IDENTIFICATION: A medium-sized, dark brown owl with no ear-tufts, a long tail, and short wings; hawk-like in posture and flight.

RANGE: Northern parts of northern hemisphere. In North America breeds across the continent in the northern forests and southward in the mountain ranges. Largely resident but occasionally wanders in fall and winter.

NESTING: In cavities in trees, usually old nesting holes of pileated woodpeckers, or sometimes in old nests of crows or hawks. Eggs, 6-7, white. (Athabasca, April 4.)

REMARKS: The hawk owl is typically a bird of the northern muskeg areas but during fall and winter it often wanders well out onto the southern prairies. It has been observed on many occasions in the mountains and one nest was found near Banff. Formerly quite common in Alberta its numbers have been considerably reduced in recent years from causes that are not apparent. Its diurnal habits and unsuspicious nature make it vulnerable to the thoughtless marksman, but more likely man's wanton destruction of its habitat is a more important cause of its depletion. One of the greatest values of preserving wilderness areas is to ensure the survival of such interesting species as the hawk owl.

The hawk owl is aptly named; its long tail and trim lines give it a hawk-like appearance. In flight it has the quick wing beat and something of the dash of the accipiters. Yet its large head, soft feathers, and large yellow eyes mark it as a true owl. The hawk owl is far more active during the day than most woodland owls. From a perch high on a dead tree or stump it surveys the surrounding muskeg watching for movement of small mammals on the ground or in the trees. If nothing stirs it moves to a similar perch in another area or flies silently and watchfully through the woods. On its winter visits to the prairies the hawk owl uses fence posts or stooks as vantage points from which to capture mice and voles which fatten on grain left in the fields.

OWLS — Family Strigidae

PYGMY OWL
Glaucidium gnoma   subsp. (p. 492)

Scarce Resident.
Length 6½ in.

DESCRIPTION: Upperparts dark grayish-brown with small indistinct round spots of buffy on crown and hindneck and a few irregular spots on wings; whitish collar on hindneck bordered behind by black; face and bar across throat white with some dusky marks on face; brownish bar across lower throat; rest of underparts white with large grayish-brown patches on sides of breast and streaks of same color elsewhere; tail dark grayish-brown with six or seven narrow white bars; iris pale yellow.

IDENTIFICATION: A very small dark owl not likely to be confused with any other species except perhaps the saw-whet; the pygmy owl is much smaller and is blackish-brown instead of cinnamon-brown.

RANGE: Western North America. Breeds from Alaska south to Guatemala mainly west of the Rockies. Resident throughout range.

NESTING: In woodpecker holes or other cavities in trees. No nest is made. Eggs, 3-4, white or cream.

REMARKS: The range and status of the pygmy owl in Alberta are not well defined. It is fairly common in Banff National Park. It has also been observed at Jasper, Grassland, Nordegg, Peers, Ft. Assiniboine, McLeod Valley, Phoenix, Sedgewick and Calgary. Pygmy owls breed in the interior of B.C. and might be expected to nest on the eastern slopes of the Rockies but there are no nesting records for Alberta as yet.

The pygmy owl frequents open coniferous and mixed wood forests. A favorite perch for hunting is the tip of an evergreen near a clearing from which it can drop onto a rodent in the grass below. All its hunting is done during daylight hours but it is most active in the morning and in late afternoon. Like a shrike the pygmy owl swoops from a perch, flies low near the ground, and then rises abruptly to the top of another tree. Its wing-beats are fairly rapid and not at all owl-like. Especially on hot summer afternoons the pygmy owl sits quietly in the shade close to the trunk of an evergreen. It is not at all wary or easily alarmed and no doubt often escapes attention through its stillness.

During spring and early summer pygmy owls may call at any time of the day. A series of whistled toots, more rapidly repeated and at a higher pitch than those of the saw-whet owl, makes identification easy for those who have once heard it. An imitation of this call will often bring a curious pygmy owl into view if the caller has both skill and patience; it may also bring a worried aggregation of small woodland birds anxiously searching for the marauder.

227

OWLS — Family Strigidae

BURROWING OWL
Speotyto cunicularia subsp. (p. 492)

Fairly Common Summer Resident.
Length 9½ in.

DESCRIPTION: Ads. — Upperparts tawny-brown streaked on crown and hindneck and spotted on back and wings with buffy-white; face grayish or whitish; line across upper throat mixed black and buffy; line across lower throat and extending down middle of body to abdomen white; sides of breast tawny-brown spotted and barred with buffy-white; tail short, brown with buffy bars; legs long, feathered mainly on front; iris yellow. Im.—Similar but lighter; very young birds may show only a tinge of brown on underparts instead of spotting and barring.

IDENTIFICATION: A small ground owl with stubby tail, long legs, and no ear-tufts. The only other owl likely to be found in similar habitat is the short-eared; the burrowing owl is smaller, has longer legs, barred instead of streaked underparts, and white instead of black around eyes.

RANGE: North and South America. Breeds from southern Manitoba and B.C. south to Florida and Panama. Winters from southwestern states to southern South America.

NESTING: In burrows in the ground made by mammals. Nest of dry horse manure at end of burrow. Eggs, 6-10, white. (Langdon, May 20.)

REMARKS: As a breeding bird the burrowing owl occurs on the prairies of southern Alberta and in the southern parklands north to about Red Deer Lake, but its distribution is local and its appearance from year to year rather erratic. The northernmost record, a specimen taken east of Edmonton in September, was a bird of the year.

The home of the burrowing owl is the shortgrass prairies and Richardson's ground squirrels, chestnut-collared longspurs, and vesper sparrows are its neighbors. Standing on a mound of earth thrown up by some industrious badger the burrowing owl advertises the location of its nest each spring. By early summer several ungainly youngsters are likely to join the parents for a siesta on the mound but they scurry down the burrow at the first sign of danger while the parents fly off with slow full strokes of their wings. At this season, particularly in dull weather, burrowing owls may hunt during daylight hours to provide for the needs of their large family but normally they are most active at daybreak and after dusk in the evening. At such times they often perch on fenceposts listening for the telltale rustle of an insect or the squeak of a mouse in the grass nearby. In autumn when fledged families have augmented the population the ghostly flare of their wings, white in the headlights' glare, startles the night driver as they rise from the roadside. The number of mangled feathery bodies on prairie roads indicates one reason why burrowing owls are not as abundant as they once were.

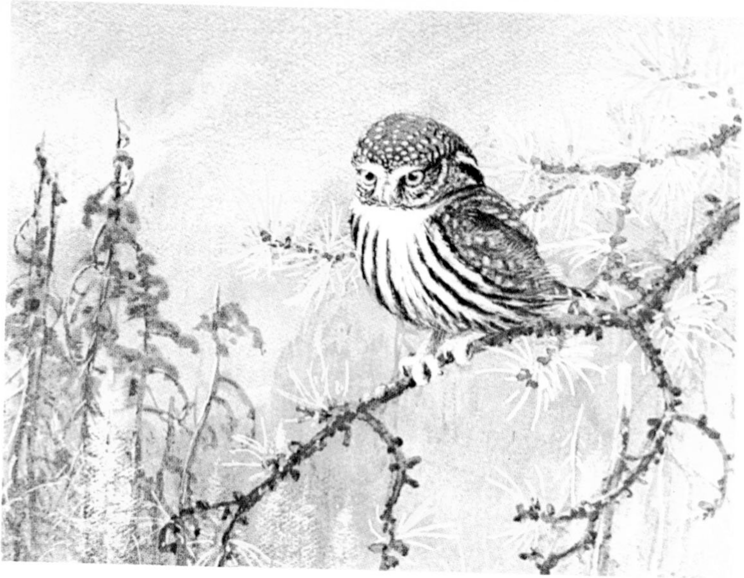

PYGMY OWL ALLAN BROOKS

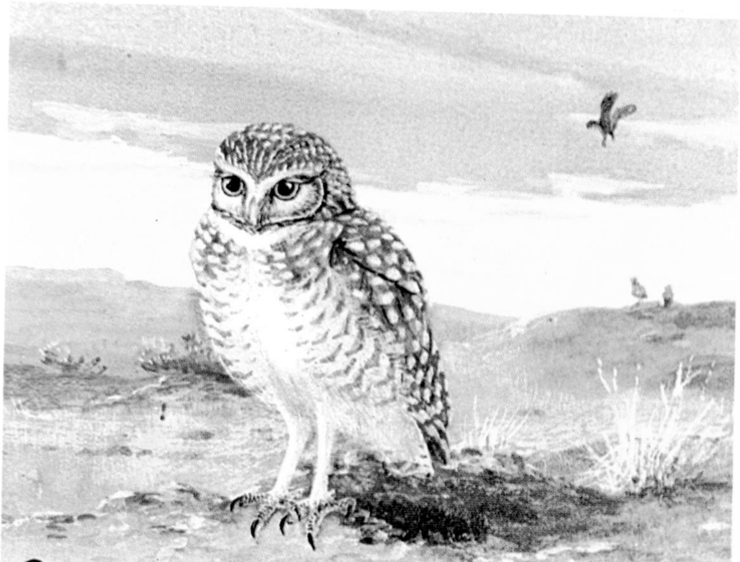

BURROWING OWL ALLAN BROOKS

BARRED OWL
Strix varia   subsp. (p. 492)

Scarce Resident.
Length 17-22 in.

DESCRIPTION: All upperparts and tail dark grayish-brown heavily barred with white or light buff; facial disks gray with faint concentric rings of darker gray; throat white with dark brown spots; underparts white or buffy-white barred on upper breast and broadly streaked elsewhere with grayish-brown; iris dark brown; beak yellow.

IDENTIFICATION: A large brown owl with large round head and no ear-tufts, decidedly barred above and on the breast and streaked on sides and abdomen. The dark eyes are distinctive.

RANGE: North America. Breeds across northern Canada and south into United States mainly east of the Rockies. Largely resident wherever found.

NESTING: In hollow trees or in old nests of hawks or crows. Eggs, 2-3, white.

REMARKS: Until recently there were but two records of the barred owl in Alberta: a specimen taken near Calgary in 1912, and one heard near Ft. McMurray in 1934. Since 1945, however, there have been quite a number of records and it is now believed that the species breeds in small numbers throughout the forested regions of northern and western Alberta. A family of barred owls was seen at Prairie Creek south of Lesser Slave Lake in July, 1949. Other barred owls have been seen or collected at Smoky River north of Jasper, Wembley, Rocky Mtn. House, Obed, Flatbush, Calling Lake, Grosmont and Corbett Creek. In April and May, 1963, a barred owl was seen on several occasions within the boundaries of the city of Edmonton and its voice was recorded.

The barred owl inhabits deep, dark woods and is nocturnal in habit. For this reason it may be easily overlooked unless one is familiar with its call. Southerners claim that the barred owl says, "*Who-are-you—Who-are-you-all.*" Certainly these words give the rhythm of its call and anyone familiar with the deep-throated hoot of the great horned owl would note immediately this difference even through the timbre might be the same.

Since mice, voles and other small mammals which are active at night are staple foods of the barred owl the species is definitely beneficial. The prey is located by sound rather than by sight. Owls have remarkably large ear openings which can pick up sounds of low intensity. Furthermore, the two ear openings differ in size and shape, an adaptation which facilitates accurate location of the source of the sound. A barred owl can capture a mouse which rustles the grass or squeaks without ever seeing it. Its eyes, however, are adapted to see in dim light; bright light dazzles the bird and it usually seeks a dark secluded perch during the daytime.

OWLS — Family Strigidae

GREAT GRAY OWL
Strix nebulosa subsp. (p. 492)

Scarce Resident.
Length 25-33 in.

DESCRIPTION: Facial disks large, light gray with several concentric rings of dark gray; upperparts dark grayish-brown, almost black, streaked with light gray; flight feathers and tail barred with same colors; chin black; light line across throat; rest of underparts gray heavily streaked with black; iris yellow; no ear-tufts.

IDENTIFICATION: A very large gray owl lacking ear-tufts. Most like the barred owl but larger, grayer, and with longitudinal streaking on crown and neck where the barred owl is cross-barred.

RANGE: Northern hemisphere. In North America breeds in northern forests across continent south to Idaho and Minnesota. Resident throughout its range.

NESTING: In old nests of hawks or crows, at considerable height. Eggs, 3-5, white. (Belvedere, April 30.)

REMARKS: The great gray owl inhabits deciduous and mixed-wood forests in unsettled areas of western and northern Alberta. It has been found nesting near Rocky Mt. House, Edson, Jasper, Belvedere, Whitemud Lake, and Ft. Chipewyan. A recent survey of the status of the great gray owl in the province showed it to be present but very scarce in a few remote areas south as far as Sundre.

The great gray owl sits erect in a tree with its head lifted well above its shoulders accentuating its length. Its great size is due largely to a very thick coat of feathers for it actually weighs less than either the snowy or the great horned owl. It is unsuspicious to the point of stupidity and will allow an observer to approach quite close. Perhaps this accounts for its scarcity for few hunters can resist shooting at such a large sitting target even though it is legally protected. The great gray owl is a beneficial species very close to extermination in Alberta. It does not prey upon game birds but takes large numbers of mice and other small rodents.

The great gray owl is most active in the early morning and late evening; all of its hunting is done at these times. From a vantage point in a tree it watches for tell-tale activity beneath and, on silent wings, swoops upon its unsuspecting prey. Having fed, however, it spends most of its time sitting close to the trunk of a tree or hidden among evergreen boughs. On winter days when the temperature drops to fifty degrees below zero such a sedentary creature might be expected to freeze to death but it merely fluffs out its feathers to form an insulating blanket some three inches thick and dozes in comfort.

BARRED OWL

GREAT GRAY OWL

232

C. HAMPSON

LONG-EARED OWL
sheltering young

KAY HODGES

SHORT-EARED OWL
female on nest

233

OWLS — Family Strigidae

LONG-EARED OWL
Asio otus subsp. (p. 492)

Fairly Common Summer Resident.
Length 13-15 in.

DESCRIPTION: A medium-sized owl with long ear-tufts. Upperparts blackish-brown, the feathers speckled on the head and finely barred elsewhere with buffy and white; buffy bases of feathers show on surface in many places; flight feathers and tail show broader barring; facial disk buffy-brown shading to black above and below eye; underparts light gray and buff streaked and barred with brownish-black; feathers on toes very short; iris yellow.

IDENTIFICATION: An owl with long ear-tufts, larger than screech, smaller than great horned owl. The ear-tufts of this owl are longer in proportion, and set more toward the middle of the head than those of horned owl; they often point straight upward close together, rather than slanting far apart as in horned owl.

RANGE: North America. Breeds from California and Virginia north to about tree limit. Winters from southern Canada to Mexico.

NESTING: In old nest of hawk, crow, or magpie. Eggs, 4-6, white, (Rosebud, May 14.)

REMARKS: Although the long-eared owl has been taken as far north as Ft. Simpson, N.W.T., it is not known to breed north of Grimshaw in Alberta. It is most common in the poplar groves of the parklands and the lightly wooded coulees of the prairies. It has been taken at Crowsnest Lake in the mountains. Occasionally a few long-eared owls winter in the province.

Thick, almost impenetrable bushy tangles on the sides of prairie coulees are favorite nesting sites of the long-eared owl. Incubating birds sit very close and will often allow a person to climb to the nest and remove them by hand. When released they join their mates in protesting from the bushes nearby, some of their calls resembling the long-drawn-out *meeaauw* of a cat. As with other owls incubation starts when the first egg is laid. Consequently when the young have hatched they are of assorted sizes, the largest being more than a week older than the smallest. Cannibalism is not uncommon and it is only rarely that the youngest members of the family survive. Even during the nesting season the long-eared owl is active only at night. Its food consists almost entirely, therefore, of small nocturnal mammals such as shrews and mice.

Not a great deal is known of the spring and fall movement of long-eared owls. In September and October they are often seen in areas where they do not nest, sitting out the day in a thick bush and waiting until dusk puts them on the move again. Dispersal during these movements must be great; a fledgling banded at Rosebud was recovered in Minnesota when it was only five months of age.

234

OWLS — Family Strigidae

SHORT-EARED OWL
Asio flammeus subsp. (p. 492)

Common Summer Resident.
Length 13-16 in.

DESCRIPTION: Crown and hindneck yellowish-buff streaked with dark brown; ear-tufts extremely short or absent; back and wings yellowish-buff streaked on back with blackish-brown and some white, and barred on wings with blackish-brown; tail barred with grayish-brown and buffy, becoming almost white on tip and outer feathers; ring around eye black; chin and beside beak white; rest of face brownish; underparts buffy becoming almost white towards tail, streaked with brownish-black most heavily on breast; iris yellow. There is little variation for age or sex.

IDENTIFICATION: A medium-sized owl with barely noticeable ear-tufts centrally placed above eyes. Larger than burrowing owl with longer tail and black ring around eyes.

RANGE: Nearly world-wide. In North America breeds from subarctic to northern states. Winters from southern Canada to Guatemala.

NESTING: On the ground. Nest, a depression lined with grass and feathers. Eggs, 5-7, white. (Balzac, June 5.)

REMARKS: The name short-eared owl is misleading for it is only on rare occasions that any suggestion of ear-tufts can be seen. The species breeds throughout the province except in the heavily wooded regions. Like the burrowing owl the short-eared is a ground owl but it prefers marshlands, meadows, crop lands, and buckbrush to the shortgrass plains and it does not nest underground. It hunts more commonly by day than any other species of owl but it is most active at dusk. Beating slowly over the grass or stubble it depends largely on its ears to locate mice and voles and will come readily to investigate an imitation of their thin squeak. Its flight is characteristic; the downstroke is slow and steady but the upstroke is fast bringing the wing tips well up over the back.

Incubation commences when the first egg is laid and the young hatch at intervals. The older ones soon creep from the nest to hide in the surrounding grass or brush. They are fed almost exclusively on small rodents. In some winters short-eared owls remain in the province in fair numbers feeding on mice in the unharvested grain. At this season they sometimes show a sociability not usually found in owls. On December 5, 1959, thirty-two short-eared owls were flushed from less than one acre of grass and low brush near Edmonton. Such a large aggregation is rare but groups of eight or ten are not unusual. The owls can hardly be said to flock for they are only casually associated and the group breaks up very easily.

C. HAMPSON

BOREAL OWL

KAY HODGES

SAW-WHET OWL

OWLS — Family Strigidae

BOREAL (RICHARDSON'S) OWL
Aegolius funereus subsp. (p. 492)

Scarce Resident.
Length 10 in.

DESCRIPTION: Upperparts dark grayish-brown with numerous small white spots on forehead, crown, and around facial disks, and with large indistinct white spots across hindneck and on wings; tail with five narrow white bars; facial disk gray except black beside beak; underparts white with a bar of brown across throat and broad blotches and streaks of brown on breast and sides; iris lemon yellow.

IDENTIFICATION: A small dark brown owl with large head and no ear-tufts. Darker than screech owl and lacking ear-tufts. Most easily confused with saw-whet owl but larger, grayer, and with spots instead of streaks on forehead and crown.

RANGE: Northern parts of northern hemisphere. Breeds from central Canada north to tree limit. Largely resident but sometimes wanders south as far as northern states in winter.

NESTING: In cavities in trees, usually woodpecker holes. Eggs, 4-7, white. (Belvedere, April 15.)

REMARKS: More northerly in distribution than the saw-whet Richardson's owl breeds in the mixed-wood forests from the parklands to the northern boundary of the province. It also occurs in the mountains where it probably breeds although it has been found nesting only near Jasper. It is largely resident throughout its range but during the winter it sometimes wanders southward onto the prairies. Specimens have been taken at this season at High River and Rosebud.

Richardson's owl is similar in habits as well as appearance to its smaller relative the saw-whet owl but it has retreated more rapidly before human encroachment into its territory. During daylight hours it sits motionless in a bush or on a low branch of a tree, usually escaping attention through its stillness. At such times it may be approached closely and occasionally be picked up by hand. But while lethargic by day it becomes quite active and more wary as night approaches. A skilful hunter it captures bats, mice, and other small nocturnal mammals with ease; small birds, which are normally not active at night, are taken only rarely. Richardson's owl is a beneficial species which deserves complete protection, the more so because its numbers at present are at a low ebb.

While little is known of the factors which control the number of Richardson's owl it appears that the species is highly dependent upon cavities in trees. Not only are these used as nesting sites but in winter they serve as shelters during severe weather. It is probable that this need for shelter is the reason that winter incursions of Richardson's owls often end in disaster unless the little birds gain entry to a granary or other outbuilding.

237

SAW-WHET OWL   Fairly Common Resident.
Aegolius acadicus subsp. (p. 492)   Length 8 in.

DESCRIPTION: Upperparts reddish-brown streaked with white on forehead and around facial disks and splotched with white around hindneck; tail with three narrow white bars; facial disk white above eye, remainder gray streaked with brown; throat buff bordered with brown; underparts white with broad streaks of reddish-brown on breast and sides; iris lemon yellow.

IDENTIFICATION: A small reddish-brown owl with large head and no ear-tufts. Can be confused only with Richardson's owl but is smaller, browner, and has streaked instead of spotted forehead.

RANGE: North America. Breeds in Alaska, across southern Canada, and in all except southeastern states. Mostly resident but there is some southward movement in winter.

NESTING: In cavities in trees usually an old woodpecker hole. Eggs, 4-7, white; time of nesting variable. (Camrose, April 12 to June 8.)

REMARKS: The saw-whet owl frequents dense deciduous woods in the parklands especially those bordering lakes and rivers. It is found less commonly in the mixed-wood forests north as far as Big Mouth Creek on the Athabasca River and has been observed in the mountains near Banff in May and July. It occasionally occurs on the prairies outside the breeding season.

Late in a spring evening the courtship song of the saw-whet owl, a series of whistled toots with a metallic quality, may be heard coming from the thick woods, indicating that a nesting territory has been established. The female selects a woodpecker hole for her nest and lays an egg every day or so. Incubation commences with the laying of the first egg so newly-hatched and fully-fledged young may be found in the same brood. The saw-whet owl has a large bump of curiosity; when the nesting tree is tapped with a stick the head of the female appears at the opening. She is not at all wary and will sit close by as the nest is examined.

Outside the nesting season saw-whet owls spend the day sitting on a branch only a few feet from the ground. They are usually easily approached and will sometimes allow themselves to be touched. In the evening however, they become alert and active. At this time and in the early hours of the morning they hunt the woods for mice and small mammals which comprise most of their food.

GOATSUCKERS — Family Caprimulgidae

Goatsuckers are birds of medium size with long pointed wings and short weak feet. Their heads are broad, their beaks very small, but their mouths wide and edged with bristles. They sit about on the ground or along a branch during the day but at dusk they fly back and forth capturing insects on the wing. The name goatsucker comes from an old superstition that they sucked the milk from goats with their large mouths.

POOR-WILL
Phalaenoptilus nuttallii   subsp. (p. 492)

Scarce Summer Resident.
Length 7½ in.

DESCRIPTION: Upperparts streaked, spotted, and barred with pale gray, black, brown, and buffy, producing a pale brownish-gray effect; sides of face brown; large throat patch of white; breast brownish-black lightly marked with gray; rest of underparts buffy-white barred across lower breast and sides with black; tail similar to back but outer three pairs of feathers broadly tipped with white. Sexes alike.

IDENTIFICATION: Similar to the nighthawk but much smaller and lacking white on wings; white marks at tip of tail instead of part way up as in the nighthawk.

RANGE: Western North America. Breeds from extreme southeastern B.C. and South Dakota south to Kansas and Mexico. Winters in extreme southwestern states and Mexico.

NESTING: On the ground. The eggs are laid directly on the ground usually in a fairly exposed place. Eggs, 2, white, unmarked.

REMARKS: The poor-will, which occurs in both southern B.C. and southern Saskatchewan, was unknown in Alberta until 1945 when several were heard and one was collected in the Cypress Hills. There have been no further records of the species in the province. It should be watched for in the wooded valleys and coulees of the southern prairies.

The poor-will is more of a nocturnal species than the nighthawk. During daylight hours it remains crouched inconspicuously on the ground or along the limb of a tree. As night falls, however, it takes flight and hawks for insects along a woodland path or at the edge of a clearing. Unlike the nighthawk it rarely rises high into the air but, bat-like, flutters below tree-top level where, in the failing light, it offers only fleeting glimpses to the observer. These habits make it easy to overlook poor-wills; fortunately they identify themselves during summer evenings by frequent mournful repetitions of their name, *poor-will*, or *poor-will-uck*, the accent being on the second syllable. Since their activities are carried on far into the night they are sometimes caught in the beam of headlights as a car slowly winds along a wooded road.

GOATSUCKERS — Family Caprimulgidae

COMMON NIGHTHAWK
Chordeiles minor   subsp. (p. 492)

Fairly Common Summer Resident.
Length 10 in.

DESCRIPTION: Ad. m.—Upperparts black, spotted and barred with gray, buffy, and white; the crown is usually darkest and a band across the hindneck buffiest; primaries black with a white band across their middle; tail black barred with gray, a white band crossing all but middle feathers; broad white V extends from throat onto sides of neck; rest of underparts white barred with black, darkest on upper breast. Ad. f.—Similar but lacks white bar across tail.

IDENTIFICATION: A dark brownish-black bird most often seen in flight in the evening; the outline resembles that of a small falcon but the wing beat is slow and deliberate; white throat and white bar across tips of wings are quite evident in flight.

RANGE: All of North and South America. Breeds from Yukon and Newfoundland south to Central America. Winters in all of South America.

NESTING: On the ground or on flat roofs of buildings. No nest is made. Eggs, 2, pale olive-buff speckled with black, brown, and gray. (Spruce Grove, June 20.)

REMARKS: On the prairies of southern Alberta nighthawks are usually unable to find suitable nesting territory except in the river valleys. Elsewhere they are widely but rather locally distributed in all parts of the province. This is a species which has adapted very well to man's encroachment upon its natural habitat. In most of our cities nighthawks nest on the gravelled roofs of buildings and the backyard naturalist is treated on a summer evening to spectacular flight displays which often include steep dives ending in a resounding boom as the bird catches itself and swings upward.

Small patches of gravel are favorite nesting sites of the nighthawk but there must be some shelter from the sun provided by bushes or boulders. Where gravel is not present the eggs are laid in an open spot in the woods. In either place the eggs, the young, and the sitting birds blend so well with the surroundings that they are rarely detected without an intensive search. Nighthawks rest during the day squatted upon the ground or along a branch. At dusk, however, they perform marvellous aerial acrobatics, darting about erratically but gracefully as they capture insects which have risen into the cool air. From time to time they utter a loud strident, *beentz.* The last half of their name gave rise to much unwarranted persecution in the past; a glance at the small beak and weak feet should have convinced even the most sceptical that a nighthawk could not harm anything larger than an insect.

POOR-WILL

C. HAMPSON

COMMON NIGHTHAWK

241

SWIFTS — Family Micropodidae

Swifts and swallows are much alike and are separated on the basis of structures hardly recognizable to the inexperienced eye. The beak in swifts is even smaller than that of swallows; the feet are small and weak; the three front toes are approximately the same length whereas in swallows the middle toe is much longer than the others. Swifts do not have colorful plumage. They never alight in trees but cling to vertical surfaces such as cliffs and walls using their tails to aid in support.

BLACK SWIFT   Scarce Summer Resident.
Cypseloides niger   subsp. (p. 492)   Length 7 in.

DESCRIPTION: Ads.—Head dark sooty-brown, paler on throat, feathers of crown edged with white; rest of plumage sooty-black; wings very long; tail slightly forked, less in female than in male; beak small, black; gape very wide.

IDENTIFICATION: A black swallow-like bird resembling a small purple martin; in flight the front edges of the wings of the swift form a well bowed arc and the tail is usually spread; the martin lacks these characteristics.

RANGE: Western North America and Central America. Breeds in mountains from Alaska to Mexico and along coast from Washington to California. Winters in Central America.

NESTING: In crevices on cliffs. Nest of grass and rootlets. Eggs, 1, white.

REMARKS: The black swift is not a common bird in Alberta yet the first nest to be found in the Rocky Mountains was discovered in Johnston's Canyon near Banff on September 2, 1919. It contained one well-fledged young. No other nests have been recorded in the province although black swifts have been observed at various places in the Banff and Jasper National Parks. They have not been seen outside of the mountain regions.

Deep mountain canyons with steep rock walls are the haunts of black swifts. They seem to prefer a nesting site near water, often so close to a waterfall that the nest is wet with spray. The young are fed at infrequent intervals by regurgitation and require about four weeks to reach maturity and leave the nest. On fine days black swifts fly high in the air, often beyond range of the unaided eye, but on dull days they descend to lower levels, wheeling and gliding on tireless wings. They are entirely insectivorous and all their food is caught in the air.

There are sight records of Vaux's swift in the Jasper area but as yet no concrete evidence of the occurrence of this species in Alberta has been obtained. This is a very small swift, brown in color with pale throat, closely resembling the more easterly chimney swift. The tail is short and rounded at the tip.

242

HUMMINGBIRDS — Family Trochilidae

Very small size, long narrow wings, small legs, and needle-like beaks characterize the hummingbirds. Their plumage is iridescent and in many cases brightly colored. With wings vibrating so rapidly that they produce a humming sound they hover before flowers sipping nectar or capturing small insects with long protrusible tongues. In flight they move forward, backward, or sideways with equal ease.

RUBY-THROATED HUMMINGBIRD
Archilochus colubris

Scarce Summer Visitor.
Length 3½ in.

DESCRIPTION: Ad. m.—Upperparts iridescent green; black mark from chin, under eye to ear; small white spot behind eye; throat ruby-red, iridescent, feathers may be puffed out to form a gorget; white collar behind gorget incomplete on hindneck; sides dusky green; rest of underparts white; center tail-feathers green, rest brownish, tail slightly forked. Ad. f.—Above iridescent green, less brilliant than male; underparts white or dusky-white, with pale buffy on sides and under tail; no red on throat; outer three tail feathers tipped with white.

IDENTIFICATION: Size and mode of flight identify as a hummingbird. Males with large patch of ruby-red on throat are distinctive; females paler below than rufous, larger than calliope.

RANGE: North America east of the Rockies. Breeds from central Canada to Florida and Texas. Winters in southern states and Central America.

NESTING: In trees. Nest, a dainty cup of lichens and mosses lined with plant down, saddled on a branch with spider webs. Eggs, 2, white.

REMARKS: The ruby-throated hummingbird is an eastern species, in fact it is the only species of hummingbird found in eastern North America. In Alberta it occurs west as far as Calgary and Red Deer where its range overlaps slightly that of the rufous hummingbird. It is most common in the parklands but occurs north as far as Peace River and Ft. Chipewyan. On the southern prairies it has been recorded at Rosebud and Brooks, and in the Cypress Hills. In eastern Alberta the ruby-throat is the only species likely to be present but in the western part of the province identification of hummingbirds should be made carefully.

Ruby-throated hummingbirds are most often seen in gardens where they seek nectar and small insects attracted to flowers but they also visit wild flowers especially the blossoms of saskatoon, chokecherry and wolf-willow. Their hovering flight and the drone of their wings causes many people to dismiss them with a glance as large insects; a more careful scrutiny, however, will reveal them as iridescent beauties.

BLACK SWIFT

RUBY-THROATED HUMMINGBIRD
female   *male*

RUFOUS HUMMINGBIRD
male above   *female below*

CALLIOPE HUMMINGBIRD
male   *female*

245

RUFOUS HUMMINGBIRD
Selasphorus rufus

Fairly Common Summer Resident.
Length 3½ in.

DESCRIPTION: Ad. m.—Crown metallic bronze-green; rest of upperparts cinnamon-rufous; chin and throat iridescent scarlet; breast white becoming cinnamon-rufous on sides and under tail. Ad. f.—Above iridescent metallic green; throat white usually with a patch of iridescent scarlet or gold; underparts dull white becoming cinnamon-rufous on sides; tail rufous basally, black towards tip, the outer three feathers tipped with white.

IDENTIFICATION: Small size, mode of flight, and burnished copper color will identify males. Females are difficult to distinguish from other hummers but spot on throat, large amount of rufous on sides and tail will help.

RANGE: Western North America. Breeds from Alaska to California from Rockies to coast. Winters from California to Mexico.

NESTING: In trees. Nest of lichens lined with plant down fastened on a branch. Eggs, 2, white. (Jasper, June 10.)

REMARKS: The rufous hummingbird occurs in the mountains from the Waterton Lake area to north of Jasper. Occasionally it wanders eastward as far as Red Deer where its range overlaps that of the ruby-throated hummingbird.

Although rufous hummingbirds are often seen around flower gardens in mountain towns burned-over areas choked with fireweed and clearings in the mountain forest are more natural haunts. The male is a tiny jewel of burnished copper against the dark green of spruce boughs. With a temper as fiery as his colors he brooks no intrusion into his territory attacking sparrows, thrushes, and chipmunks alike, and going out of his way to pick a fight with his own kind. Wings moving so rapidly that they appear only as a blur, the duller colored females are easily mistaken for hawk moths as they visit flowers to sip the nectar. Hummingbirds are so small and move so fast that sight identification especially of females is difficult; for this reason the ranges of the three species found in Alberta are imperfectly known.

Male hummingbirds make poor fathers. Once the eggs are laid they desert the female and leave to her the task of raising the family. After about twelve days of incubation tiny naked black forms emerge from the eggs. The young thrive on a liquid diet fed directly into their throats by regurgitation from the mother's crop but they are not ready to leave the nest until three weeks after hatching.

HUMMINGBIRDS — Family Trochilidae

CALLIOPE HUMMINGBIRD
Stellula calliope

Scarce Summer Resident.
Length 2¾ in.

DESCRIPTION: Ad. m.—Upperparts iridescent metallic green; throat iridescent reddish-purple, the feathers of the gorget very long on sides of throat and with white bases; rest of underparts dull white with buffy tinge on sides. Ad. f.—Upperparts iridescent green; underparts dull white spotted on throat with gray and washed on sides with buffy; tail largely rufous at base, black towards tip and the three outer feathers tipped with white.

IDENTIFICATION: The smallest Canadian bird. Males with gorget of pointed violet feathers are distinctive. Females difficult to separate from females of other hummers; smaller and more brown on tail than ruby-throat, smaller and lacking dark throat patch of rufous.

RANGE: Western North America. Breeds from B.C. and Alberta south to southern California in Rocky Mountain region. Winters mainly in Mexico.

NESTING: In trees. Nest of moss and lichens lined with plant down. Eggs, 2, white. (Jasper, June 13.)

REMARKS: The calliope hummingbird is a western species, quite common in the interior valleys of B.C., which occurs in Alberta only along a strip of the Rocky Mountains from the international boundary north to Jasper and perhaps farther. It has been found nesting only a few miles from the town of Jasper where rufous hummingbirds also nest. While males of the two species are easily separable females should be identified carefully.

In his courtship flight the male calliope hummingbird dives back and forth like a pendulum, his wings humming and his gorget fanned out like a brilliant spiked collar beneath his chin. The female is apparently impressed for on the strength of this ardent display she builds her tiny nest near the tip of a horizontal evergreen bough and lays two eggs hardly the size of beans. She defends her home with vigour and will drive away marauders as large as squirrels with a dive-bombing attack which effectively routs them. Males are equally pugnacious until incubation commences, when they lose interest in family matters and take off for a care-free summer. Since the male crop will not provide the regurgitated food which the young require this desertion is of no importance to the future of the nestlings. The female can well look after the needs of such a small family and they grow rapidly. Hummingbirds eat the nectar from flowers but they also like the small insects attracted to them.

KINGFISHER

YELLOW-SHAFTED FLICKER
female   *male*

KINGFISHERS — Family Alcidinidae

Kingfishers are heavy-set birds with short tails, large heads, and strong pointed beaks used for capturing fish. The legs and feet are small, the outer two toes being joined for about half their length. Dense oily plumage sheds water easily. Only one species of kingfisher occurs in Canada.

BELTED KINGFISHER
Megaceryle alcyon   subsp. (p. 493)

Fairly Common Summer Resident.
Length 12-13 in.

DESCRIPTION: Ad. m.—Upperparts grayish-blue except white collar across hindneck; primaries show white patch near bases in flight; large double crest on back of head; face grayish-blue except small white spot in front of eye and white lower eyelid; underparts white except broad grayish-blue band across breast and some bluish on sides; beak black, heavy, more than 2 in. long; legs small, bluish-gray. Ad. f.—Similar but sides and a band across lower breast dark chestnut, this latter band separated from the upper blue one by a thin band of white. Im.—Similar to adults but breast bands usually show some brown in the blue.

IDENTIFICATION: Kingfishers might be confused with blue jays but have long heavy beaks, short tails, and show less white above.

RANGE: North and South America. Breeds in most of North America except extreme northern arctic. Winters from northern states south to northern South America.

NESTING: In banks near water. The eggs are laid on bare sand at the end of a long burrow. Eggs, 5-8, white.

REMARKS: On migration in early May and late August the belted kingfisher occurs throughout Alberta but during the nesting season its distribution is extremely local. At this time kingfishers frequent only those streams and lakes which have clay banks sufficiently high to provide safe nesting places. The birds sit motionless on a branch overhanging the water watching for fish, frogs, or large aquatic insects. Then diving head first beneath the surface they come up with the slippery prey firmly grasped in their large beaks. The food habits of kingfishers have brought them into disfavor among fishermen in some areas but it is doubtful that they have any serious effect upon game fish in Alberta.

With a loud rattling call the kingfisher attracts attention as he flies towards a perch on some dead branches leaning well out over the water. He has the patience of all good fishermen but if he misses a dive off he goes to another perch rattling his chagrin along the way and perhaps looking for clearer waters where his chances of success are greater for he fishes by sight alone.

WOODPECKERS — Family Picidae

The woodpeckers are arboreal birds with strong chisel-pointed beaks and long protrusible tongues. The feathers of the tail are stiff and pointed. Except in the three-toed species two toes point forward and two back. By grasping slight irregularities in the bark with short curved claws and using their tails as props, woodpeckers move along the tree trunks with ease. In the air most woodpeckers alternately rise with a few rapid strokes of the wings, then glide with wings closed; this produces a characteristic undulating flight.

YELLOW-SHAFTED FLICKER   Common Summer Resident.
Colaptes auratus   subsp. (p. 493)   Length 12 in.

DESCRIPTION: M.—Head and neck gray, brownish at base of beak, a black moustache mark running from base of beak along side of throat, a scarlet band across nape; back and wings grayish-brown with dark brown bars on feathers, under surface of wings golden yellow; breast and abdomen fawn with numerous circular black spots, a strong black crescent separating breast and throat; upper tail coverts white; upper surface of tail black; under surface golden yellow. F.—Similar but lacking black streaks on sides of throat. Immatures like adults.

IDENTIFICATION: The large amount of brown in the plumage separates the flickers from all other woodpeckers. The yellow lining of wings and tail identify this species.

RANGE: North America west to the Rockies. Breeds throughout range north as far as tree limit. Winters in southern part of range.

NESTING: In holes bored in trees. Nest, the unlined bottom of the nesting cavity. Eggs, 5-9, glossy white. (Rosebud, May 15.)

REMARKS: The yellow-shafted flicker is the most common and the most widely distributed of our woodpeckers. It has taken kindly to human settlement and where natural sites are not available it will occupy specially constructed nest boxes. It is a noisy bird, not always welcome around the house. Between harsh *flicker* cries the male hammers out a loud tattoo on a hollow tree or a tin roof.

Flickers commonly feed on the ground. They are especially fond of ants which they lick up from the ant-hill with their long tongues. In addition to insects they eat small fruits, berries and seeds.

In lightly wooded areas where suitable nesting sites are not numerous flickers often make use of the same hole year after year. That recent immigrant, the European starling, has taken over many of the nesting cavities formerly used by flickers and other birds. It will be interesting to observe the effect of this introduced vermin upon our native species.

WOODPECKERS — Family Picidae

RED-SHAFTED FLICKER
Colaptes cafer subsp. (p. 493)

Fairly Common Summer Resident.
Length 12 in.

DESCRIPTION: Similar to the yellow-shafted flicker but upperparts more decidedly brown, wing linings and under tail light red instead of yellow, moustache marks scarlet instead of black, and no scarlet on nape. The flickers are the only brown woodpeckers in Alberta.

IDENTIFICATION: The two species of flicker may be easily separated on the basis of the above markings. However, hybridization is common and various mixtures of these characteristics produce some confusing individuals.

RANGE: North America from Rocky Mountains westward. Breeds from Alaska to Mexico. Winters from southern B.C. to Central America.

NESTING: In holes in trees. Eggs, 7-9, glossy white; laid on unlined bottom of nesting cavity. (Rosebud, May 20.)

REMARKS: The red-shafted flicker occurs in a pure form along the Rocky Mountains, but east of the foothills hybrids are commonly found. One focus of hybridization is the Cypress Hills; another is the Rosebud valley northeast of Calgary where, however, the predominant species is the yellow-shafted.

The food habits and general behavior of the red-shafted flicker are similar to those of the yellow-shafted. It requires trees large enough to be suitable for nesting sites and in lightly wooded areas the same nesting hole, often in a dead tree, may be occupied year after year. Such trees are usually of little commercial value and should be left standing for the use of flickers and other birds which nest in tree cavities.

Both species of flicker show a preference for fairly lightly wooded areas in which poplars and other deciduous trees predominate. The wooded coulees and river valleys of the prairies form excellent habitat. In heavily wooded areas they occur mainly around the borders of clearings for they like to feed on the ground as well as in the trees. Flickers are hardy birds. The first migrants usually return from the south early in April although they have been observed as early as February. Most of them have gone south again by the end of September but occasionally laggards remain until December. Flickers winter regularly in southern B.C. but only rarely in Alberta. Their diet includes more fruit and berries than that of our usual wintering woodpeckers and this, together with their habit of feeding on the ground, may prevent their wintering where snow lies deep.

PILEATED WOODPECKER   Scarce Resident.
Dryocopus pileatus   subsp. (p. 493)   Length 18 in.

DESCRIPTION: Ad. m.—Entirely dull brownish-black except for scarlet crown and crest, scarlet moustache mark, white throat, white line extending from below eye down side of neck to flanks where it is barred with black, and white bases of flight feathers which are not noticeable at rest. Ad. f.—Similar but moustache mark black instead of scarlet, and scarlet on crown confined mainly to crest. Im.—Similar to adults but the red paler.

IDENTIFICATION: Large size and scarlet crest will identify at rest. In flight large size and large white wing patches are distinctive.

RANGE: Forested regions of North America. Resident throughout its range.

NESTING: In holes drilled high in a decaying tree trunk. Eggs, 3-4, white, laid on wood splinters at bottom of cavity. (Camrose, May 16.)

REMARKS: The pileated woodpecker is a bird of the heavy woods. It occurs, therefore, mainly in the mountains and in the northern and western parts of the province. Its bright contrasting colors and its large size attract attention, and since it is not particularly wary, many are killed by the curious hunter with his .22. This slaughter and the steady destruction of the mixed-wood forests combine to keep the numbers of this species at a low level and to drive it farther into the wilderness areas. In the winter it wanders about and may be seen even in the cities and towns.. Until quite recently at least one pair nested within the city limits of Edmonton.

The pileated woodpecker feeds mainly on wood-boring insects and their larvae. With a few deft strokes it breaks out pieces of the decaying wood to get at the delicacies beneath. The blows of its beak resound through the woods; its presence is further announced from time to time by a loud flicker-like call.

Unlike the smaller woodpeckers pileated woodpeckers require quite large territories and two pairs are rarely found nesting within a mile of each other. Within this territory they have several nesting holes, each in a tall stump of a deciduous tree, and if unmolested, they occupy these nests in rotation from year to year.. It is possible that at least one of the adults is resident on this territory throughout the year and that the young wander widely from it finally settling in a region which may be far removed from their birth-place.

C. HAMPSON

RED-SHAFTED FLICKER
male

KAY HODGES

PILEATED WOODPECKER
male

RED-HEADED WOODPECKER
Melanerpes erythrocephalus subsp. (p. 493)

Scarce Summer Visitor.
Length 9½ in.

DESCRIPTION: Ads.—Head and neck crimson; upper back, wings and tail glossy black except secondaries which form a large white patch on wing; lower back, breast and abdomen white. Im.—Similarly marked but head and neck light brown streaked with dark; upper back, wings and tail brownish-black except secondaries which are white with black bars; lower back, breast and abdomen white, often with grayish or brownish tinge.

IDENTIFICATION: The strikingly colored adults cannot be mistaken for any other species. Immature birds can be identified at rest or in flight by the large amount of white on wings and lower back.

RANGE: Eastern North America west to the Rockies, north to southern Canada. Winters in southern states.

NESTING: In holes in trees. Eggs, 3-5, white.

REMARKS: Some confusion exists about the status of this species because many people erroneously apply the name red-headed woodpecker to any woodpecker with a red mark on the head and especially to the flickers. The red-headed woodpecker is an erratic wanderer which has been reliably recorded from Waterton Lake, Foremost, Medicine Hat, Calgary, Rosebud, Viking, and Elk Island Park. It is seen fairly frequently in the Cypress Hills and may breed there since it is known to nest on the Saskatchewan side of the hills. The most westerly record is a specimen taken in the foothills about 20 miles west of Turner Valley on June 13, 1961.

The red-headed woodpecker prefers open country interspersed with lightly wooded areas. Favorite spots are orchards and farm plantations where it can find small fruits, berries and nuts in addition to insects. Like Lewis' woodpecker and the yellow-bellied sapsucker it often catches insects on the wing, dashing out from a high perch to snap them up as they pass. When there is an abundance of food, especially nuts, the red-headed woodpecker providently stores a supply in any convenient nooks and crannies. It has one bad habit, that of eating the eggs and young of smaller birds. Always aggressive the red-headed woodpecker holds its own against most other birds and small mammals. It seems to take delight in driving off English sparrows and starlings which try to usurp its nesting and roosting cavities. Since it is equally unafraid of man it makes an easy and interesting object of study.

254

WOODPECKERS — Family Picidae

LEWIS' WOODPECKER
Asyndesmus lewis

Scarce Summer Resident.
Length 10½ in.

DESCRIPTION: Ads.—Upper parts glossy black, dark crimson at base of bill and under eyes; breast silvery gray, a narrow band of this color extending around the back of the neck; lower breast and abdomen red mixed with gray; tail black. The feathers of the breast and abdomen have a loose, hair-like texture. Im.—Similar but lacking crimson face and gray collar, abdomen grayer.

IDENTIFICATION: Red on the abdomen distinguishes this from all other species of woodpecker.

RANGE: Western North America north to southern B.C.; rarely found east of the Rocky Mountains. Migratory; winters mainly in southern states although individuals may winter throughout range.

NESTING: In holes in trees. Eggs, 5-9, white. (Devona, June 19.)

REMARKS: Although it is not a common species Lewis' woodpecker breeds irregularly in the mountain region of Alberta at least as far north as the Jasper areas. Further information is necessary before the breeding range can be accurately outlined. Away from the mountains individuals have been recorded at Brooks, Strathmore, Rosebud, Sullivan Lake, Camrose, Belvedere and Lesser Slave Lake, mostly during migration periods.

Lewis' woodpecker has some peculiar habits; it eats wild and cultivated fruits as well as insects; it captures much of its insect food on the wing after the manner of a flycatcher; it gathers into flocks for migration; and it flies with steady wing-beats like a crow. Otherwise, however, in behavior and in structure it is a typical woodpecker. In preference to thick forests Lewis' woodpecker frequents open woods with scattered large trees. Burned-over areas where scattered skeletons of trees rise above the shorter new growth are much to its liking. Instead of perching vertically like most woodpeckers, Lewis' woodpecker sits across a high blackened branch and waits to dash out after a passing insect. If no branch is handy it is not averse to sitting on a fence or telephone wire.

In defending a desirable nesting hole against starlings or against sparrow hawks Lewis' woodpeckers show a pugnacity which augurs well for the survival of their race. At such times, and also during the squabbles attendant on the selection of a mate, they are quite noisy, uttering a variety of harsh notes unlike those of most other woodpeckers. Once the nesting season is over, however, they are as quiet as any members of the woodpecker tribe.

ALLAN BROOKS

RED-HEADED WOODPECKER
adult   *immature*

ALLAN BROOKS

LEWIS' WOODPECKER

YELLOW-BELLIED SAPSUCKER
female   *male*

HAIRY WOODPECKER
male

257

WOODPECKERS — Family Picidae

YELLOW-BELLIED SAPSUCKER
Sphyrapicus varius subsp. (p. 493)

Common Summer Resident.
Length 8½ in.

DESCRIPTION: Ad. m.—Crown and throat crimson, remainder of head black with white streaks above and below eye extending onto neck; back and wings black with irregular white marks, a large patch of white on wing coverts; upper breast black sharply delineated from yellowish lower breast and abdomen; sides grayish heavily barred with dark gray; tail black except for white on central two feathers. Ad. f.—Similar but the crimson of throat may be replaced by white. Im.—Similar but overwashed with brownish, usually slight indication of crimson on crown and throat.

IDENTIFICATION: Yellowish underparts and crimson crown will identify. In flight the white wing patch is prominent.

RANGE: North America, except arctic. Breeds throughout range. Winters in middle and southern states and Mexico.

NESTING: In holes in trees, usually not lower than 15 ft. in a live tree. Eggs, 4-7, glossy white. (Camrose, May 21.)

REMARKS: The yellow-bellied sapsucker drills rows of small pits through the smooth bark of trees to the succulent green wood beneath. It visits these trees periodically to lap up the sap which has oozed into the holes. Unfortunately this drilling is injurious to the trees; fungus diseases gain entrance through the pits or, if the drilling is extensive, the tree is girdled and killed. Sapsuckers are not sufficiently numerous in Alberta to cause much trouble, but in the regions where they congregate in the winter damage to orchards and timber stands may be extensive.

The home of the yellow-bellied sapsucker is small and the family soon outgrows its accommodation. The adults seem to be unable either to supply the young with sufficient food or to keep the nesting hole clean. The young protest constantly, probably against both conditions, for as soon as they are able they climb to the opening where food and fresh air are readily available. As they grow older they clamber out on the bark and later join their parents in foraging for food. Sap and the soft cambium layer of the wood form a large part of the food, but wild fruits, berries, and insects are also eaten. Insects are often captured in flight.

The yellow-bellied sapsucker occurs throughout the mixed-wood forests of central and northern Alberta and out onto the prairies as far as suitably wooded valleys are found. In the mountains a subspecies, the red-naped sapsucker, occurs.

WOODPECKERS — Family Picidae

HAIRY WOODPECKER
Dendrocopos villosus subsp. (p. 493)

Fairly Common Resident.
Length 9½ in.

DESCRIPTION: Head except throat black, a strong white line over eye ending, in the male, in a red bar on the nape, another strong white line running under eye to the neck; hindneck, back and wings black with white bars on the wings and a broad white streak down the middle of the back; underparts white; two outer feathers on each side of tail white, the third white towards tip, others black.

IDENTIFICATION: The white stripe running down the back separates this from all other species of woodpecker except the downy from which it is distinguished by larger size and unmarked outer tail feathers.

RANGE: Wooded parts of North and Central America; resident throughout its range.

NESTING: In holes in trees. Eggs, 4-6, glossy white. (Belvedere, May 10.)

REMARKS: The heavier woods of the unsettled regions are the usual habitat of the hairy woodpecker but occasionally, especially in winter, it may wander into the wooded valleys of the prairies. It is more wary than the downy woodpecker and rarely comes to the feeding shelf. What sense it uses to locate dormant wood-boring insects in winter is not known but it cuts into infested trees with uncanny precision to reach them. Occasionally, high on some hollow tree, it pauses in its search for food and, with rapid blows of its beak, rolls out a resounding tattoo.

In late summer, after the young have become self-reliant, the family groups break up and individuals wander far from their birthplace. This is not a migration for the movement may be in any direction. It results, however, in a thorough intermingling of the broods before the following breeding season and probably accounts for the fact that hairy woodpeckers are rarely seen in groups.

The tongue of the hairy woodpecker is long, pointed and protrusible. Small backward-projecting barbs cover the sensitive tip and glands keep it covered with a sticky secretion. With its tongue the woodpecker can explore the depths of holes and crevices in wood and can feel a grub when it touches it. The barbs and the sticky secretion enable the hairy woodpecker to extract an insect from its burrow. The tongues of other species of woodpeckers are similarly adapted for securing their food.

DOWNY WOODPECKER
male

BLACK-BACKED THREE-TOED WOODPECKER
female   *male*

DOWNY WOODPECKER
Dendrocopos pubescens subsp. (p. 493)

Fairly Common Resident.
Length 6.5 in.

DESCRIPTION: A small replica of the hairy woodpecker. The only color difference is in the tail where the central two feathers are black, the remainder being white with black bars. The beak is quite short for a woodpecker.

IDENTIFICATION: White stripe down the back, small size, and short beak are the best field marks. In the hand black marks on outer tail feathers will identify.

RANGE: Wooded parts of North America north of Mexico; resident throughout its range.

NESTING: In holes in trees. Eggs, 3-6, glossy white.

REMARKS: The downy woodpecker is more commonly found in poplar woods and birch thickets than in the deep forest. In winter it wanders well out onto the prairies following the sparsely wooded coulees and creek bottoms and appearing in the shelter-belts of farmsteads where, with a little encouragement, it may remain until spring. On the farm or in the city it is an attractive guest at the winter feeding shelf to which it may be lured, along with chickadees, by a marrow bone filled with suet. Like the hairy woodpecker it is solitary in habit at this season.

The short beak of the downy woodpecker is better adapted for probing irregularities in the bark than for digging in wood, yet each year a nesting cavity is excavated in the trunk or branch of a tree. Male and female co-operate in this work. They also share the more arduous task of supplying insect food for an ever-hungry family. Naked and blind when they are hatched the young thrive under constant care and soon appear at the opening of the nest cavity in plumage similar to their parents'. In summer downy woodpeckers are easily overlooked among the more colorful and more vocal immigrants from the south for they go about their business quietly. A sensitive ear, however, may pick out a tattoo more gentle than that of the flicker or the hairy woodpecker as the downy hammers out his call on a hollow tree in typical woodpecker fashion. Ants and wood-boring beetles and their larvae form a large part of the downy woodpecker's diet but other insects and soft caterpillars are commonly eaten. Plant food, including berries and the soft inner bark of trees, forms a smaller part of their diet. The downy woodpecker is a highly beneficial species which should be encouraged to remain around any woodlot.

261

WOODPECKERS — Family Picidae

BLACK-BACKED THREE-TOED WOODPECKER   Scarce Resident.
Picoides arcticus   Length 9½ in.

DESCRIPTION: Ad. m.—Upperparts glossy black except large yellow patch on forehead and some white spotting on primaries and secondaries; under parts white except a black line from base of beak to neck, and much black barring on sides; central two tail feathers black, remainder white. Ad. f.—Same but lacks yellow crown. Im.—Similar but duller black and yellow on crown reduced; both sexes may show some yellow. The foot bears only three toes.

IDENTIFICATION: This is the only small woodpecker with a plain black back.

RANGE: The coniferous forests of North America south in the mountains to California. Breeds throughout range.

NESTING: In holes in trees. Eggs, 4-5, glossy white.

REMARKS: The black-backed, or arctic, three-toed woodpecker is most commonly found in the evergreen forests of the mountains and the northern parts of the province, but occasionally in winter it moves out of these regions, often in considerable numbers, and appears in the spruce groves of the parklands and the prairie coulees. For its nesting territory it prefers areas which have been burned over where many dead stumps and decaying trees remain standing. These provide both nesting sites and food.

This woodpecker feeds almost entirely on the larvae of wood-boring beetles, but it eats also the spiders and ants which hide in crevices of the bark. It commonly works on low stumps and even on fallen trees, flaking off the bark with deliberate blows, and pausing every now and then as though listening for movement beneath. Whatever sense is used to locate the food must be quite keen for the probing beak accurately locates the white grubs.

The arctic three-toed woodpecker is quite unsuspicious and usually allows close observation. It is more often located by the sound of its hammering than by its call. When approached it hides behind a tree trunk poking its head around occasionally for a look at the intruder. Unless alarmed by sudden movement however, it is soon reassured and goes about its business with no apparent concern. Holding itself on the bark with tail and feet it peers into all likely spots and tests them with a few blows of its beak. This probably tells it whether the wood beneath is sound or not and helps it to decide whether further excavation would be profitable.

WOODPECKERS — Family Picidae

NORTHERN THREE-TOED WOODPECKER   Fairly Common Resident.
Picoides tridactylus   subsp. (p. 493)   Length 9 in.

DESCRIPTION: Ad. m.—Crown and face black except a yellow patch on forehead surrounded by dull white spots, and two white lines, one through eye and across nape, the other below eye and down neck; remainder of upperparts glossy black with numerous white bars across back and white spots on primaries and secondaries; tail black except two white outer feathers on each side. Ad. f.—Same but lacks yellow on crown which is spotted with white. Im.—Similar but black duller and amount of yellow reduced. The foot has only three toes.

IDENTIFICATION: The yellow crown identifies the male as a three-toed woodpecker; the horizontal bars, instead of vertical stripes, of white on the back distinguish this from all other black and white woodpeckers. In the hand the three toes and the barred back identify it.

RANGE: The coniferous forests of North America south in the mountains to New Mexico. Breeds throughout range.

NESTING: In holes in trees. Eggs, 4, white. (Belvedere, May 20.)

REMARKS: The two species of three-toed woodpeckers are very similar in habits and behavior. Both prefer the spruce and pine woods, both are quite tame, and neither is noisy. The northern three-toed woodpecker is perhaps quieter and more sluggish than the black-backed three-toed. Except during the breeding season it rarely uses its voice and the sound of its glancing blows does not carry far. The northern three-toed woodpecker is the more common of the two species especially in the mountains. In winter it wanders as far east as Camrose and Drumheller. Because of the white bars on its back it is known in some districts as the ladder-back woodpecker.

Coniferous forests are the home of northern three-toed woodpeckers although they are often found in mixed-wood forests if there are good stands of spruce and pine here and there. Rarely the nest cavity is bored only eight or ten feet from the ground but twenty-five to forty feet is a more usual height. Most woodpeckers are good parents and this species is no exception; incubation duties are shared by both male and female and the young are attended for some time after they have left the nest and learned to fly. These little family groups are occasionally seen in our mountain parks during the summer working either up or down the tree trunks in the never ending search for insect food. Bark beetles, which do not bore into wood but remain immediately beneath the bark, are a staple part of their diet.

FLYCATCHERS — Family Tyrannidae

Flycatchers have wide flattened beaks with bristles at the base which assist them in catching and holding insects. Most of them are woodland birds but the Arkansas kingbird and Say's phoebe occur regularly on the prairies. The smaller species are so confusingly similar in color that only the expert can identify them in the hand. In the field they are most easily identified by their notes.

EASTERN KINGBIRD
Tyrannus tyrannus

Common Summer Resident.
Length 8¼ in.

DESCRIPTION: Upperparts dull black, darkest on head; a concealed patch of red feathers on crown; a few wing feathers narrowly edged with white; underparts white except for a light gray band across upper breast, becoming darker gray as it continues down sides; tail black with terminal band of white. Sexes alike.

IDENTIFICATION: Slightly smaller than a robin. Like a dull blackbird with white underparts. The white-tipped black tail is distinctive.

RANGE: North and South America. Breeds from Newfoundland and central B.C. south to Florida and New Mexico. Winters from Mexico to Peru.

NESTING: In trees or shrubs usually only a few feet above the ground; occasionally on stumps or fenceposts. Nest of grasses, string and feathers lined with fine grasses, wool and cottonwood fibres. Eggs, 3-4, white heavily marked with light and dark brown. (Rosebud, June 15.)

REMARKS: The eastern kingbird is found throughout the province but it is scarce in the heavily forested regions and in the mountains. Lightly wooded areas interspersed with open fields and meadows, so characteristic of the parklands, are its preferred habitat. It also occurs commonly in farm shelterbelts and the wooded coulees of the prairies, often sharing them with the western kingbird in the southeastern parts of the province.

Disdaining to skulk in the foliage the kingbird perches well out in the open on a branch, a post or a wire where it can see and be seen. It is a true flycatcher; nearly all of its food is caught in the air. On quivering wings it darts out to catch a passing insect, often with an audible click of its beak then, returning to its perch, it flicks it tail, utters a steely cry of success and waits for another morsel to come along. Its harsh voice protests all intrusions whether human or otherwise but it does not stop with vocal protests; hawks and crows which wander through its territory are driven off with savage attacks that make the feathers fly. The kingbird comes by its name honestly.

T. M. SHORTT

NORTHERN THREE-TOED WOODPECKER
male

C. HAMPSON

EASTERN KINGBIRD

FLYCATCHERS — Family Tyrannidae

WESTERN KINGBIRD
Tyrannus verticalis

Fairly Common Summer Resident.
Length 8½ in.

DESCRIPTION: Crown, back, throat and upper breast ashy-gray, lightest on throat; concealed vermilion patch on crown; wings light olive-brown; lower breast and abdomen lemon yellow; tail black, outer web of outermost feather white. Sexes alike.

IDENTIFICATION: A pale gray bird with yellow underparts and black tail. Sometimes confused with Say's phoebe but larger and lemon yellow not cinnamon or buffy below. Black tail with narrow white stripe down each side is distinctive.

RANGE: Breeds from southern prairie provinces and B.C. south to Oklahoma and California. Winters in western Central America.

NESTING: In shrubs or trees, or on telephone poles or buildings, usually 15-30 feet above ground. Nest of grasses, feathers, wool, hair, cottonwood down and any other fibrous material available. Eggs, 3-5, white heavily marked with various shades of brown. (Beynon, June 16.)

REMARKS: The western kingbird is a prairie species confined to the southeastern section of the province. It has been found breeding north as far as Scollard and Bodo and west to Pearce, Rosebud and Munson. There are recent indications that this range is being extended; in June, 1956, a western kingbird was seen near Lac Ste. Anne and in late May, 1965, one was observed for some time at Wembley in the Peace River area.

Along the valleys of the Milk River and the tributaries of the South Saskatchewan tall poplars are the home of the western kingbird. It is a noisy bird and one of the first to greet the dawn with shrill chatter. From a high exposed perch it keeps a restless vigil over its domain but it is a little more tolerant of hawks and crows than the eastern kingbird and rarely will it go far out of its way to pester them. Western kingbirds also make themselves at home around farmsteads and in prairie villages where telephone poles and grain elevators may provide the only suitable nesting sites. While most birds are seeking shelter from the heat of the summer sun western kingbirds bicker among themselves or sally out after real or fancied perils. Their seemingly boundless supply of nervous energy comes from a diet of insects mostly caught on the wing. Grasshoppers, which form a large part of their food in Alberta, are captured near the ground as the kingbird flies over the grass.

FLYCATCHERS — Family Tyrannidae

SCISSOR-TAILED FLYCATCHER
Muscivora forficata

Accidental Wanderer.
Length 12-15 in.

DESCRIPTION: Body about the size of a kingbird's but tail very long (7-10 in.) and very deeply forked. Ad. m.— Head and body pale ash-gray, paler below; concealed scarlet patch on crown; delicate flush of salmon-pink on sides and abdomen, strongest near bend of wing; wings gray-brown, undersurface washed with salmon-pink; 3 longest outer tail feathers on each side white with black tips, remainder black. Ad. f.—Similar in color but with shorter tail. Immature birds usually lack crown patch.

IDENTIFICATION: A pale gray bird beautifully marked with red; outer tail feathers much longer than body, middle ones much shorter.

RANGE: Breeds in Kansas, Oklahoma and Texas and adjacent parts of Arkansas and Louisiana. Winters mainly in Mexico and Central America.

NESTING: In trees, or on buildings, bridges, poles or towers, in cities as well as in the country. Nest of small twigs and rootlets lined with hair, wool, feathers, grass, twine, etc. Eggs, 4-6, white spotted and blotched with browns.

REMARKS: Individuals of this species wander erratically from the normal range and have appeared in practically all parts of North America. There are several records from Canada including two from the shores of Hudson Bay. In Alberta a scissor-tailed flycatcher was seen at close range at Claresholm on August 20, 1943; another was under observation for over an hour in Ft. Chipewyan, Lake Athabasca, on June 17, 1952.

It is unthinkable that such a spectacular bird should go unnoticed but, as though deliberately attracting attention, the scissor-tailed flycatcher habitually opens and closes its long tail when at rest, performs remarkable gyrations in the air, and shrieks exultantly at every opportunity. Like the kingbirds it seems to take pleasure in attacking any large birds which wander into its territory.

The scissor-tailed flycatcher prefers open country in which, from a perch on a telephone pole or a tree, it can dash out to capture passing insects. It rarely alights on the ground. The long tail feathers give it a grace of movement in the air which is unmatched among birds. As though aware of this it performs remarkable aerial gymnastics in view of the female during the period of courtship.

WESTERN KINGBIRD

ALLAN BROOKS

SCISSOR-TAILED FLYCATCHER

EASTERN PHOEBE

F. C. HENNESSEY

SAY'S PHOEBE

ALLAN BROOKS

EASTERN PHOEBE
Sayornis phoebe

Common Summer Resident.
Length 7 in.

DESCRIPTION: Upperparts dark grayish-brown, darkest on crown and sides of head; secondaries and tertiaries narrowly edged with white; underparts white or cream with dusky chin and sides, and sometimes a faint dusky band across breast; beak black. Sexes alike.

IDENTIFICATION: Similar to wood pewee but larger, lacking wing bars, lighter below, and lower mandible black. Differs from olive-sided flycatcher in having dusky chin and lacking dark mottling on crown, back and sides. Plain white under tail coverts separate it from both above species.

RANGE: North America east of the Rockies. Breeds throughout range. Winters in southern states and Mexico.

NESTING: In crevices on cliffs, on ledges in buildings, under bridges, or in a great variety of other sites usually protected from above. Nest of mud, grass and moss, lined with fine plant fibres and hair; sometimes attached to sides of beams or walls. Eggs, usually 5, white occasionally lightly marked with brown. (Winterburn, May 24.)

REMARKS: The eastern phoebe is a woodland bird preferring the edges of clearings to the depths of the forest. Wooded banks of streams and lakes are favorite haunts. It occurs throughout the province but is scarce on the prairies. The only mountain record is from Jasper.

As it repeats its name, accenting the first syllable, the voice of the phoebe is as soft and subdued as its colors. All its actions indicate a gentleness of manner characteristic of the species. In flight it resembles a butterfly, delicate and graceful. As restless as most flycatchers it nervously flirts its tail even when at rest. Yet it is not a shy bird for it frequently nests close to, or even in, human habitations. For an insectivorous species the phoebe is an early spring migrant arriving in central Alberta about the third week of April. During the periods of cold and snow which usually follow, it gets sustenance from seeds and berries while the insects are dormant. At other times, like all the flycatchers, it prefers to capture insects on the wing.

This is a species which is easily attracted to a secluded cottage in the woods. A shelf under the eaves protected from strong sunlight and not accessible to predators is often sufficient invitation to bring a pair of phoebes for the summer. They and their family will blend unobtrusively into the quiet surroundings making up in grace what they lack in color and demonstrating conclusively that fine feathers are not a requisite of fine birds.

SAY'S PHOEBE
Common Summer Resident.
Sayornis saya subsp. (p. 494)
Length 7 in.

DESCRIPTION: Upperparts brownish-gray darkest on head and primaries; tall dark brownish-black; throat and breast brownish-gray lighter on throat; abdomen and under tail coverts cinnamon-buff. Sexes alike.

IDENTIFICATION: A flycatcher of medium size, browner than any other species. In flight the tail appears black but lacks the white tip of the eastern kingbird and the white edges of the western kingbird. The rust-colored abdomen is distinctive.

RANGE: Western North America. Breeds from southern Manitoba to Alaska south to New Mexico and California. Winters in southwestern states and Mexico.

NESTING: In crevices and on ledges of cliffs or in cavities in banks or trees; in inhabited regions any sheltered ledge or cavity around buildings. Nest, a flat structure of grasses, wool and hair, lined mainly with the last two fibers. Eggs, usually 4-5, white. (Rosebud, May 11.)

REMARKS: Say's phoebe is similar to the eastern phoebe in habits and behavior, but in habitat it is characteristically a bird of the prairies and the canyons. It breeds commonly throughout the prairies, less commonly in the parklands, and rarely north to Athabasca. There are as yet no breeding records from northern Alberta although it nests along the Mackenzie river north of the provincial boundary. In the mountains and the foothills it is seen fairly commonly from the Crowsnest Pass to Cochrane, but rarely at Banff and Jasper.

Say's phoebe is a friendly species which seems to prefer inhabited regions to the wilder spots. Few prairie farms lack a nesting pair. Quiet in voice, soft of flight, and gentle in manner, they are well worth encouraging at any farmstead. Say's phoebes live almost entirely on insects caught in flight yet, unlike swallows, they do not spend a great deal of time on the wing. Instead, like most other flycatchers, they wait upon a perch until an insect passes by, flit out to pick it from the air, and then return to a perch again. To those who are accustomed to seeing Say's phoebes around human habitations it comes as something of a surprise to find them in out of the way places, yet they nest not uncommonly in the canyons and river banks of the foothills and in late August fair numbers may be found slowly migrating along the valleys at the eastern foot of the Rockies. They return to southern Alberta during the last week of April, usually alone or in twos and threes, gradually working northward during the daytime in short flights from one fencepost to another.

YELLOW-BELLIED FLYCATCHER

TRAILL'S FLYCATCHER

FLYCATCHERS — Family Tyrannidae

YELLOW-BELLIED FLYCATCHER
Empidonax flaviventris

Scarce Summer Resident.
Length 5½ in.

DESCRIPTION: Head, neck and back olive-green; narrow yellow eye-ring; wings brownish-black with two yellowish wing bars and tertiaries margined with white; tail brownish-black, feathers margined with green; throat, breast and sides yellowish-olive, lighter on throat; abdomen yellow. Sexes alike.

IDENTIFICATION: The most brightly colored of the small flycatchers, decidedly greenish above and yellow below; wing bars decidedly yellowish.

RANGE: North America east of the Rockies. Breeds in coniferous forests of Canada and northern states. Winters in Mexico and Central America.

NESTING: On or near the ground, often on the sides of hummocks. Nest of moss and grass lined with fine rootlets. Eggs, 3-4, white finely dotted with light and dark brown. (Glenevis, June 13.)

REMARKS: Since the depths of the mixed-wood and coniferous forests are the preferred habitat of the yellow-bellied flycatcher it is not a well known species. Although by no means wary, it is so quiet and retiring that it remains inconspicuous among the foliage except when it flits into the open to snap up an insect. It is a rather common inhabitant of the forested regions between Athabasca and Lesser Slave Lake but appears to be scarce in wooded areas elsewhere. It has not been reported from the mountains or the foothills; the western flycatcher, very similar to the yellow-bellied in color and habits, has recently been found in the mountains southwest of Calgary. The yellow-bellied flycatcher is found occasionally in the parklands of central Alberta during spring and fall migrations. As shy then as it is on its nesting grounds it still keeps rather close to coniferous woods and their adjacent shrubbery.

The muskeg areas of northern Alberta are perhaps the best places to find yellow-bellied flycatchers during the nesting season but alder swamps, especially those bordering streams and lakes, often contain a pair. In these almost impenetrable places they keep to the lower branches of the densest thickets, very rarely appearing on the tops of the bushes or at the edge of a clearing. To catch a glimpse of such a shy bird in these surroundings requires the patience of Job. Fortunately although it is not particularly vocal its voice is fairly easily identified. The call is a clear *choo-wheee*, or *tyoo-wheee*, with the second note higher and more prolonged than the first. The quality is sweeter than one usually expects of a flycatcher.

FLYCATCHERS — Family Tyrannidae

TRAILL'S (ALDER) FLYCATCHER   Common Summer Resident.
Empidonax traillii   subsp. (p. 494)   Length 5¾ in.

DESCRIPTION: Head, neck and back dull olive-green; yellowish-white eye-ring; wings brownish-black with two pale olive wing bars and white margins on tertiaries; tail brownish-black; sides of neck, a band across breast and down sides olive; throat white; lower breast and abdomen white with yellowish tinge. Sexes alike.

IDENTIFICATION: Not as gray above as the least nor as green as the yellow-bellied; abdomen yellower than former but not as yellow as latter. Best identified in the field by voice and habitat.

RANGE: Western North and South America. Breeds in North America mainly west of the Mississippi. Winters in Central America and northwestern South America.

NESTING: In bushes about 3-4 feet from ground. Nest of grasses lined with shredded plant fibers, placed in fork of branches; deep cupped. Eggs, 3-4, cream with ring of blotches and dots of light and dark brown. (Spruce Grove, June 30.)

REMARKS: The alder flycatcher inhabits dense willow and alder shrubbery bordering streams or clearings in the forest, avoiding the poplar clumps preferred by the least flycatcher and the coniferous forests inhabited by the yellow-bellied. It is widely distributed in the mixed-wood forests of the northern half of the province and in the parklands. In suitable habitat along the rivers and in the coulees of the prairies Traill's flycatcher is not uncommon. It has also been reported from the river valleys of the mountains and in the Cypress Hills.

Like all the flycatchers, Traill's flycatcher is very restless but its activities never carry it into the open for more than a moment. Dashing out to catch an insect with an audible click of its beak it returns immediately to a perch on an outer branch of the alders. It does not hide yet its colors blend so well with the foliage that it takes a good eye to pick it out. Unlike the least flycatcher it is rather retiring in habit; even the incubating female will not allow a close approach. Traill's flycatcher is so similar in appearance to other species of flycatchers that sight identification appears impossible. Fortunately, especially in early summer, it is fairly vocal and a soft call, *vee - feel,* with the second note only slightly accented over the first, readily identifies it. Among the fall migrants which go through central Alberta in late August and early September Traill's flycatchers are quiet and inconspicuous.

274

FLYCATCHERS — Family Tyrannidae

LEAST FLYCATCHER
Empidonax minimus

Common Summer Resident.
Length 5½ in.

DESCRIPTION: Sexes alike. Crown, back and tail olive-brown, sometimes with vague dark streaks on crown; wings brownish-black with two dull white bars; face, breast and sides gray or brownish-gray; white ring around eye; throat white or ashy; abdomen white or yellowish-white.

IDENTIFICATION: Very similar to other small flycatchers but grayer and with a very noticeable eye-ring. The best field identification is its note, a loud *che-bec* accented on the second syllable.

RANGE: North America mainly east of the Rockies; breeds throughout. Winters south to Central America.

NESTING: In the fork of a tree from 5-25 feet from ground. Nest, a deep cup, compactly woven of grasses, bark fibres, feathers and spider-webs. Eggs, 3-5, white or very pale buff. (Edmonton, June 3.)

REMARKS: This is the best known of our small flycatchers. Its familiar *che-bec* note, loud out of proportion to its size, is heard in urban as well as rural areas. The least flycatcher prefers open woods to dense forests; light growths of poplar and aspen along the roadside or at the edge of a clearing are favorite nesting spots. On the prairies it is a common inhabitant of the poplar clumps in river valleys and coulees. In the mountains it has been recorded in some of the lower river valleys but elsewhere its place is taken by the dusky flycatcher. The two-note call of the dusky flycatcher can be confused with that of the least flycatcher but it is not so harsh and lacks the staccato quality of a *chebec*. Flycatchers in the mountains should be identified carefully.

The least flycatcher is a restless bird, flitting from one perch to another but never leaving leafy shelter for more than a moment. Although it catches much of its food on the wing, like other flycatchers it searches the leaves and bark for ants and beetles which constitute a large part of its food. Normally a tame friendly bird, the male during the nesting season resents intrusion into his territory and will drive away much larger birds than himself. The female sits very close upon the nest. After 12 days the eggs hatch and 11 days later the young are fledged. They remain dependent upon the parents for some time after they have left the nest begging for food with quivering wings and appealing cries. Long before they start their southward migration in September, however, the family groups have broken up and the young fend for themselves.

FLYCATCHERS — Family Tyrannidae

HAMMOND'S FLYCATCHER
Empidonax hammondii

Scarce Summer Resident.
Length 5½ in.

DESCRIPTION: Upperparts grayish-olive; wing with two light gray bars; underparts olive-gray darkest on breast and palest on throat and abdomen; sides faintly tinged with olive-yellow.

IDENTIFICATION: Hammond's and the dusky flycatchers, even in the hand, can be separated only by the expert who has handled many specimens of both species. In the field they are quite similar in color; when seen together Hammond's appears smaller than the dusky and darker both above and below, giving the general appearance of a small wood pewee. In habitat and in voice they differ markedly.

RANGE: Western North America. Breeds mainly west of the Rockies from Alaska to central California. Winters in southern Mexico and Central America.

NESTING: In trees, usually conifers, at considerable height. Nest of fine grasses and plant fibers placed in the fork of a branch. Eggs, 3-4, white or yellowish; unmarked or sprinkled with fine brown dots.

REMARKS: During the breeding season Hammond's flycatcher is most frequently found at high altitudes in coniferous forests where the upper branches form its home. It behaves like most small flycatchers, changing perches often and flirting its tail nervously each time it alights. The male guards the nest jealously, driving away any other birds which come near the incubating female and, in so doing, often calling the attention of any human observer to it. Hammond's flycatcher is not at all shy or wary and since it often perches in the open it may be readily observed. Despite this, its similarity to other species of flycatchers makes recognition extremely difficult. Its tameness, however, may be used as a means of identification, for other flycatchers will rarely allow such close approach, especially near the nest.

Hammond's flycatcher has been recorded infrequently in Alberta although it is a common species in British Columbia. All Alberta specimens have been secured in the mountains from Jasper south to Waterton. During late summer dusky and Hammond's flycatchers may often be found in the same habitat. At this time the notes of Hammond's may be more helpful in identifying it than is its color. They are usually of one syllable, *pzeect,* or *peect,* with a rising inflection; occasionally a low, *tzur-r-r-p,* definitely burred, is included.

LEAST FLYCATCHER

HAMMOND'S FLYCATCHER

277

FLYCATCHERS — Family Tyrannidae

DUSKY FLYCATCHER
Empidonax oberholseri

Fairly Common Summer Resident.
Length 6 in.

DESCRIPTION: Very similar to Hammond's flycatcher in color but somewhat grayer on the back and lighter below; throat often almost white; outer web of outer tail feathers much lighter than inner web.

IDENTIFICATION: Similar to Hammond's but lighter gray in general tone. In the field the dusky flycatcher appears larger and has longer tail with pale outer margin on outermost feather. The habitat and the notes of the two species are quite different.

RANGE: Western North America. Breeds mainly in the Rockies and west, from British Columbia south to Arizona and California. Winters in western Central America.

NESTING: In trees, usually deciduous, at heights of 3-8 feet. Nest of grasses and fine plant fibers usually in the upright crotch of a branch. Eggs, 3-4, white or creamy, unmarked.

REMARKS: This is the species which, until 1957, was known as Wright's flycatcher. Adding to the confusion which has long existed in naming the flycatchers, taxonomists have given the name Wright's to another species which does not occur in Alberta and have called this the dusky flycatcher.

Although a mountain species, the dusky flycatcher is usually found during the breeding season at lower altitudes than Hammond's. Here it frequents the alders, willows and poplars rather than the coniferous growths. This is the type of habitat which, away from the mountains, is inhabited by Traill's and least flycatchers. The notes of the dusky flycatcher are *see - whik* and *see - whee* often repeated several times in not too rapid succession. They are much higher pitched than the notes of Hammond's flycatcher; they may sound to a casual listener something like the *che-bec* of the least flycatcher but the notes are softer.

This is the flycatcher most commonly seen in the burns and at the edges of clearings in our Rocky Mountain valleys and in thin deciduous woods along their slopes. It also occurs in the aspen poplar groves which dot the sides of the foothills but its range appears to be delimited by altitude for it never moves down onto the prairies. It has been recorded from the higher parts of the Cypress Hills in both Alberta and Saskatchewan in the same type of habitat which it occupies in the mountains.

278

FLYCATCHERS — Family Tyrannidae

WESTERN FLYCATCHER   Scarce Summer Resident.
Empidonax difficilis subsp. (p. 494)   Length 5½ in.

DESCRIPTION: Sexes alike. Crown and back olive-green; wings and tail brownish-black, two buffy bars on wings; face, throat, breast and sides light buffy-yellow, lightest on throat; abdomen pale yellow; a narrow light ring around eye.

IDENTIFICATION: The western and the yellow-bellied flycatchers both show much yellow on the underparts and might easily be confused. Fortunately they occur in widely separated areas, the western in the mountains, and the yellow-bellied in the northern coniferous forests. The western is more buffy and has the sixth primary longer than the first. A flycatcher nesting on the ground in the mountains is probably this species.

RANGE: Western North America from Alaska to Mexico mainly west of the Rockies. Winters in Mexico.

NESTING: Sometimes in trees but commonly on the ground near a stump or on a bank near a stream. Nest, a ball of green moss with a deep depression. Eggs, 3-5, creamy-white with fine spots of cinnamon. (Gorge Creek, July 16.)

REMARKS: The western flycatcher was unknown in the province until 1954 when it was found nesting on the shale banks of Gorge Creek in the foothills west of Turner Valley. Specimens were taken and positively identified the following year. Since that time the species has been found at various places in the foothills and in mountain valleys south to Waterton and north to Jasper but its complete range will not be known until much more field work has been done in these areas. A flycatcher in the mountains showing a decided yellow tinge on the underparts is likely to be a western flycatcher.

During the nesting season the western flycatcher frequents deciduous woods along mountain streams, especially those whose banks are precipitous. The young are raised under a slight overhang of the cliff and fed on insects captured in flight over the stream. When they are on the wing family groups scatter more widely but they still show preference for poplar woods and aspen groves rather than shrubby thickets and conifers. Their migration must be in a westerly or southwesterly direction since the species has not been encountered on the prairies. Migration dates have not yet been ascertained but most western flycatchers have left their usual habitat by late August.

DUSKY FLYCATCHER

WESTERN FLYCATCHER

280

WESTERN WOOD PEWEE

C. HAMPSON

OLIVE-SIDED FLYCATCHER

T. M. SHORTT

FLYCATCHERS — Family Tyrannidae

WESTERN WOOD PEWEE
Contopus sordidulus subsp. (p. 494)

Common Summer Resident.
Length 6¼ in.

DESCRIPTION: Crown, neck and back grayish-olive; wings and tail gray-brown, wings with two faint light wing bars; throat, breast and sides gray, lightest on throat, abdomen white or cream; under tail coverts white with dusky centers; upper mandible black, under mandible buffy. Sexes alike.

IDENTIFICATION: A gray flycatcher, grayer below than any other. Like eastern phoebe but smaller and with light wing bars; under tail coverts with dark centers.

RANGE: Breeds in western North America from Alaska to Manitoba south through Mexico and Central America. Winters in Central America and northwestern South America.

NESTING: On a horizontal branch or in the fork between branch and trunk of a tree at heights of 10-50 feet. Nest, a flat structure of grasses and plant fibers bound with spider web. Eggs, 2-4, white or cream irregularly marked around larger end with browns and purples. (Lake Wabamun, June 19.)

REMARKS: The wood pewee is widely distributed in the forested regions of Alberta diminishing in numbers, however, toward the northern boundary and toward the mountains where it has been recorded from Waterton, Jasper, and along the Bow River near Banff. In the parklands it is found only in the heavier stands of timber. On the prairies it breeds in the large cottonwoods in the coulees and along the rivers. It is absent, peculiarly, from the Cypress Hills where there is an abundance of suitable habitat.

Generally quiet and staid in manner the wood pewee is a little less active than most other species of flycatchers. While at rest it sits quietly with few nervous movements and none of the flirting of the tail so commonly seen in the phoebe. Yet in general behavior it is a true flycatcher and there is no mistaking it. Sitting erect and trim on a twig it watches for a passing insect then flies out to pick it from the air. As likely as not it moves on to another perch to await its next victum and its forays are as often into the woods as into the clearings. From time to time, except in the fall, it gives a plaintive, high-pitched call, *pee - wee* or *pee - a-wee*, from which its name is derived.

The wood pewee is a true woodland bird rarely seen far from trees even on migration. Unlike the phoebe it usually avoids human habitations but this is probably because of its different nesting requirements rather than from wariness for in its normal habitat the pewee is not a particularly shy bird.

FLYCATCHERS — Family Tyrannidae

OLIVE-SIDED FLYCATCHER   Fairly Common Summer Resident.
Nuttallornis borealis   Length 7½ in.

DESCRIPTION: Upperparts sooty-gray often with slight olive tinge on back, tertiaries margined with white; sides of throat, breast and flanks olive-brown, many feathers with darker centers; stripe down middle of throat, breast and abdomen cream or white; tail dark brownish-black; under tail coverts cream with dusky centers. Sexes alike.

IDENTIFICATION: A woodland bird most likely to be confused with the phoebe and the wood pewee. Large size and the dark sides separated by a medial light line from throat to tail distinguish this species.

RANGE: North and South America. Breeds in coniferous forests across Canada and United States. Winters mainly in northwestern South America.

NESTING: In conifers usually at considerable height. Nest of mosses, grass and needles, on horizontal branch. Eggs, 3-4, creamy-white with ring of brown spots near larger end. (Lamont, June 16.)

REMARKS: The olive-sided flycatcher shows a decided preference for burnt timber adjacent to coniferous and mixed-wood forests; it is also frequently found in tamarack swamps and spruce muskegs. Although not a common bird it is well distributed in such habitat in northern and western Alberta including the mountains.

Olive-sided flycatchers, unlike most flycatchers, are rarely seen in settled areas, preferring the seclusion of the muskegs and the forests particularly those in which spruce and tamarack predominate. Even in these wilderness surroundings they are wary birds difficult of approach. If it were not for their habit of choosing a high, open perch, often on the topmost dead limb of a conifer, they would rarely be seen. There is never doubt of their presence in an area, however, for their alarm notes, *quip - quip - quip*, and their song, a not unmusical *quick - three beers*, are uttered loud and often. Both calls are distinctive. In the nesting season they resist intrusion into their territory driving off those of their own kind with the aggressiveness of a kingbird. Human beings are subjected to vociferous attacks which increase in intensity with nearness to the nest, thus defeating their purpose.

Sitting erect and straight on a dead limb the olive-sided flycatcher watches for flying insects which comprise over ninety-five percent of its food. It dashes out and pursues them, often twisting and turning through remarkable gyrations before capturing a particularly elusive moth or bee. Then back it goes to its high perch to wait for further food to approach.

HORNED LARK

VIOLET-GREEN SWALLOW

LARKS — Family Alaudidae

Larks are dull-colored ground birds which walk instead of hopping. They have thin sharp beaks and a very long hind toe nail. In the nesting season they are not gregarious but during migration they visit cultivated fields in flocks. They have delightful songs usually given on the wing; the English skylark is the most celebrated member of the family.

HORNED LARK

Eremophila alpestris subsp. (p. 494)

Common Summer Resident.
Length 7 in.

DESCRIPTION: Ad. m.—Face and forehead white except a strong black moustache mark; black band across crown extending back over ears into erectile feathers or 'horns'; remainder of crown, hindneck, and bend of wing pinkish-brown; back and sides buffy streaked with grayish-brown; middle tail feathers brown, remainder black; throat white or yellow; dark crescent across upper breast; underparts white. Ad. f.—Similar but darker above and black markings subdued.

IDENTIFICATION: The black breast band, moustache mark, and forecrown are good field marks; in flight the tail shows black except for the lighter central feathers.

RANGE: The northern hemisphere. In North America breeds throughout the northern states and Canada. Winters from southern Canada to northern South America.

NESTING: On the ground on prairies and meadows. Nest, a depression lined with grass usually unconcealed. Eggs, 3-5, white speckled heavily with browns and pale blue. The horned lark usually produces two broods. (Calgary, April 25 and June 10.)

REMARKS: A number of geographic races of the horned lark occur in Alberta; one nests commonly on the prairies, another breeds in the open lands farther north, a third nests in the alpine meadows of the Rockies, and a fourth migrates through the province to its breeding grounds in the arctic. Members of this last race often winter in southern Alberta.

In those parts of the province which have escaped the plough the horned lark is a characteristic species. It rises from the ground and flies low with undulating flight to perch on a hummock or fence-post. There it may sing its cheery tinkling song, but its best performance is given in the air while the female covers her eggs on the ground below. In central Alberta horned larks are most commonly seen as early spring migrants appearing along roadsides long before the snow has disappeared. They often associate with snowbirds and Lapland longspurs at this season; mixed flocks of hundreds of birds settle on fallow early in April feeding on weed seeds and insects and filling the air with cheerful twitterings.

SWALLOWS — Family Hirundinidae

Swallows are famed for their graceful flight. Their primaries are very long, the secondaries relatively short, forming a long, narrow wing. Their beaks are short and flat but the gape is enormous. Their legs are small and weak. All swallows are insectivorous.

VIOLET-GREEN SWALLOW   Fairly Common Summer Resident.
Tachycineta thalassina subsp. (p. 494)   Length 5 in.

DESCRIPTION: Ad.m.—Face, cheeks and all underparts white, this white extending onto lower back near base of tail but never reaching mid-line; crown, hindneck, and back dark iridescent green; tail iridescent violet, slightly forked. Ad. f.—Similar but grayish-brown above with green and violet reflections. Im.—Similar to female but duller.

IDENTIFICATION: Like the tree swallow but showing green instead of blue reflections; the white patches on the sides of the rump and on the face are distinctive.

RANGE: Western North America from California to Alaska mainly from the Rockies westward. Winters in Central America.

NESTING: In crevices on mountain cliffs, in holes in trees, in birdhouses, or in holes about buildings. Nest of grass usually with a few feathers. Eggs, 4-5, white. (Banff, June 25.)

REMARKS: The violet-green swallow is a mountain species which is locally common on the eastern slopes of the Rockies from Waterton to north of Jasper. Visitors to Lake Louise are almost sure to see it skimming over the water or darting about the buildings in pursuit of insects. The species seems to have become more abundant and to have extended its range in recent years. It is now found in many mountain localities formerly occupied solely by the tree swallow. Where the two species are found together they present an interesting challenge in identification to the tyro.

The species occurs in a few spots away from the mountains. In 1892 Frank Farley found a pair of violet-green swallows nesting near his homestead southeast of Red Deer. In 1937 violet-green swallows were discovered nesting close to this same spot. They have also occupied nesting-boxes near Penhold and at Hinton on several occasions during the past few years. Violet-green swallows are very similar to tree swallows in habits as well as appearance. They make themselves at home around buildings and go about their business undisturbed by human activity. Like all swallows they are fond of feeding over water; in the southwest corner of the province violet-green swallows are often seen over ponds hawking for insects in company with bank, cliff, and tree swallows.

SWALLOWS — Family Hirundinidae

TREE SWALLOW
Iridoprocne bicolor

Common Summer Resident.
Length 6 in.

DESCRIPTION: Ad. m.—Upperparts blue-black with a steely gloss on all except the flight feathers; tail brownish-black, slightly forked; cheeks and underparts white except for a light grayish tinge on sides and sometimes on breast. Ad. f.—Very similar but usually a little duller than male. Im.—Above soft grayish-brown; below white, shaded on sides and breast with pale grayish-brown.

IDENTIFICATION: A small swallow, glossy black above and white below is most likely a tree swallow. Like the violet green swallow but larger and lacks white on sides of rump and above eye.

RANGE: North and Central America. Breeds from central states north to tree limit in Canada and Alaska. Winters in southern states and Central America.

NESTING: In holes in trees or poles, or in birdhouses. Nest of dry grass usually with a few feathers. Eggs, 4-7, white. (Frog Lake, June 8.)

REMARKS: The tree swallow nests regularly in the parklands and the forested areas of the province. It also breeds in the mountains usually at lower altitudes than the violet-green swallow although there has been considerable overlapping of range of these two species during recent years. On the prairies the tree swallow occurs only as a migrant except in those towns and cities where good stands of shade trees and suitable bird-houses form a combination too strong for a pair of tree swallows to resist.

As lumbering and agriculture have destroyed its natural nesting sites the tree swallow has adapted itself to man-made substitutes. Even in the cities a nest-box on a pole or high on the garage wall will often attract a pair of these graceful birds. It is best set up about the middle of April after the English sparrows have built their nests but before the tree swallows have arrived. The tree swallow is the first of the swallows to appear in the spring; at Camrose the average date of arrival over a twenty-five year period is April 25th. Swallows which arrive too early often starve to death if the weather is severe, since they cannot find their insect food. Late in summer when the young are strong on the wing, tree swallows congregate in large flocks before migrating. Day after day, twittering incessantly, they weave intricate patterns in the air or perch in long rows on the telephone wires. Then, suddenly, in the third week of August, they are gone on the first leg of their southward journey.

SWALLOWS — Family Hirundinidae

BANK SWALLOW
Riparia riparia   subsp. (p. 494)

Common Summer Resident.
Length 6 in.

DESCRIPTION: Ads. — Upperparts grayish-brown darkest on wings and tail; throat and underparts white except a definite band of grayish-brown across upper breast; sides lightly tinged with brown. Im.—Similar but feathers of upperparts often edged with whitish and underparts usually tinged with rusty.

IDENTIFICATION: A small brown swallow with white throat and dark band across breast. Likely to be confused only with the rough-winged swallow which lacks white throat.

RANGE: Almost world-wide. In North America breeds from southern states north to about tree limit. Winters in South America from Brazil to Peru.

NESTING: In colonies in sand or clay banks. Each nest is built at the end of a narrow tunnel two or three feet long which slopes slightly downward towards its entrance to prevent flooding by rain. Nest, a few bits of grass and feathers. Eggs, 4-7, white. (Rosebud, July 1.)

REMARKS: The bank swallow is locally common throughout the province even in the mountain valleys but is restricted during the breeding season to those regions where there are suitable nesting cliffs. Clay banks sufficiently extensive to house colonies of a hundred or more birds are most commonly found bordering rivers but as highways have been cut through hills the bank swallow has been quick to take advantage of these man-made cliffs. The same site is used by the colony for many years; the number of deserted sites probably indicates that the colony likes a change from time to time for the species does not appear to have diminished in numbers in recent years.

In company with other species of swallows, the bank swallow may be found in the spring skimming the surface of lakes and sloughs as it hawks for insects. Although not as colorful as the rest, it is equally graceful on the wing. In summer around banks in which a colony nests the swallows weave intricate patterns in the air as they approach and leave the burrows. They live harmoniously for each pair knows its own burrow; only occasionally is there bickering among birds returning to adjacent holes at the same time. Their only vocal effort is a lively chitter which cannot be called a song. Bank swallows arrive in southern Alberta about the end of April or the beginning of May and fall migrants pass through the province during the third week of August. Even on migration they will spend the night in burrows if any are handy, particularly during inclement weather.

TREE SWALLOW

H. PEGG

BANK SWALLOW

ALLAN BROOKS

ROUGH-WINGED SWALLOW Fairly Common Summer Resident.
Stelgidopteryx ruficollis subsp. (p. 494) Length 6 in.

DESCRIPTION: Ads. — Upperparts grayish-brown, darkest on wings and tail; throat, breast and sides light grayish-brown; remainder of underparts white; the barbs of the outer webs of the outer wing feathers are hooked and therefore the wing edge feels rough when stroked, hence 'rough-wing'. Sexes alike but the 'rough' wing may be absent in the female. Im.—Similar but browner above and below and with two light wing bars.

IDENTIFICATION: A small brown swallow most likely to be confused with the bank swallow; differs in having dark throat and breast.

RANGE: North and South America. Breeds throughout North America. Winters from Mexico south to Chile.

NESTING: In holes in banks, in crevices in rocks or walls, in drain-pipes and similar places; usually solitary but occasionally two or three pairs may nest on the same cliff; sometimes may nest with a colony of bank swallows. Nest of dry grass and feathers at end of two or three foot tunnel. Eggs, 4-7, white. (Rosebud, June 27.)

REMARKS: Taverner, in his 'Birds of Canada' (1934), says of this species, 'not so far detected in . . . Alberta'. Since that time the rough-winged swallow has been found breeding fairly commonly throughout the prairies and the parklands as far north as Camrose. In the mountains it is known to nest at Jasper and Banff.

Perhaps because the needs of only one pair have to be considered, the rough-winged swallow usually selects nesting sites quite unlike those of the bank swallow. Low banks, only a few feet high, so commonly found in prairie coulees or along streams and irrigation ditches are favorite spots. In such places neither the birds nor the small entrance to their tunnel attract attention; it is no wonder the species escaped notice for so many years. Out of the breeding season rough-wings may be found with other species of swallows, usually in the vicinity of water. In such company it takes a practiced eye to separate this species from the more numerous bank swallows.

Although more solitary in habit than bank swallows rough-winged swallows are occasionally found in groups but these never approach the size of a bank swallow colony. They often rest on fence wires which may be the only perch available in some of the areas where they nest. In flight rough-wings are as skilful and graceful as other swallows but their drab color and the short unforked tail makes them less spectacular.

SWALLOWS — Family Hirundinidae

BARN SWALLOW
Hirundo rustica subsp. (p. 494)

Fairly Common Summer Resident.
Length 7 in.

DESCRIPTION: Ad. m.—Forehead chestnut; rest of upperparts dark steely-blue with purple reflections; tail deeply forked, outer feathers 1½ inches longer than middle; throat and breast chestnut, changing to buff on rest of underparts; partial or complete band of bluish-black on upper breast. Ad. f.—Similar but underparts paler and tail not so deeply forked. Im.—Similar but much duller all over; tail forked less than one inch.

IDENTIFICATION: A small dark swallow with deeply forked tail and reddish-orange underparts. Even in the juveniles the tail is more deeply forked than in any other species of swallow.

RANGE: North and South America. Breeds in most parts of North America. Winters from Mexico south to Chile and Argentina.

NESTING: On beams or rafters in barns or old buildings, under bridges, in crevices on cliffs, or in hollow trees; often solitary, sometimes in small groups. Nest, a shallow cup made of mud plastered on a horizontal or vertical surface, always protected from above; lined with grass and feathers. Eggs, 4-6, white marked with shades of brown. Sometimes raises two broods. (Rosebud, June 23. Camrose, August 11.)

REMARKS: Although it is nowhere abundant the barn swallow is widely distributed throughout the province especially in the settled areas. It has extended its breeding range westward in the past few years; recently barn swallows have been found nesting at Johnson's Canyon and Lake Louise in the mountains and at several places in the Peace River District.

This is another species which has found association with mankind so much to its advantage that it is rarely seen far from human habitations. Rural and suburban areas, especially those near streams, are favored, for here are found ideal nesting sites and an abundance of insects flying over stock, gardens or water. Although its name indicates association with but one type of building the barn swallow finds any beamed structure to its liking if there is an opening large enough to permit entrance by direct flight. In towns it may even nest under eaves like the cliff swallow. Graceful in form and flight, soft of voice, and bright in color, it is an attractive guest wherever it locates.

In the fall adults and young mingle on migration sitting on telephone wires for a rest or swooping over a muddy slough for a meal. Often, particularly on cool days, they hawk for insects around cattle and horses darting over and under the grazing animals to snap up the insects which have been disturbed from the grass. Their soft twittering carries but a short distance.

ROUGH-WINGED SWALLOW

BARN SWALLOW

KAY HODGES

CLIFF SWALLOW

C. HAMPSON

PURPLE MARTIN

293

CLIFF SWALLOW   Common Summer Resident.
Petrochelidon pyrrhonota   subsp. (p. 494)   Length 6 in.

DESCRIPTION: Ads.—Forehead white; crown blue-black; black mark from beak to eye; throat and sides of head chestnut extending as a band around hindneck; back blue-black streaked with whitish; rump cinnamon; wings and tail dull brown, tail slightly forked; upper breast and sides buffy-brown with central black mark on breast; rest of underparts white. Sexes alike. Im.—Similar but the blue-black largely replaced by grayish-brown and the chestnut by cinnamon.

IDENTIFICATION: A dark swallow with striking head-markings and slightly forked tail; the cinnamon rump is a good field mark. Nesting habits help to identify.

RANGE: North and South America. Breeds throughout most of North America. Winters in Brazil and Argentina.

NESTING: On cliffs or on the sides of buildings especially under the eaves, in colonies. Using small pellets of mud each pair builds a gourd-like structure whose opening is at the end of a short neck, recurved to prevent the entrance of rain. Hundreds of these may be packed tightly together on the face of the nesting site. Within this mud structure the real nest is built of grass and feathers. Eggs, 4-5, white spotted with light and dark browns. (Calgary, June 23.)

REMARKS: The cliff swallow occurs throughout the province but during the breeding season it is very local. Clusters of nests plastered on the steep banks of rivers and on the walls of canyons and mountains indicate the distribution of the species. Cliff swallows have deserted many of these natural sites, and have established colonies on man-made structures; those on the concrete bridges crossing the Bow river in Calgary and Banff now consist of hundreds of birds. Where houses and schools have been selected the swallows are not always welcomed; parasites from the nests have been known to enter the buildings.

Cliff swallows are highly gregarious at all times of the year. About the middle of May small flocks appear in Alberta, usually feeding in the vicinity of lakes or rivers until they reach their nesting grounds. On calm days they skim the water, often in company with other species of swallows, picking insects from the surface as easily as from the air above. Near a nesting colony, particularly after the young have hatched, there is apparent confusion as scores of parents wheel to and fro, yet each unerringly returns to its own offspring with food. About the middle of July the young are flying and the cliff swallows begin to range farther from their nesting grounds. By the middle of August flocks are on the move again, this time heading southward.

PURPLE MARTIN   Fairly Common Summer Resident.
Progne subis subsp. (p. 494)   Length 8 in.

DESCRIPTION: Ad. m.—Entirely glossy blue-black with purplish reflections except flight feathers and tail which are brownish-black; tail forked about ½ inch. Ad. f. —Above brownish-black with some bluish reflections and a gray band across hindneck; throat, breast and sides sooty-gray; rest of underparts white, most feathers with dark streaks. Im.—Similar to female but duller above and paler below.

IDENTIFICATION: A large swallow with moderately forked tail either entirely black or largely black above and gray below. Males might be confused with blackbirds but their manner of flight is distinctive.

RANGE: North and South America. Breeds from southern Canada through the United States into Mexico. Winters mainly in Brazil.

NESTING: In crevices in cliffs, in holes in trees, in old buildings, or in bird-boxes; usually in small colonies. In Alberta most purple martins nest in martin-houses specially erected for them in towns and cities. Nest of grass and feathers. Eggs, usually 4-5, white. (Edmonton, June 8.)

REMARKS: The purple martin has an irregular distribution in the province; it breeds from Sylvan Lake and Penhold east to the Saskatchewan border and north to Ft. McMurray and the Peace River district. Strangely, although it almost certainly migrates over the southern regions, it has not been found breeding there. Perhaps a few martin-houses in the towns along its route might prove an irresistible attraction.

Purple martins are sociable birds. They prefer to nest in large apartment-type houses providing separate quarters for six or more pairs. Never wandering very far from home they wheel and turn high over the gardens, picking insects from the air with remarkable agility. They have the loudest voice of the swallows but their constant chatter is not objectionable. It is quite distinctive and serves as an excellent means of identification.

When the young are flying well purple martins disappear from urban areas and resort to rural wooded areas where they join those of their brethren which have raised families in this natural habitat. In August mixed companies of adults and young are often seen around woodland lakes. During the day they feed in flight above the tree tops or over water; in the evening they fly in loose flocks to some favorite roosting spot. By early September their flights carry them gradually southward and migration has begun.

CANADA (GRAY) JAY

C. HAMPSON

BLUE JAY

W. A. LEA

296

CROWS, MAGPIES, JAYS — Family Corvidae

The members of this family are large or medium sized birds with stout beaks and feet. Their nostrils are covered with a tuft of bristly feathers. All Alberta species except the crow are non-migratory. They are omnivorous birds; the economic effect of the food habits of some species is the subject of much controversy.

GRAY (CANADA) JAY
Perisoreus canadensis subsp. (p. 494)

Common Resident.
Length 11 in.

DESCRIPTION: Plumage soft and fluffy. Beak smaller than in other jays. Ads.—Front half of crown white, shading back into a black band across hindneck; remainder of upperparts smoky-gray; throat and cheeks white; rest of underparts light smoky gray. Im.—Much darker and browner; whole crown nearly black; no white anywhere.

IDENTIFICATION: A gray bird with white forehead and black nape; juveniles sooty-brown with black crown. Best identified in the field by habits.

RANGE: Northern states and Canada north to tree limit. Resident throughout range.

NESTING: In trees, usually coniferous. Nest, a bulky mass of twigs, grass and moss with a deep cup lined with feathers and hair. Eggs, 4-6, greenish-gray blotched with browns and lavender, usually laid in March. (Boyle, March 2.)

REMARKS: In the mountains and in the heavily wooded northern parts of the province the Canada jay is a common bird. Periodically, and for no apparent reason, it wanders into the western parklands to spend the winter but by early March it is back again on its nesting grounds.

Canada jay, whiskey jack, or camp robber, no matter by what name they know him, all travellers in the wild unsettled forests and in our mountain parks are familiar with this friendly rogue who does so much to relieve the tedium of camp life. At the sound of the camper's axe or the hunter's rifle he puts in a prompt appearance to claim his share of the lunch or the spoils. Thief he may be about the camp site but most of his pilferings are done in the open, much to the amusement of the camper, and he repays manifold, in cheerfulness and sociability, the food that he borrows.

Appearing out of nowhere gray jays approach and scrutinize an observer in the woods in a manner which raises the question of who is watching whom. Once their curiosity is satisfied however, they disappear as noiselessly as they came. Their flight is soft; their movements quiet and unhurried; nothing is left to reveal their presence except that occasionally, at any season of the year, loud clear calls, less harsh and more varied than those of the blue jay, tell that gray jays are in the vicinity.

CROWS, MAGPIES, JAYS — Family Corvidae

BLUE JAY

Fairly Common Resident.

Cyanocitta cristata subsp. (p. 495)

Length 12 in.

DESCRIPTION: Ads.—Head with conspicuous crest; upperparts blue with purplish tinge on back; wings bright blue barred with black, a bar on wing and tips of secondaries white; tail bright blue tipped with white, most feathers barred with black; face and throat white or pale gray bounded by a black line extending from behind ears down across breast; rest of underparts smoky-gray shading to white on the abdomen. Im.—Similar but duller and markings less definite.

IDENTIFICATION: A blue bird with a conspicuous crest; shows much white on wings and tail in flight. Much larger than the mountain bluebird.

RANGE: United States and southern Canada east of the Rockies. Resident throughout range.

NESTING: In trees, usually conifers in Alberta. Nest, a bulky mass of twigs, bark, moss, rags and wool lined with fine rootlets. (Edmonton, May 11.)

REMARKS: The blue jay breeds in central Alberta from about Red Deer to Ft. McMurray and the Peace River District. In recent years it has reappeared in the Calgary-Cochrane-Okotoks areas, a region from which it has been largely absent for three or four decades. It does not occur in the mountains although there is a single record from Gorge Creek. On the prairies it has been recorded at several places including Craigmyle, Sullivan Lake, Beynon and Brooks.

During the summer the blue jay is a quiet, wary bird which keeps to the confines of leafy trees and thickets. At this season it has the bad habit, common to all members of the family, of eating the eggs and young of small birds. Insects, seeds, berries and carrion are also included in the diet. It is remarkable that, with such omnivorous habits and so few apparent enemies, blue jays have never become numerous in Alberta.

Their nesting duties over, blue jays show all the traits usually associated with their name; they become inquisitive, mischievous, quarrelsome and talkative. In winter they frequent farmsteads and even enter towns and cities. Scraps of meat and suet will bring them to the feeding shelf where their bright colors and saucy behavior make them interesting visitors. Sunflower seeds are an irresistible attraction. Even better are a few sunflower heads left standing in the garden or tied to a tree where the jays must perform gymnastics to extract the kernels. When undisturbed they feed with their crests down but at the slightest alarm up go the crests and away go the jays.

CROWS, MAGPIES, JAYS — Family Corvidae

STELLER'S JAY   Scarce Resident..
Cyanocitta stelleri   subsp. (p. 495)   Length 13 in.

DESCRIPTION: A conspicuous crest on head; whole of head and neck black with a few light blue feathers on forehead; upper back black; lower back, wings and tail dark blue, some feathers faintly barred with black; throat and foreneck black; rest of underparts dark blue.

IDENTIFICATION: Resembles a blue jay in size and behavior but very dark blue with black head; shows no white in flight. A mountain species.

RANGE: North and Central America in the western mountain regions from Alaska south to Nicaragua and Guatemala. Resident throughout range.

NESTING: In coniferous trees. Nest, a bulky mass of twigs, bark and dead leaves cemented with mud and lined with fine rootlets. Eggs, 3-5, pale bluish-green irregularly marked with browns.

REMARKS: Not a great deal is known of the status of Steller's jay in Alberta. It occurs during the breeding season in Waterton Lakes National Park but no nest has been found. It is probably resident in the western parts of our mountains for it is seen fairly regularly in Banff and Jasper Parks and is quite common on the B.C. side of the Rockies. Occasionally in fall and winter individuals wander eastward. There are a few records of the occurrence of Steller's jay at this season as far east as Glenevis, Whitecourt, the Swan Hills, Cochrane and Edmonton.

Steller's jay frequents coniferous forests at altitudes of 4000 feet or more during the summer. Secretive and wary at this season it is a difficult bird to locate or approach. During the winter, perhaps emboldened by hunger, it often appears around settlements at lower altitudes. In voice and in general behavior Steller's jay is quite similar to the blue jay.

Jays are the busy-bodies of the woods. If a horned owl sleeps against the trunk of a spruce or a coyote stretches out in a small sunny glade the jays are the first to find him and the first to declaim in loud voice that there is a villain about. Within a few minutes all the jays within hearing have joined in the clamor to drive the marauder from the vicinity or, if he won't move, to make his life miserable until they tire of the sport. Yet Steller's jay is not above a little marauding himself; on his nest-robbing forays none can be quieter nor can anyone appear more self-righteous when caught in the act.

BLACK-BILLED MAGPIE

Common Resident.

Pica pica subsp. (p. 495)

Length 18-22 in.

DESCRIPTION: Glossy jet black except white on lower breast and abdomen, white tertiaries which form a V on the back when at rest, and white inner webs of flight feathers not visible except in flight; lower back grayish; tail almost as long as body, outer feathers shorter than middle and graded in length; black on head and back has bluish iridescence, on wings and tail a coppery iridescence; beak and legs black; iris brown. Sexes alike.

IDENTIFICATION: The long tail and the contrasting black and white colors are so distinctive that the magpie can be confused with no other bird.

RANGE: Western North America. Resident from Alaska and southern Saskatchewan south to New Mexico and eastern California. Wanders erratically, especially in fall and winter.

NESTING: In trees and bushes. Nest, a large domed structure made of twigs with one or more entrances in sides; the real nest within this is a cup of grasses set in mud, sparingly lined with grass and rootlets. Eggs, 6-9, usually 8, greenish-gray blotched with brown. (Drumheller, April 15.)

REMARKS: The magpie is resident in most parts of the province except the far north. Its range includes the foothills, the lower mountain passes, the parklands and those parts of the prairies where a bush in a shelter-belt or coulee is large enough to support its nest. It was not always so numerous nor so widely distributed; during the period 1892-1911 Frank Farley saw only two magpies in the Red Deer-Lacombe district.

Its liking for flesh, living or dead, has brought upon the magpie the anger of both sportsman and farmer. The eggs and young of wild and barnyard fowl are a favorite food in early summer when the magpie has several young of its own to feed. The effect of this food preference upon game bird populations has been hotly debated. In weighing the economic importance of the magpie its value as a scavenger and an insectivore must not be overlooked. Sporadic campaigns against the magpie have not resulted in any appreciable decrease in its numbers and may actually have hastened an extension of its range. They have also demonstrated that here is a species which can thrive in the face of persecution.

Regardless of its reputation the magpie is a beautiful and interesting member of our birdlife. It is justifiably wary of mankind and almost impossible of approach except when nesting. But if an observer will remain well hidden he may be fortunate enough to see the antics of a magpie at play and hear its repertoire of "soft-talk" as it goes unconcernedly about its business, and this will give him a new outlook on the species.

STELLER'S JAY

BLACK-BILLED MAGPIE

301

CROWS, MAGPIES, JAYS — Family Corvidae

COMMON RAVEN   Fairly Common Resident.
Corvus corax   subsp. (p. 495)   Length 24-27 in.

DESCRIPTION: Entirely glossy jet black with purplish iridescence on upperparts; feathers of throat and upper breast somewhat elongated and pointed; legs and beak black; iris brown. Immature birds are duller and lack the gloss.

IDENTIFICATION: Similar to the crow but much larger and with pointed feathers on throat; beak stouter than the crow's. Flies more leisurely than the crow and often soars. The note is a hoarse, guttural croak.

RANGE: Northern parts of northern hemisphere. In North America from Labrador and Alaska south to northern states; in mountains south to Central America. Resident throughout range.

NESTING: In trees or on cliffs. Nest, a mass of sticks and twigs lined with grass and bark. Eggs, 4-7, greenish blotched with brown.

REMARKS: During the breeding season the raven is an inhabitant of the wild unsettled forests of the northern part of the province. It is also seen regularly, but in varying abundance, on the eastern slopes of the mountains where it undoubtedly breeds although no nests have yet been found. In winter it appears around the northern settlements feeding on carrion and refuse of all sorts. At this season it regularly gets as far south as Lac La Biche and Athabasca. Occasionally it wanders much farther; during mild winters it has been seen in the Edmonton and Mundare districts and in August, 1965, one was seen near Pigeon Lake.

While with us in the winter the raven is an unsuspicious bird which responds readily to friendly overtures and becomes a regular visitor at those farmsteads where it may feed unmolested. But on its nesting grounds it is an entirely different bird, wary, secretive, and destructive. To satisfy the voracious appetites of its growing young it takes the eggs and young of other birds and even kills small mammals. These are added to the usual diet of carrion, insects, seeds and berries.

In our Rocky Mountain National Parks ravens occur at all seasons of the year. They are seen to best advantage in the winter when a dozen or more may congregate daily at the carcass of a winter-killed elk until, with the aid of coyotes and other mammalian scavengers, they have reduced it to a mass of bare bones. When disturbed they rise with heavy wing beats and disappear into the woods protesting the intrusion occasionally with various croaking tones quite unlike the repetitious cawing of the crow. In summer they retreat into the solitudes to raise their brood and the tourist who never gets far from his car will not likely see them.

CROWS, MAGPIES, JAYS — Family Corvidae

COMMON CROW Common Summer Resident.
Corvus brachyrhynchos subsp. (p. 495) Length 17-20 in.

DESCRIPTION: Entirely glossy jet black with some purplish iridescence on upperparts; beak and feet black; iris brown. Immature birds are duller and less glossy.

IDENTIFICATION: Not likely to be confused with any species but the raven. In the field the two species can be separated only by size, which is a poor criterion, and by voice. Crows do not winter in Alberta; ravens do. In the hand the crow lacks pointed feathers on the throat and breast.

RANGE: North America. Breeds throughout except in the arctic. Resident over most of its range but migrates from northern parts to south of Canadian border except in Ontario and B.C. Young birds banded in Alberta have been shot in Kansas and Oklahoma.

NESTING: In trees or bushes. Nest, a bulky structure of twigs lined with bark, grasses, and rootlets. Eggs, 4-7, greenish or bluish blotched with brown. (Strathmore, May 17.)

REMARKS: As a breeding bird the crow is found in all parts of the province but it is very local in the northern areas and on the prairies. It is more widely distributed as a migrant.

While raising their young, crows are not gregarious. In the fall, however, they assemble in large flocks before migrating south and their evening flights to favorite roosting spots are an impressive sight.

The voracious appetite and omnivorous habits of the crow have brought it into direct conflict with man's interests. The farmer objects to the destruction of his crops and the sportsman to the destruction of the eggs and young of game birds. That they consume large numbers of cutworms, wireworms, grasshoppers, and noxious weeds is usually overlooked. Whether the harm done by the crow outweighs the good is a controversial question whose answer probably varies from district to district. Various methods of control which have been tried in Alberta and elsewhere indicate that the crow cannot be exterminated but that local populations can be kept within reasonable limits. The most expensive, and probably the least effective, of these methods is the bounty system; the most effective methods take advantage of their gregarious behavior during the winter, using explosives to kill them at their roosts.

RAVEN

T. M. SHORTT

COMMON CROW

CLARK'S NUTCRACKER

BLACK-CAPPED CHICKADEE

CROWS, MAGPIES, JAYS — Family Corvidae

CLARK'S NUTCRACKER   Fairly Common Resident.
Nucifraga columbiana   Length 12 in.

DESCRIPTION: General color of body smoky-gray becoming almost white around base of beak; wings jet black except white terminal parts of secondaries which form a large white patch on wing; tail white except two middle feathers which are black; legs and beak black; iris brown. Immature birds duller and with some brown tinge on wings.

IDENTIFICATION: A gray bird about the size and general color of the Canada jay but showing large black and white areas on wings and tail. Tail much shorter and beak much larger than in Canada jay.

RANGE: Western North America. Resident in Rocky Mountains and western ranges from Alaska to Lower California. Wanders erratically in winter.

NESTING: In coniferous trees usually well out on a horizontal limb. Nest, a platform of twigs with a cup lined with conifer needles, grass, and shredded bark. Eggs, usually 2-4, greenish with small spots of brown. A very early nester.

REMARKS: Clark's nutcracker is restricted during the breeding season to the sub-alpine coniferous forests of the mountains. In late fall and winter it descends to lower altitudes, appearing in small groups around the settlements in search of food. In Banff, Clark's nutcrackers share the household garbage with Canada jays. Individuals may wander some distance from the mountains; there are records from the Porcupine Hills, Beaverlodge, and Belvedere. The species occurs on the Saskatchewan side of the Cypress Hills and may be expected on the Alberta side.

As the nutcracker moves about the tree tops high on the mountain side its long beak and the undulating flight from tree to tree may give the general impression of a woodpecker, but its crow-like shape, its raucous voice, and its curiosity mark it as a member of the Corvidae. It is fond of circling out over the valley with widespread wings and tail and performing peculiar aerial gyrations before dropping into the forest below. In the wilds it is rather wary and difficult of approach yet, particularly in the National Parks it responds readily to friendly overtures and soon learns to accept the camper's offerings of food. Under these circumstances Clark's nutcracker shows by its general behavior its close relationship to the jays. In summer insects form a large part of the food but at other seasons carrion, berries, and the seeds of conifers are its mainstay. Its name is derived from its dexterity in opening cones and nuts to get at the seeds within.

CHICKADEES — Family Paridae

Chickadees belong to a family widely distributed in the northern hemisphere whose members are known in the British Isles as titmice. Small size, short rounded wings, fairly long tails, short stout beaks, and fluffy plumage are characteristic of the chickadees. They are active, inquisitive, friendly birds, mostly gregarious after the mating season. None of our species is brightly colored.

BLACK-CAPPED CHICKADEE
Parus atricapillus subsp. (p. 495)

Common Resident.
Length 5¼ in.

DESCRIPTION: Crown and hindneck jet black; back bluish-gray; wings and tail brownish-gray, the edges of the secondaries white forming a narrow white streak along wing; sides of neck and face below eye white; throat black; rest of underparts white but sides tinged with buff. Sexes alike.

IDENTIFICATION: A small fluffy gray bird with broad white face-mark separating black crown and throat.

RANGE: North America. Breeds from tree limit in north to south central states. Largely resident wherever found.

NESTING: In holes in rotting stumps or trees, usually only a few feet from ground. Nest of grass warmly lined with rabbit hair. Eggs, 6-9, white speckled with brown. (Camrose, May 10.)

REMARKS: The black-capped chickadee breeds in all parts of the province but is scarce in the mountains and on the prairies where it is restricted to the more thickly wooded coulees and river valleys. In summer when the woods are full of birds black-capped chickadees are inconspicuous members of the throng, but when their more colorful fellows have retreated to warmer climates and the verdure has gone from the trees their busy ways and cheery calls become noticeable. Clearly whistled notes, *chick-a-dee-dee-dee,* announce their passage through the woods. Busily they search each tiny crevice in the bark, hanging sideways or upside down to peer beneath a branch, or hammering like woodpeckers to get at some well lodged insect. Gradually they pass through the trees but in an hour or so they, or another group, will be back in the same area again in the never-ending search for food. Around settlements they are frequent visitors at the winter feeding shelf, sharing suet and marrow bones with the downy woodpeckers. What they lack in color they make up in irrepressible good spirits.

MOUNTAIN CHICKADEE

BOREAL CHICKADEE

MOUNTAIN CHICKADEE
Parus gambeli subsp. (p. 495)

Fairly Common Resident.
Length 5 in.

DESCRIPTION: Crown and hindneck jet black except a narrow white line over the eye; rest of upperparts smoky-gray, darkest on wings and tail; face and sides of neck white; throat black; underparts and sides white tinged with gray. Sexes alike.

IDENTIFICATION: Similar to black-capped chickadee but grayer and with definite white streak above eye and no light streak on wing. A mountain species.

RANGE: Western North America. Breeds in the mountain regions from northern B.C. to California and southwestern Texas. Largely resident throughout range..

NESTING: In natural cavities in trees or in old woodpecker holes, usually only a few feet above ground. Nest of mosses lined with fur and hair. Eggs, 6-12, white, unmarked or faintly spotted with reddish-brown. Two broods may be raised in one year. (Jasper, May 25, June 30.)

REMARKS: During the breeding season the mountain chickadee inhabits the coniferous forests high in the mountains, leaving the valleys largely to the black-capped chickadee. In winter it descends to lower altitudes and may even wander out into the foothills; it has been observed in spruce trees along the Bow River near Calgary and has been taken in spruce woods near Edmonton.

In our mountain parks mountain chickadees are usually found in coniferous woods. They often associate with the black-capped and brown-headed chickadees for all chickadees are sociable birds seldom found alone. In these mixed flocks the mountain chickadees are not conspicuous either in numbers or behavior. As the flock works it way through the trees, however, there is ample time to notice differences in voice and the mountain chickadees may identify themselves before they are seen. Their notes have something of a guttural quality, not as pleasing as those of the black-caps nor as wheezy as those of the brown-headed chickadees. It is remarkable that, especially on a wintery day, all chickadees look as cheery as they sound. Keeping mainly to the crowns of coniferous trees they pass slowly through the forest in loose flocks. Each bird is constantly on the move flitting from branch to branch and from tree to tree, yet somehow the flock keeps together. It is not a quiet group. Long after the bustling forms have disappeared from sight through the woods their cheerful twitter comes floating back to the ears. In an hour or so the whole flock may be back travelling this time in the opposite direction and thus they work back and forth through a territory which may support them for several weeks.

309

CHICKADEES — Family Paridae

BOREAL CHICKADEE
Parus hudsonicus subsp. (p. 495)

Fairly Common Resident.
Length 5¼ in.

DESCRIPTION: Crown, hindneck and back ashy-brown; wings and tail brownish-gray; throat black; face under eye white shading to gray on ears and sides of neck; sides reddish-brown; breast and abdomen dull white. Sexes alike.

IDENTIFICATION: Like a black-capped chickadee but dull brown above and browner on flanks. The white face mark does not extend back onto sides of the neck. The call notes are distinctive.

RANGE: Northern North America. Breeds mainly in northern states and in Canada north to tree limit. Resident throughout range.

NESTING: In holes in trees and stumps. Nest of hair and fur at bottom of cavity. Eggs, 4-9, white with small reddish-brown spots. (Fawcett, May 20.)

REMARKS: The boreal, or brown-headed, chickadee prefers dense coniferous and mixed-wood forests and is therefore largely restricted to the northern and western parts of the province. It occurs in small numbers in the mixed woods along the larger rivers of the parklands. It breeds in Jasper and Banff National Parks but has not been recorded from Waterton. There are no records from the Cypress Hills.

If it were not for their wheezy notes, like those of a black-capped chickadee with a cold, the brown-headed chickadees could be easily overlooked as they work their way through the winter forests, for they prefer the higher branches of the coniferous trees where such small forms are not conspicuous. With typical chickadee acrobatics they swing from twig or cone examining every likely spot for hibernating insects. Despite their somewhat dreary vocal efforts they seem as cheerful and happy as the black-capped chickadees which often accompany them. Certainly they are as curious, for the observer who can produce a mouse-like squeak will bring the whole flock into the lower branches peering about for its source.

Chickadees are more or less resident throughout much of their range but in the mountains there is often a seasonal movement from high to lower altitudes in the fall with a reversal of direction in the spring. This usually results in fall and winter concentrations of chickadees in the lower valleys especially those with mild climates. The mountain valleys of western Alberta through which warm chinook winds sweep periodically are excellent wintering spots for boreal chickadees. In Banff and Jasper National Parks visitors should have no difficulty in finding boreal chickadees either in summer or winter.

310

NUTHATCHES — Family Sittidae

Nuthatches are small woodland birds with long beaks, short strong legs, and short tails. They creep about on the trunks and branches of trees, moving head downwards, sideways, or upwards with equal ease. Although they eat insects, their main food is seeds and nuts; in fact their name is derived from a habit of poking a nut into crevice and then 'hatching' or hacking it open.

WHITE-BREASTED NUTHATCH
Sitta carolinensis subsp. (p. 495)

Scarce Resident.
Length 6 in.

DESCRIPTION: Beak nearly as long as head. Ad. m.—Crown, hindneck and upper back glossy black; rest of upperparts dull blue with some black streaks on wings; tail feathers bluish-gray, all except middle pair with large white terminal patches; face and underparts white except some rusty in flanks and under tail. Ad. f.—Similar but duller and more rusty on sides.

IDENTIFICATION: Larger than red-breasted nuthatch; face entirely white with no strong black line from beak through eye. The pure white face is the only distinctive feature since some plumages may show a definite pinkish tinge on the underparts.

RANGE: North America. Resident in most of southern Canada, the United States and Mexico.

NESTING: In holes in trees. Nest of bark, grass, and hair. Eggs, 6-9, white marked with brown and lilac.

REMARKS: Information sent by many observers in response to an appeal in the first edition of this book has clarified considerably the status and the range limits of the white-breasted nuthatch in Alberta. It is now apparent that the species occurs regularly in small numbers in the west-central part of the province bounded by Calgary, Red Deer, Edmonton and Athabasca on the east and by Dickson, Pigeon Lake, Glenevis and Flatbush on the west. Most observations have been made during late fall and winter but there are enough summer sightings to indicate that the white-breasted nuthatch probably breeds locally within this area and there is one definite nesting record. Observations of the species outside this area are few and far between; it has been seen as far north as Salt Prairie near Grouard, and south as far as the Oldman River near Lethbridge.

The white-breasted nuthatch is similar in habits to its red-breasted relative but it is a bulkier bird looking almost as large as a downy wood-pecker as it works its way down the trunk of a dead poplar. It shows a decided preference for deciduous woods rather than conifers and the two species of nuthatch are, therefore, unlikely to be found together. The call, a sharp *quank, quank,* louder and less nasal than that of the red-breasted nuthatch, first attracts the observer's attention and since the bird often works at low levels and is not particularly wary it will probably allow close examination.

311

NUTHATCHES — Family Sittidae

RED-BREASTED NUTHATCH Fairly Common Summer Resident.
Sitta canadensis Length 5½ in.

DESCRIPTION: Ad. m.—Crown and nape black; rest of upperparts dull blue; central pair of tail feathers dull blue, outer ones black with white spots near ends; head below crown white except a black line from beak through eye becoming very broad on sides of neck and fading into back; chin dull white; rest of underparts cinnamon or rusty. Ad. f.—Similar but black on head replaced by blue-gray and underparts paler.

IDENTIFICATION: A small creeping woodland bird mostly bluish above and buffy below. Distinguished from white-breasted nuthatch by strong dark line through eye and along sides of neck with definite white line immediately above it. In the field the note is distinctive.

RANGE: North America. Breeds from Alaska through forests of Canada and northern states south in the Rockies to California.. Winters from southern Canada through United States.

NESTING: In holes in trees or stumps. Nest of grass. Eggs, 4-7, white with spots of brown and lavender. (Lake Wabamun, June 5.)

REMARKS: The red-breasted nuthatch breeds throughout the wooded areas of the province. In the south it is usually seen as a migrant in the more heavily wooded coulees and river valleys. Small numbers remain over winter in the protection of coniferous bluffs.

A soft nasal, *nyaa, nyaa,* from the upper levels of the forest canopy is often the only indication that red-breasted nuthatches are in the vicinity, for although they are rarely still they are difficult to see. Mouse-like they creep along the limbs, well hidden in the crown of a conifer and inconspicuous even on a bare branch of a poplar. Descending the trunk they come down head first, held only by their strong toes. Their food is largely insects but they also eat the seeds from cones. They may be attracted to winter feeding stations with nuts pressed into holes drilled into a board.

About the middle of April red-breasted nuthatches arrive in central Alberta. They travel in small, loosely-associated groups, often in company with warblers and other arboreal birds but their creeping habits make them less conspicuous than their more active associates. From late August through September they move southward again still keeping well up in the trees and travelling in the same company as in spring. Even later in the year a red-breasted nuthatch or two may accompany a little band of chickadees through the woods, each species searching for the same type of food but going about it in quite different ways.

F. C. HENNESSEY

WHITE-BREASTED NUTHATCH

T. M. SHORTT

RED-BREASTED NUTHATCH

313

CREEPERS — Family Certhidae

Creepers are small woodland birds with slender down-curved beaks. Strong claws and stiff, pointed tailfeathers, as in the woodpeckers, help them to creep about on tree trunks. Only one species of creeper occurs in North America.

BROWN CREEPER
Certhia familiaris subsp. (p. 495)

Scarce Resident.
Length 5½ in.

DESCRIPTION: Ads.—Upperparts, except lower back, dark brown, each feather medially streaked with grayish-white; lower back rusty-brown; faint light streak over eye; underparts white; flanks and under tail coverts may be washed with buff.

IDENTIFICATION: A small grayish-brown bird with light streaks and light brown rump patch; long (½ in.) slender decurved beak. In the field creeping habits help to identify.

RANGE: Northern hemisphere. Various subspecies breed in most of the wooded parts of North America. Largely resident but some migration occurs from the northern part of the range.

NESTING: In cracks in bark or behind a loose piece of bark. Nest of fine twigs, shredded bark, moss and spider web. Eggs, 5-8, white marked with reddish-brown. Two broods are raised in one year. (Glenevis, May 14 and June 20.)

REMARKS: Not a great deal is known of the status of the brown creeper in Alberta. There are no nesting records from south of Edmonton nor from north of Athabasca although it is widely distributed in the coniferous and mixed-wood forests of the northern half of the province and in the mountains. In the mixed woods of the parklands and in the wooded coulees of the prairies it occurs only during the winter.

Small size, subdued colors, soft voice, and creeping habits combine to make the brown creeper one of the most inconspicuous birds in the woods. Lacking the versatility of movement of the nuthatch it spirals slowly upward along the trunk of an evergreen until, having reached the top, it flies down to the base of another tree to start upward again. Although constantly on the move, it so closely resembles a flake of bark that only a keen eye can follow it on the bare trunk; in the dense foliage of the conifers it is lost immediately. Nor can one trust to the ear to detect it for its thin, *sreep,* is so faint that it is lost in the silence of the deep woods before it has travelled a dozen yards.

DIPPERS — Family Cinclidae

Dippers, or water ouzels, are stout-bodied birds with short tails and sturdy legs. Semi-aquatic in habit they wade about in shallow water either partially or completely submerged. Only one species occurs in North America. The name dipper is derived from a habit of bobbing or dipping the whole body up and down by flexing the legs.

DIPPER   Fairly Common Summer Visitor.
Cinclus mexicanus   subsp. (p. 495)   Length 6½ in.

DESCRIPTION: Ads.—Solid dark bluish-gray all over tinged with brown on head and with light feather edges on abdomen; wings and tail darker; eyelids white. Immature birds are usually lighter below and lack brown on head.

IDENTIFICATION: A bird about the size of a robin but with short tail; slate blue with no pattern anywhere.

RANGE: Western mountains of North and Central America. Breeds in mountain regions from Alaska to Guatemala. Winters in this range wherever there is open water.

NESTING: On face of bank near water, behind waterfalls, occasionally in roots of upturned trees, or under bridges. Nest, a large ball of moss completely roofed. Eggs, 3-6, white. (Gorge Creek, June 14.)

REMARKS: During the breeding season the dipper occurs commonly throughout the Rocky Mountain regions. There is a definite migration from the province but a few individuals usually winter near waters kept open by warm springs at Canmore, Banff, Calgary, Sundre and Jasper.

Except during the summer when family groups may be found together dippers are largely solitary in habit. Invariably they are found near water; the shores of mountain lakes or the rocky margins of turbulent mountain rivers and streams are favorite resorts but even quiet pools occasionally attract dippers particularly in winter. A dipper feeding along the shore may wade directly into the water and disappear from view beneath the surface reappearing a few moments later farther downstream. It moves from water to land and back again with apparent unconcern. When disturbed it flies low over the water in a manner reminiscent of the spotted sandpiper and occasionally it dives directly into the water from the air as though to prove its mastery of the elements. The dipper can swim on the surface but its unwebbed feet propel it slowly; under water, however, its wings are brought into play and it pursues insects and minnows with dexterity. During the winter the activities of the dipper are considerably curtailed but when temperatures are well below zero and the snow lies deep a dipper can live through the winter at an ice-free pool showing that his feathers are as impervious to cold as they are to water.

BROWN CREEPER

DIPPER

HOUSE WREN

WINTER WREN

T. M. SHORTT

WRENS — Family Troglodytidae

Wrens are small, short-legged birds with thin pointed beaks. Their short tails are often held forward over their backs. Most species bustle about secretively in tangled vegetation, rarely showing themselves in the open; the rock wren is an exception. All have rollicking songs, loud out of proportion to their size.

HOUSE WREN

Common Summer Resident.

Troglodytes aedon subsp. (p. 495)

Length 4¾ in.

DESCRIPTION: Ads.—Above grayish-brown becoming cinnamon-brown on lower back and tail; dusky bars on wings, back and tail; an indistinct gray line over eye; underparts grayish-white with some fine dusky barring on sides; flanks washed with cinnamon.

IDENTIFICATION: A wren without distinctive markings. Differs from marsh wrens in lacking white streaks on back, from winter wren in having light gray underparts.

RANGE: North America. Breeds in southern half of Canada and throughout the United States. Winters in southern states and Mexico.

NESTING: In cavities in trees or in almost any small enclosure in or around buildings. Nest, a mass of twigs and rubbish filling the cavity except for a small space lined with fluff. Eggs, 6-10, white, thickly speckled with small reddish-brown dots. (Calgary, June 22.)

REMARKS: The house wren breeds throughout the province but is scarce in the mountains and on the prairies. Wherever it lives the house wren likes dense shrubbery from which it can scold with impunity. In the forest any tangled thicket will do; in towns and cities hedges and raspberry patches form attractive cover. When all is clear the wren moves out into the open to explore the garden and feast on cutworms, cabbage worms, and other pests. It is an interesting and saucy little visitor, but the gardener who sets up birdhouses to attract a variety of guests may look with some disfavor on the house wren which, having selected a box to its liking, stuffs all the others full of twigs and refuse. This is usually attributed to selfishness but it is probably merely the expression of a habit, common to most species of wren, of making a number of dummy nests in the vicinity of the real one. Another habit, that of puncturing the eggs of other birds nesting in the neighborhood, is not so readily condoned.

All the movements of the house wren are quick and abrupt. This, combined with its inquisitiveness, creates the impression of a bustling busy-body. It puts as much energy into its singing as it does into everything else; unfortunately its notes are rather harsh and the bubbling song cannot be highly rated.

WRENS — Family Troglodytidae

WINTER WREN
Troglodytes troglodytes subsp. (p. 495)

Scarce Summer Resident.
Length 3½-4 in.

DESCRIPTION: Ads. — Above dark cinnamon-brown, brightest on lower back and tail; wings, back and tail barred with dusky; tail very short; line over eye pale buff; sides of head, neck and wings flecked with white; underparts cinnamon-buff, the sides and abdomen barred with dusky white.

IDENTIFICATION: A very small wren dark brown above, lighter brown below. Like a small house wren but browner above and below.

RANGE: Canada and United States. Breeds in northern stages of Canada and Alaska. Winters in Alaska, southern B.C., and southern states.

NESTING: In crevices in a bank, in roots of an upturned tree, under a log, always close to ground. Nest, a mass of twigs and moss usually with entrance in side. Eggs, 4-7, white with fine spots of reddish-brown.

REMARKS: The winter wren has been recorded from the coniferous forests of the northern half of the province and from various parts of the mountains where it is an uncommon and rather local summer resident. In the woods the winter wren frequents dense undergrowth, the tangled roots and crowns of fallen trees, or the piles of slashings around lumber camps. It is not particularly wary yet it rarely appears in the open. If it were not for its voice this small bird would easily go unnoticed, but in typical wren fashion it harshly scolds an intruder and then bursts into a bubbling, tinkling song which goes on and on as though it would never end. It is one of the finest performers in the woods.

The winter wren spends most of its time on the ground under such a dense tangle of boughs that it is almost impossible for human eyes to follow its activities but, judging from brief glimpses obtained as it scurries from one part of the maze to another, it is one of the busiest birds in the woods. It is always on the move. With short tail cocked over its back it bustles about its business. No crevice or cranny is to small for its diminutive body to squeeze into and no insect is safe from its sharp eyes and pointed beak. Most birds expose themselves at least when they sing but not the winter wren. His song comes from the middle of the tangled brush close to the ground.

In Alberta the name winter wren is misleading. Deep snow makes it impossible for this ground-haunting bird to find sufficient food to stay alive and it does not remain over winter here.

LONG-BILLED MARSH WREN

R. CHANDLER

SHORT-BILLED MARSH WREN

WRENS — Family Troglodytidae

LONG-BILLED MARSH WREN   Fairly Common Summer Resident.
Telmatodytes palustris   subsp. (p. 495)   Length 4¾ in.

DESCRIPTION: Ads.—Crown and nape dark brown; hindneck light brown; upper back dark brown almost black, each feather with a median stripe of white; wings, lower back, and tail light brown, the tail and parts of the wings barred with dark brown; a white line over eye and ear; cheeks and sides of neck buff; underparts white except sides which are washed with cinnamon.

IDENTIFICATION: Dark back with light streaks separate this from all wrens except the short-billed marsh wren; distinguished from last species by strong white line over eye and very dark unstreaked crown.

RANGE: Southern Canada, United States, and Mexico. Winters in all except northern parts of its range.

NESTING: Over water in reeds, rushes, or cattails. Nest, a large globular structure of reeds and coarse grass woven into the leaves of the rushes from one to four feet above water; entrance in the side; several dummy nests are usually made in the vicinity of the one used. Eggs, 6-8, dull brown sprinkled with small dark brown spots. (Hay Lakes, June 15.)

REMARKS: The long-billed marsh wren is found as a breeding bird from the northern border of the province south to about Red Deer. Farther south it is scarce probably because there is little suitable habitat. A colony nests at Lake Newell. The species has not been recorded from the mountains.

Extensive beds of cattails or tules in the shallow margins of lakes and sloughs are the home of the long-billed marsh wren. In their latticed confines it finds seclusion and safety, an excellent supply of insect food, and innumerable nesting sites. Most of the wren's life is spent within a few feet of the water although it makes occasional excursions to the adjacent willow thickets on shore. Its bubbling song is delivered with the same degree of energy that goes into all its movements.

To see the long-billed marsh wren one must go to its haunts and remain motionless until it identifies itself. This usually does not take long since it is an inquisitive bird. A rustling in the cattails, or perhaps the scolding chatter so characteristic of the wrens, marks its progress through the rushes, and soon its little form may be seen scurrying from hiding-place to hiding-place just above the water. Sooner or later it shows itself, tail cocked jauntily over its back, but at the slightest movement it disappears into its reedy jungle. Long-billed marsh wrens stay with us nearly six months. The first migrants arrive in central Alberta about the third week of April; some do not leave until the second week of October.

SHORT-BILLED MARSH WREN

Cistothorus platensis subsp. (p. 495)

Rare Straggler.
Length 4 in.

DESCRIPTION: Ads.—Crown, back, and wings streaked with black, white and buff; forehead and hindneck buffy; rump and tail rusty, the tail barred with black; pale buffy line over eye; underparts white except pale buffy across breast continuing down sides as a cinnamon wash.

IDENTIFICATION: Similar to long-billed marsh wren but with streaked crown, buffy instead of white line over eye, and shorter beak.

RANGE: Eastern North America. Breeds from southern Quebec and Saskatchewan south to central states. Winters in southeastern states and eastern Mexico.

NESTING: In damp meadows and marshes. Nest, a globular mass of grass, reeds, and sedge leaves with entrance in side; attached to grasses within one or two feet of ground. Eggs, 4-8, white, unmarked.

REMARKS: The short-billed marsh wren is a rather common inhabitant of grassy meadows near reedy sloughs in Manitoba and has been observed as far west as Indian Head, Saskatchewan. Little is known of its status in Alberta. On September 19, 1927, a short-billed marsh wren was collected from a company of migrating warblers near Camrose. There are sight records from Elk Island Park, Glenevis, Innisfail, and Huxley. Since this species is quite similar to the long-billed marsh wren identification in the field is extremely difficult for observers who are not well acquainted with both species. Its song however, is distinctive. Near Glenevis short-billed marsh wrens have been seen and heard during the summer and it is believed that they may have nested there.

Although in appearance the two species of marsh wrens are quite similar, in choice of habitat they differ markedly. The long-billed marsh wren is a bird of the bulrushes and cattails which grow in water a foot or so deep; the short-billed marsh wren, however, prefers drier spots where there is little or no standing water but where the ground is damp enough to support good growth of tall grasses and sedges. If a few willows are scattered through the wet meadow they serve as favorite singing perches. This type of habitat is not abundant in Alberta; where it occurs the probability of finding short-billed marsh wrens is greatest and any unusual song should be investigated. Like all of the wrens the short-billed marsh wren is a great skulker. It will not come out into the open but remains in the tangled vegetation where it can see without being seen. However, it cannot remain still very long and a patient observer, by following the movements of the stems, may ultimately get a brief glimpse of this diminutive wren.

WRENS — Family Troglodytidae

ROCK WREN
Salpinctes obsoletus subsp. (p. 495)

Fairly Common Summer Resident.
Length 5½ in.

DESCRIPTION: Ads.—Upperparts brownish-gray indistinctly speckled with dusky brown and light gray; a small cinnamon patch on lower back; middle tailfeathers like back, remainder broadly barred towards tips with black and buff; light stripe over eye; underparts dull white indistinctly streaked with grayish-brown on throat and breast; flanks tinged with cinnamon.

IDENTIFICATION: A fairly large sand-colored wren not likely to be confused with any other bird.

RANGE: Western North America. Breeds in southern parts of Saskatchewan, Alberta and B.C., south through western states to Mexico. Winters in southwestern states and Mexico.

NESTING: In crevices under rocks or in holes in cliffs. Nest, a mass of twigs, grass, hair, and wool filling crevice or end of tunnel. Eggs, 4-10, usually 5-6, white lightly sprinkled with small reddish-brown dots.

REMARKS: As a breeding bird the rock wren is common only in the southern sections of the province, particularly in the valleys and coulees along the Red Deer, South Saskatchewan and Milk River drainage systems. Adults with young have been seen near Cochrane in the foothills. The species has been seen at several places in the mountains as far north as Jasper. Elsewhere in the province there are a few scattered records of the rock wren including one from Ft. Chipewyan.

This large wren is an inhabitant of the badlands and the prairie coulees where its drab colors blend perfectly with the sun baked cliffs. Energetically it bustles about on the rough clay banks poking its way in and out of innumerable holes and crevices. One of these will be selected as its home and the entrance will be paved with small flat stones; the rest are merely places where a good meal of insects may lie hidden. When the heat of the day is not too intense the rock wren pauses on some favorite promontory and sends out a long series of loud notes and trills quite unlike the song of any other desert bird yet sufficiently wren-like to make it recognizable to the initiate.

In the valleys and coulees of the semi-arid regions of southern Alberta those slopes which face north or east and are therefore protected from the hottest rays of the summer sun, are often wooded whereas the other slopes, dried by summer heat, are bare and precipitously eroded. Thus two extremes of habitat face each other only a few yards apart. In the former live orange-crowned and yellow warblers, brown thrashers, towhees and house wrens; the latter is home to prairie falcons, ferruginous hawks, Say's phoebes and rock wrens. Rarely indeed is there any trespass; rock wrens keep to the bare slopes as closely as towhees keep to the thickets. To follow the rock wren on the treacherous clay cliffs is next to impossible; wise observers will use powerful binoculars from the shade of the woods.

MOCKINGBIRDS, THRASHERS — Family Mimidae

The members of this family are perching birds of medium size with relatively long tails and beaks. Shy and retiring by nature they skulk in the bushes, appearing in the open only to dash from one thicket to another. They are fine songsters and great mimics.

MOCKINGBIRD
Mimus polyglottos subsp. (p. 495)

Rare Straggler.
Length 10-11 in.

DESCRIPTION: Ads.—Above ash-gray; wings darker with a white bar and with a white patch at the base of the primaries; middle tailfeathers brownish-black, outer ones mainly white; underparts grayish-white; iris yellow.

IDENTIFICATION: Might be confused with Townsend's solitaire but very light below, more white in tail, white in wing, and iris yellow.

RANGE: United States, Mexico, West Indies; occurs regularly in Canada only in extreme southern Ontario. Straggler in southern prairie provinces and B.C. Largely non-migratory.

NESTING: In trees or shrubs, often around human dwellings. Nest of twigs lined with grass and rootlets. Eggs, 3-6, bluish- or greenish-white blotched with brown. (Provost, July 10.)

REMARKS: The first recorded occurrence of the mockingbird in Alberta was in 1928 when a pair nested in a spruce tree at Didsbury and raised a brood of three. In 1964 a pair of mockingbirds nested successfully at Provost; one of these birds appears in the photograph on page 325. These are the only nesting records for the province. Mockingbirds have been observed at Huxley on two occasions. At Beynon the species was seen on June 10, 1939, and on May 23, 1959. A mockingbird was seen in Calgary on Nov. 10, 1956, and in Okotoks about two weeks later. On Nov. 21, 1964, one was seen about ten miles northwest of Pigeon Lake. These last birds must have withstood some rather severe cold but the hardiest mockingbird stayed in Calgary from early December, 1958, until January 26, 1959, during which time it survived temperatures as low as −25°F. It fed largely on berries.

The mockingbird is intolerant of intrusion into its territory and will attack birds and mammals much larger than itself. Less seclusive than other members of the family it is often seen in the open. While the colors of the mockingbird do not catch the eye, the quality of its voice and the great variety of its notes usually attract attention. In a family of fine songsters it is the most brilliant performer. As a mimic it is unsurpassed; a mockingbird has been heard to imitate 32 different birds within the space of 10 minutes.

ROCK WREN

MOCKINGBIRD

C. HAMPSON

MOCKINGBIRDS, THRASHERS — Family Mimidae

CATBIRD
Dumetella carolinensis

Common Summer Resident.
Length 8½ in.

DESCRIPTION: Ads.—Crown and nape black; rest of body and wings dark slate-gray, a little darker above than below; flight feathers very dark; tail black; under tail coverts chestnut.

IDENTIFICATION: A trim slate-gray bird with black cap and fairly long black tail. The reddish-brown patch under the tail is difficult to see but is distinctive.

RANGE: Southern Canada south to Central America. Breeds throughout most of United States and southern Canada. Winters in southern states, Mexico and Central America.

NESTING: In hedges, shrubs, or bushes, usually not more than 6 ft. above the ground. Nest of twigs, grass, and rootlets, lined with shreds of bark, cotton, horsehair, string, etc.; well hidden in dense foliage. Eggs, 2-5, deep greenish-blue. (Wetaskiwin, June 17.)

REMARKS: Except on the open prairies the catbird breeds commonly throughout the southern half of the province. It becomes progressively less abundant north of Edmonton and has not been recorded north of Lesser Slave Lake and Cold Lake.

The catbird occurs in city parks, in prairie coulees, on forest edges, wherever there are thickets or dense undergrowth to give it seclusion. Berry patches and hedges are favorite spots since they provide both excellent cover and a good supply of berries and insects for food. Like other members of the family the catbird is more often heard than seen. The familiar harsh *meee-euw* from which its name is derived is the least attractive of its vocal efforts for it is a fine songster and an adept mimic. The prolonged medley of rich notes is similar to the song of the brown thrasher but the phrases are not repeated and often a discordant *mew* is thrown in to identify the singer.

The migration of such secretive species as the catbird is never obvious but an alert observer may notice that catbirds are more abundant than usual in the third week of August and that they are rarely seen after the first week of September. During this period the fall migration is in full swing. In spring catbirds are among the last birds to arrive. They reach central Alberta during the last two or three days of May. Once here, however, they establish themselves quickly for nests with eggs can be found about the middle of June.

326

MOCKINGBIRDS, THRASHERS — Family Mimidae

BROWN THRASHER   Fairly Common Summer Resident.
Toxostoma rufum   subsp. (p. 496)   Length 11 in.

DESCRIPTION: Ads.—Upperparts light reddish-brown; two white wing bars; underparts white or buffy-white, heavily streaked on breast and sides with dark brown; tail and beak long; iris yellow.

IDENTIFICATION: Not likely to be confused with any other species; the bright reddish-brown upperparts are very noticeable in the field.

RANGE: Southern Canada and the United States east of the Rockies. Breeds throughout range. Winters in southern states.

NESTING: In thickets, bushes, shrubs or small trees; sometimes on the ground. Nest of twigs, dead leaves, grass and rootlets. Eggs, 4-5, white or bluish-white spotted with brown. (Rosebud, June 7.)

REMARKS: The brown thrasher, always a fairly common breeding bird in the river valleys and coulees of southern Alberta, has been extending its range in recent years. It was unknown at Hardisty before 1925; today it nests regularly in that district. It first appeared in the Edmonton area about 1953. Along the eastern border of the province brown thrashers have moved northward and now nest as far north as Cold Lake. A recent westward extension of range has brought the species into the Calgary district and to the edge of the foothills at Cochrane and Priddis. There are no records from the mountains.

The brown thrasher frequents dense thickets, thorn brakes, and hedges where it may skulk without being seen. Its secretive habits are no doubt the reason that the thrasher is so little known even in those districts where it occurs regularly. In early summer, however, a rich medley of notes may direct the eye to a bright brown songster perched on an exposed twig in a little copse. Its sleek form ends in a long tail which hangs straight down as though too heavy to support. Its bright yellow eye is alert for danger. The brown thrasher is too restless to stay in one place very long and, whether alarmed or not, it soon slips quietly into the thicket and is lost to view. A few minutes later its song may be heard from another bush a hundred yards or so away. The song is distinctive; in quality and tone it is similar to the catbird's but each phrase is repeated, *drop-it, drop-it, cover-it-up, cover-it-up, pull-it-up, pull-it-up, eat-it, eat-it, . . .* , on and on, tirelessly and with variations. Like Browning's wise thrush,

> ". . . he sings each song twice over,
> Lest you should think he never could recapture
> The first fine careless rapture."

C. HAMPSON

CATBIRD

F. C. HENNESSEY

BROWN THRASHER

SAGE THRASHER

W. RAY SALT

ROBIN

SAGE THRASHER
Oreoscoptes montanus

Rare Straggler.
Length 9 in.

DESCRIPTION: Ads.—Upperparts light brownish-ash indistinctly streaked with brownish-gray; wings darker with two narrow white bars; tail dark grayish-brown, the outer feathers broadly, the inner ones narrowly, tipped with white; underparts buffy-white tinged with cinnamon on sides and streaked with dark brown on sides of neck, breast, and sides; iris yellow.

IDENTIFICATION: Like a small, pale brown thrasher. In flight long tail appears dark tipped with a wedge of white on each side.

RANGE: Western North America and Mexico. Breeds from southern B.C. and Saskatchewan south to California. Winters in southwestern states and Mexico.

NESTING: In sagebush or other bushes usually not more than two feet from the ground. Nest, a bulky mass of twigs lined with grasses, wool, or horsehair. Eggs, 4-6, greenish-blue thickly spotted with chestnut.

REMARKS: There are few records of the sage thrasher in Alberta: one was seen near Orion in 1924; a singing male was collected near Walsh on June 15, 1940; an adult female was taken near Calgary on May 23, 1957; and one was seen near Drumheller on August 30, 1958. The species occurs in the dry valleys of southern B.C. and has become established in southern Saskatchewan within the past thirty years. It is possible that the sage thrasher is extending its range into Alberta as its habitat in its former range is destroyed.

Sage thrashers are birds of the sage-covered plains although they do not hesitate to seek food and cover in brushy valleys and hillsides. The abundant insect life in these places forms their staple food but berries and small fruits are occasionally eaten. Preferring to run and hide rather than take flight sage thrashers spend most of their time close to the ground. In spring, however, the males mount to the top of a bush and in typical thrasher manner, with bodies erect and tail hanging straight downward, they sing a medley of musical whistles and trills which may last for over two minutes.

THRUSHES — Family Turdidae

Thrushes are woodland birds but the robin and bluebird often live around human habitations. The young of all thrushes have dark spots or bars on light underparts and light streaks on dark upperparts. It is in the juvenile plumage that the robin, the bluebird, and Townsend's solitaire best show their relationship to the other thrushes.

ROBIN Common Summer Resident.
Turdus migratorius subsp. (p. 496) Length 10 in.

DESCRIPTION: Ad. m.—Upperparts dark slate-gray, almost black on head and tail; throat white with heavy black streaks; rest of underparts reddish-chestnut except white on abdomen and under tail coverts; outer tail feathers tipped with white; beak yellow, dusky at tip. Ad. f.—Similar but duller on breast and head. Immature birds are similar but have heavily spotted breasts and light streaks on many feathers of back.

IDENTIFICATION: Dark gray back and reddish-orange breast make the robin unmistakable.

RANGE: North and Central America. Breeds in most of United States and Canada north to tree limit. Winters from southern Canada to Guatemala.

NESTING: In trees, in bird boxes, or in almost any position around buildings. Nest of coarse grass, weeds, and straw, bound together with mud and lined with fine grasses. Eggs, 3-5, greenish-blue. Robins often raise two broods in a season. (Edmonton, May 17 - July 6.)

REMARKS: The robin occurs throughout the province in a variety of habitats. In the settled areas it is most commonly seen around gardens, parks, and farmsteads; in the wilderness it shows a preference for the vicinity of water. It was one of the most abundant breeding songbirds on the Athabasca delta in 1939.

The robin is the harbinger of spring. Other birds may arrive earlier but the cheery *chirrup* of the robin early in April is a prophecy of green grass and crocuses. Although earthworms and insects form much of the robin's food his liking for strawberries and other small fruits makes him unwelcome around the garden at times. Protection of the fruit crop with screens is sometimes necessary. Late in the fall as flocks of robins move slowly southward through the woods they fatten on the frost-nipped wild berries. Occasionally individuals remain in Alberta until after the New Year; only rarely do they survive the winter.

ALLAN BROOKS

VARIED THRUSH
male

T. M. SHORTT

HERMIT THRUSH

332

THRUSHES — Family Turdidae

VARIED THRUSH　　　　　　　　Scarce Summer Resident.
Ixoreus naevius　subsp. (p. 496)　　　　　　　Length 10 in.

DESCRIPTION:　Ad. m.—Crown and sides of head dark slate-gray or dull black except a narrow cinnamon streak extending from over eye to side of neck; remainder of upperparts dark slate-gray; wings dark brownish-gray with two cinnamon wing bars and many flight feathers edged with cinnamon; tail dark brownish-gray, the outer two pairs of feathers splashed with white at tips; throat and breast reddish-cinnamon with a narrow black band across upper breast; rest of underparts cinnamon with much gray on sides and white on abdomen. Ad. f.— Similar but duller.

IDENTIFICATION:　Like a robin but with much tawny in the wings and with black band across breast.

RANGE:　Western North America. Breeds from Alaska to California from the Rocky Mountains to the Pacific coast. Winters throughout this range but only a few individuals remain in the more northerly areas.

NESTING:　In trees, especially conifers. Nest of twigs and mosses bound with mud and lined with grass and shredded bark. Eggs, 2-5, greenish-blue with a few small spots of brown.

REMARKS: This is a mountain species which appears on the prairies only as an accidental straggler well off its usual migration route. As a breeding bird it occurs in the Rocky Mountains from the international boundary to north of Jasper. There is recent evidence that it nests about 35 miles south of Grande Prairie.

The varied thrush is easily mistaken for a robin, which it resembles in both habits and color. However, it is more of a woodland bird keeping pretty much to the depths of the coniferous forest. It feeds commonly on the ground as well as in the trees. It lacks the friendly confidence of the robin and is difficult to approach. Watch for it near damp trails through dense evergreens in our Rocky Mountain National Parks and listen for its notes, an unmusical attempt at a song, quite unlike the cheery tune of the robin.

Like other thrushes the varied thrush scratches among the dead leaves, turning them over to get at the insects beneath. When berries ripen, however, it is commonly found in trees and bushes feasting on soft fruits. The varied thrush is an early spring migrant which sometimes arrives in the Banff area in March. In the fall it may not leave until early October. It is during migration periods that varied thrushes are occasionally seen east of their usual mountain haunts.

THRUSHES — Family Turdidae

HERMIT THRUSH   Common Summer Resident.
Hylocichla guttata subsp. (p. 496)   Length 7 in.

DESCRIPTION: Ads.—Upperparts dark olive-brown except rump and tail which are reddish-brown; ring around eye light gray; underparts white streaked with dark brown on upper breast; sides light olive. Sexes alike.

IDENTIFICATION: Similar to olive-backed and gray-cheeked thrushes but with brownish tail. More heavily streaked on breast than veery. In the field most easily identified by song.

RANGE: North and Central America. Breeds in northern states and in Canada from southern Quebec to southern Yukon. Winters mainly in southern states, Mexico and Guatemala.

NESTING: On the ground hidden under low hanging branches or in short undergrowth. Nest of twigs, grass, and moss, lined with fine rootlets and fine plant fibers. Eggs, 3-4, light greenish-blue. (Athabasca, May 25.)

REMARKS: The hermit thrush breeds mainly in the heavily forested areas of the unsettled parts of the province including the mountains and the foothills. Rarely it may nest in the thickly wooded valleys of the parklands as far south as Red Deer. On the prairies and in the Cypress Hills it occurs only as a migrant.

The hermit thrush is a quiet unobtrusive bird usually found on the floor of the forest or in the lower branches of the undergrowth. It remains quite still for long periods as though meditating its next move. Then off it flits through the trees to pose motionless upon another branch. Even when feeding it pauses repeatedly as though alert for signs of danger. Late on a summer evening it identifies itself to the naturalist who may have searched the woods fruitlessly for it all day. Its beautiful flute-like song, *Oh, holy, holy, — ah, purity, purity, — ehh, sweetly, sweetly,* is sung in three parts with long pauses between phrases. The first is low in pitch, the second nearly an octave higher, and the third so thin and high-pitched that it is inaudible at any great distance.

The hermit thrush resembles its more abundant relative the olive-backed thrush in habits as well as appearance. It is most active during the early and late hours of the day. At these times it is more apt to take a higher, more exposed perch where one can see as well as hear it. Yet it does not lose it caution for its slips into the denser foliage at lower levels when approached and, apparently fortified with a sense of security, scolds an intruder with sharp notes, *chuk, chuk.* It takes patience to become well acquainted with the hermit thrush.

334

THRUSHES — Family Turdidae

SWAINSON'S THRUSH
Common Summer Resident.
Hylocichla ustulata subsp. (p. 496)
Length 7 in.

DESCRIPTION: Ads.—Upperparts dark olive; eye-ring buffy; sides of head buffy streaked with olive; throat and breast pale buff, the throat bordered with streaks of dark brown and the breast heavily spotted with dark brown; remainder of underparts white; sides pale olive. Sexes alike.

IDENTIFICATION: Separated from hermit thrush by lack of reddish-brown tail; from veery by more heavily spotted breast. Almost identical to gray-cheeked thrush but has buffy cheeks and a distinct buffy eye-ring.

RANGE: North and South America. Breeds from Alaska to Newfoundland south in the mountains to California and West Virginia. Winters from southern Mexico to Argentina.

NESTING: In trees usually not over 7 ft. from ground. Nest of twigs, grass, and moss lined with dead leaves. Eggs, 3-5, greenish-blue spotted with light brown.

REMARKS: Over most of its range Swainson's thrush is more appropriately called the olive-backed thrush. It breeds in the wooded areas of the province including the mountains and the Cypress Hills. It also nests in parts of the parklands. In the prairie regions, it occurs only on migrations.

During the day the olive-backed thrush spends much of its time on the forest floor searching for insect food. Since it keeps to the cover of the dense woods and rarely utters a sound it is not a conspicuous bird. Whether on the ground or in the trees short spurts of activity are interspersed with periods of motionless attention. But as the sun sets on a quiet summer evening the olive-backed thrush breaks the silence with a sweet clear, *Oh, Aurelia, will ya, will ya,* starting on a low note and spiralling rapidly upward to the end. It is over in a moment, but if the singer is not disturbed the rich performance will be repeated often in the gathering darkness. It sings equally well in the morning; in fact a camper who has pitched a tent near the woods in the Cypress Hills or in most of our National Parks will likely waken on a June morning to a serenade in which olive-backed thrushes take a prominent part.

Anyone who wishes to become well acquainted with these thrushes must be willing to rise early and stay up late. At dawn and again at dusk they are least elusive as well as being most vocal. The dawn period is most pleasant and most rewarding for a great variety of species show to best advantage at this time.

THRUSHES — Family Turdidae

GRAY-CHEEKED THRUSH

Hylocichla minima subsp. (p. 496)

Fairly Common Migrant.
Length 7 in.

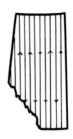

DESCRIPTION: Ads.—Upperparts dark olive; sides of head gray; throat white; breast pale buff; sides of throat streaked and breast spotted with dark brown; rest of underparts white shaded with light olive on sides. Sexes alike.

IDENTIFICATION: Distinguished from hermit thrush by lack of brown tail; from veery by more heavily spotted breast. Colors and markings exactly like those of olive-backed thrush but sides of head gray and distinct eye-ring absent. Does not occur in Alberta during nesting season.

RANGE: Northeastern Asia, North America, and northern South America. Breeds from northeastern Siberia and Alaska across Northwest Territories into Nova Scotia and northeastern United States. Winters in northern South America.

NESTING: In evergreens or in dwarf willows and alders along arctic streams. Nest of finely woven grass, leaves, and shredded bark. Eggs, 3-5, light greenish-blue sparingly marked with cinnamon.

REMARKS: The gray-cheeked thrush breeds mainly in the river valleys and the wooded parts of the sub-arctic regions, but it has been found nesting in northern B.C. and might, therefore, be expected to breed in northern Alberta. So far there are no nesting records for this province. On migration the species is widely distributed. Even in the Rocky Mountains it is apparently only a migrant, although it has been observed there as late as the first week of June.

The gray-cheeked thrush resembles the olive-backed in behavior as well as appearance. It is rarely seen out of the shadows of the woods where it keeps to the ground in its search for food. Although largely insectivorous like all of the brown thrushes, it is fond of small fruits especially the blueberries and cranberries on its northern nesting grounds. The song is said to be of fine quality but on migration it is rarely heard.

Gray-cheeked thrushes pass northward through southern Alberta during the second and third weeks of May. This is the time of arrival of the olive-backed, or Swainson's thrush, and very often the two species may be found in the same woods. They cannot be said to associate however, for thrushes are solitary in habit and rarely form groups. In the fall gray-cheeked thrushes move southward through the province from late August to late September.

336

RAY SALT

SWAINSON'S THRUSH

F. C. HENNESSEY

GRAY-CHEEKED THRUSH
Swainson's Thrush (below)

337

THRUSHES — Family Turdidae

VEERY Fairly Common Summer Resident.
Hylocichla fuscescens subsp. (p. 496) Length 7 in.

DESCRIPTION: Ads.—Upperparts brownish-olive; no distinct eye-ring; upper breast and sides of throat buffy indistinctly streaked or spotted with brown; sides light gray; remainder of underparts white. Im.—Similar to adults but many feathers of upperparts with pale centers and more heavily spotted with brown below.

IDENTIFICATION: The brownest of our brown thrushes; the hermit thrush has a browner tail but, like the olive-backed and gray-cheeked thrushes, it is grayer on the back. The veery is less distinctly spotted on the breast than these other species.

RANGE: North and South America. Breeds in southern Canada and the northern states. Winters in Brazil.

NESTING: On or very close to the ground. Nest, a mass of dead leaves lined with dry leaves and rootlets. Eggs, 3-5, greenish-blue usually unmarked. (St. Albert, June 26.)

REMARKS: The veery is most abundant as a breeding bird in the parklands and in the wooded river valleys of the prairies, ranging westward in the south as far as the aspen forests of the lower foothills. There is a sight record from Banff but normally it is not to be expected in the mountains. It is not uncommon north of Edmonton as far as Athabasca and Valleyview but farther north it is scarce. Early investigators found it in the Peace River District but later workers failed to find it there. In 1964, however, singing males were heard in the region indicating that this is once more a breeding area.

The veery is an elusive bird although it is not particularly wary. Its favorite haunts are deciduous woods with thick undergrowth into which the sun penetrates as rarely as man. Even in the drier parts of Alberta such places have that touch of dankness which appears to be essential in the habitat of the brown thrushes. The veery spends most of its time on the ground, or close to it, finding insects under the decaying leaves or fruit in the bushes. Like the other brown thrushes it has a beautiful song which is heard to best advantage at dusk. But while their songs ascend in scale the veery sings a rich rolling, *veery, veery, vaary, vaary*, on a descending scale, each phrase lower in tone than the preceding. In the Cypress Hills it is possible to hear veerys and Swainson's thrushes singing in close proximity, their dulcet voices blending beautifully. Thrushes, including the veery reach central Alberta on migration about the middle of May although early individuals may arrive ten days earlier, only to be greeted by a late spring snowfall. In the fall thrushes move south early in September but some laggards may be found late in that month.

338

THRUSHES — Family Turdidae

MOUNTAIN BLUEBIRD
Sialia currocoides

Fairly Common Summer Resident.
Length 7 in.

DESCRIPTION: Ad. m.—Head and entire upperparts including wings and tail bright azure-blue; underparts lighter blue shading to white on abdomen. Ad. f. — Upperparts blue overwashed with brownish-gray which largely obscures the blue except on flight feathers, lower back and tail; underparts brownish-ash becoming white on abdomen. Im.—Similar to female but with light marks on back and spotted with brown and white on breast.

IDENTIFICATION: The male could be confused only with the indigo bunting which is much smaller and is rare in Alberta. The female, especially in flight, shows enough blue in wings and tail to identify her.

RANGE: Western North America and Mexico. Breeds from Alaska across to southern Manitoba and south to New Mexico and California. Winters in western states south to Mexico.

NESTING: In cavities in trees, buildings, or cliffs, or in nest boxes. Nest of grass and shredded bark often lined with feathers. Eggs, 4-8, pale blue. Sometimes two broods are raised in one season. (Beynon, May 15.)

REMARKS: Despite its name the mountain bluebird occurs as commonly on the prairies and in the parklands as it does in the mountains. It breeds throughout southern Alberta and as far north as Ft. McMurray. From there north the status of the mountain bluebird is not well defined. There are a few records from Ft. Chipewyan and Wood Buffalo Park during the summer but nests have not been found.

A fairly common bird only thirty years ago the mountain bluebird is now diminishing in numbers at a rate which is alarming. The invasion of its habitat by the house sparrow and the starling seems to be the most obvious reason for its decrease; certainly in the competition for suitable nesting sites the bluebird stands little chance against these aggressive bullies. If given adequate protection mountain bluebirds will occupy bird houses in either urban or rural areas but the nature-lover who is interested in saving this species must be prepared to take extreme measures against all competing pests such as house sparrows, starlings, house wrens and cats. The reward could be worthwhile: a pair of bluebirds, soft of voice, gentle in manner, and beautiful in color are attractive guests around any home. The youngsters, although not so colorful, will prove their relationship to the thrushes by their spotted breasts.

The eastern bluebird, which looks like a mountain bluebird with a red breast, has recently extended its range into Manitoba and Saskatchewan. There have been sight records from Beynon and the Drumheller area during recent years but there is so far no concrete proof of the occurrence of the species in Alberta.

VEERY

MOUNTAIN BLUEBIRD

ALLAN BROOKS

TOWNSEND'S SOLITAIRE

RAY SALT

GOLDEN-CROWNED KINGLET

341

TOWNSEND'S SOLITAIRE Fairly Common Summer Resident.
Myadestes townsendi subsp. (p. 496) Length 8 in.

DESCRIPTION: Ads.—Smoky slate-gray all over; conspicuous white eye-ring; wings dark grayish-brown with a tawny patch near the base of the flight feathers which shows best in flight; tail dark brownish-gray, outermost pair of feathers largely white and next pair tipped with white. Im.—Similar but feathers of body with white center spots giving a spotted appearance.

IDENTIFICATION: Like a pale catbird but tawny patches on wings, and white on outer tail feathers shows well in flight.

RANGE: Western North America and Mexico. Breeds from Alaska to northwestern Mexico from Rocky Mountains to Pacific coast. Winters from southern B.C. to Mexico.

NESTING: On the ground or on a bank, usually protected from above by an overhang. Nest of twigs and pine needles lined with grass and moss. Eggs, 3-5, white or bluish-white splotched and scrawled with shades of brown. (Gorge Creek, June 12.)

REMARKS: The forests of the mountains and the foothills are the summer home of Townsend's solitaire, but during migration it often appears farther east in the parklands and the prairie coulees. There are records from Brooks, Beynon, Rosebud, Sullivan Lake, Camrose, Elk Island Park, and Clyde.

Like the brown thrushes Townsend's solitaire usually makes itself inconspicuous but it is not as shy as the other thrushes. It spends less of its time on the ground and more on some exposed perch at the edge of the woods from which it may sally forth to capture flying insects in the manner of a bluebird. Its flight is soft, its manner quiet, and its colors subdued; casual observers will miss it completely. Yet it is an interesting bird well worth watching for in our Rocky Mountain National Parks where it nests fairly commonly.

Townsend's solitaire is a somewhat erratic migrant which may appear irregularly almost anywhere in southern Alberta except on the open prairies. Individuals occasionally arrive early in April; some do not leave until well on in October. The solitaire is not dependent upon insects for food; especially during early spring and late fall berries and soft seeds form a large part of its diet.

KINGLETS — Family Sylviidae

Kinglets belong to a large family which includes the Old World warblers, but only two species occur in Alberta. Arboreal in habit, leaf green in color, and diminutive in size, they are easily overlooked by the casual observer.

GOLDEN-CROWNED KINGLET
Regulus satrapa subsp. (p. 496)

Scarce Resident.
Length 4 in.

DESCRIPTION: Ad.m.—Center of crown bright orange bordered narrowly with yellow, then broadly with black; thin white line over eye extending forward over beak; black line through eye; rest of upperparts grayish olive-green, darker on wings and tail; throat and underparts light greenish-olive. Ad.f.—Similar but center of crown is entirely yellow with broad black border.

IDENTIFICATION: A very small greenish bird with rather short tail. Similar to ruby-crowned kinglet but strong black and yellow markings on head are distinctive.

RANGE: North and Central America. Breeds throughout North America except in the central prairie regions. Winters throughout most of its breeding range and south to Guatemala.

NESTING: In conifers usually towards the tip of a high branch. Nest, a globular mass of lichens, mosses, and leaves with opening at the top; lined with shredded bark, rootlets, hair, and feathers. Eggs, 5-10, creamy white spotted and blotched with brown.

REMARKS: Except for the mountain regions where it is widely distributed in the coniferous forests as a breeding bird, not a great deal is known of the status of the golden-crowned kinglet in Alberta. It has been observed during May and June at Wood Buffalo Park, Ft. Chipewyan, the Swan Hills, and the Peace River district and might be expected to nest in these areas. Elsewhere it appears most commonly during the winter in small flocks.

Outside the nesting season golden-crowned kinglets are erratic wanderers which frequent, in settled areas, thick stands of coniferous trees in river valleys and coulees. Fluttering about the upper branches of the evergreens they look like large moths rather than birds. When they alight among the needles their colors blend and they are lost to view. Their call note, a thin *tzeet,* attracts as little attention as their tiny forms. Unlike ruby-crowned kinglets, whose voices are robust out of all proportion to their size, golden-crowned kinglets have a weak song. It is largely a repetition of their *tzeet* note, high pitched and weak in quality.

343

ALLAN BROOKS

RUBY-CROWNED KINGLETS *(male — female)*
Golden-crowned Kinglets (below)

T. M. SHORTT

WATER PIPIT

KINGLETS — Family Sylviidae

RUBY-CROWNED KINGLET Fairly Common Summer Resident.
Regulus calendula subsp. (p. 496) Length 4 in.

DESCRIPTION: Ad.—Center of crown bright red often concealed by surrounding feathers; rest of upperparts grayish olive-green; wings with two white bars; a conspicuous white eye-ring; underparts grayish-white tinged with buff on abdomen. Ad. f.—Similar but lacks red crown patch.

IDENTIFICATION: A very small greenish bird with no very distinctive markings. The light eye-ring and wing bars are the best means of identification; the scarlet crown patch of the male is distinctive.

RANGE: North America. Breeds in northern states and Canada north to tree line. Winters from southern Canada to Mexico.

NESTING: In conifers. The nest is usually hung under a high branch towards its end. It is a globular mass of lichens and mosses with a deep cup lined with hair and feathers. Eggs, 5-11, white with brown spots and blotches. (Edmonton, June 5.)

REMARKS: The ruby-crowned kinglet nests in mixed-wood forests from our northern boundary south as far as the edge of the parklands and in the Rocky Mountains south to the International boundary. It is a common migrant in the southern part of the province even on the prairies where it follows the wooded coulees and river valleys.

When pussy willows are bursting with pollen and red catkins dangle from cottonwood boughs the ruby-crowned kinglet flits among them picking off insects as daintily as the orange-crowned warblers which often accompany him and for which he is often mistaken. By the time the leaves have appeared the kinglet has arrived at his nesting grounds and here, in some muskeg forest, his diminutive form would be completely lost to view if he were not such an active mite. Restlessly he moves about the higher branches, nervously fluttering his wings and often bursting into loud song. When the large brood has hatched all the energy of both parents is required to satisfy insatiable appetites and there is little time for singing.

During the breeding season ruby-crowned kinglets frequent coniferous or mixed-wood forests for the nest is always built in a conifer. They do not, however, confine their activities to the evergreens. Wherever insects can be found there the ruby-crowns will go. On migration they are sociable birds usually found in mixed flocks with golden-crowned kinglets, warblers, or any other small birds. They arrive in southern Alberta shortly after the middle of April; in the fall only an occasional laggard remains until October.

Pipits are small ground-feeding birds which frequent open meadows and prairies, cultivated fields, and muddy flats. Although somewhat similar in appearance to sparrows, pipits walk rather than hop and have slender pointed beaks. The nail of the hind toe is greatly elongated as in the longspurs and larks.

WATER (AMERICAN) PIPIT

Anthus spinoletta subsp. (p. 496)

Common Migrant.
Fairly Common Summer Resident.
Length 6½ in.

DESCRIPTION: Ads.—Upperparts brownish-olive, the feathers of crown and back with dark centers; wings dusky black with two vague light bars; tail brownish-black, the outermost feather mainly white and the next with white at tip; buff line over eye; underparts cinnamon-buff; breast and sides streaked with dusky brown.

IDENTIFICATION: A plain earth-brown bird with decidedly buffy underparts streaked on breast and sides; shows white stripe on each side of tail in flight.

RANGE: Breeding range circumpolar. In North America breeds in arctic across continent, south in mountains to northern New Mexico. Winters in southwestern B.C., throughout the United States and south to Guatemala.

NESTING: On the ground. Nest of fine twigs and grasses among sparse vegetation and rocks. Eggs, 4-7, dull white, so heavily marked with dark brown that the ground color is almost obscured. (Junction Mt., June 22.)

REMARKS: American pipits pass through Alberta in flocks, appearing for a short time in April and in September on their way to and from their arctic nesting grounds. Some, however, find suitable nesting terrain in our Rocky Mountain regions. On the alpine meadows above tree line, often in company with horned larks and white-tailed ptarmigan, these may be observed in our mountain National Parks.

Migrating American pipits are highly gregarious. Swinging out of the sky in twittering hundreds they settle in fields to feed or on lake shores to quench their thirst. Their drab colors blend well with the ground as they crouch for a moment looking for danger. Then all move at once walking about much in the manner of larks. After a good feed of weed seeds and small insects they are ready to take off again in unison on the next lap of their journey. Pipits migrate a little later in the spring and earlier in the fall than Lapland longspurs but mixed flocks containing these two species, and sometimes horned larks and snow buntings, are occasionally seen in April.

PIPITS — Family Motacillidae

SPRAGUE'S PIPIT
Anthus spragueii

Fairly Common Summer Resident.
Length 6½ in.

DESCRIPTION: Ads. — Upperparts streaked with brownish-black and pale buff, each feather having a dark center and a pale border; wings grayish-brown; tail brownish-black, the two outer feathers on each side largely white; cheeks and underparts pale buff becoming almost white on abdomen; sparsely streaked with dusky across breast.

IDENTIFICATION: Very similar in color to vesper sparrow and Baird's sparrow; distinguished from former by lack of chestnut on wing and from latter by white outer tailfeathers, from both by slender beak and very long hind toenail. Aerial song is distinctive.

RANGE: Plains of North America. Breeds from central Prairie Provinces south to western Minnesota and Montana. Winters in south central states and Mexico.

NESTING: On the ground. Nest of grasses sunk into ground often overarched with grass. Eggs, 4-5, dull white thickly covered with purplish-brown markings. (Suffield, May 14.)

REMARKS: Early in the century Sprague's pipit nested in numbers on the short-grass plains of Alberta, but as these regions yielded to the plough, the species became less abundant. It still nests in many parts of the southern prairies, the parklands, and the Peace River district where the sod has not been destroyed, but its distribution is quite local. It occurs in the foothills as far west as the Yaha Tinda prairies just east of Banff National Park.

High overhead a thin metallic *ching-a-ring-a-ring-a-ring-a*, decreasing in scale and intensity, like a silver chain swirled around a silver basin, tells that the male pipit has established his claim to an area of virgin prairie where the female is probably incubating on a well-hidden nest. After each performance the tiny songster circles in the blue sky almost at the limit of human vision, gaining altitude until ready to set his wings and pour out his jingle again. For as long as an hour he may remain in the air before dropping like a stone to the ground. Here among the abundant insect life of the prairie and the seeds of grasses and weeds it finds its food. On the ground Sprague's pipit is a shy bird avoiding approach with long undulating flights, and since his colors blend well with parched prairie grass he is difficult to find. Perhaps for this reason Sprague's pipits go unnoticed in regions where they are reasonably abundant unless their aerial song is recognized.

WAXWINGS — Family Bombycillidae

Smooth, soft brown plumage, conspicuous erectile head crest, and yellow tipped tail readily identify the waxwings. Small extensions on the shafts of the secondaries, the color and texture of sealing wax, give the waxwings their name, but unfortunately are not readily seen in life and are not always present. Except during the nesting season waxwings are quite gregarious. At rest they usually sit erect on a branch, their long crests accentuating their length.

BOHEMIAN WAXWING
Bombycilla garrula subsp. (p. 496)

Fairly Common Resident.
Length 8 in.

DESCRIPTION: Ads.—Head with long, pointed crest. General color soft grayish-brown becoming grayer on sides and rump; throat, and a line from beak over eye black; forehead and sides of throat pale chestnut; wings blackish-brown with white wing bar and most primaries and secondaries striped with white or yellow; secondaries usually with small, red, waxlike appendages; tail gray darkening towards tip but with yellow terminal band; under tail coverts chestnut. Im.—Crest small; general color grayer than adult becoming dull white below and streaked with dusky brown; head markings indistinct; white markings on wings; tail as in adult.

IDENTIFICATION: Similar only to cedar waxwing. Distinguished at any age by larger size, white on wings, and chestnut under tail coverts.

RANGE: Circumpolar. In North America breeds from northeastern Manitoba to Alaska south to central Alberta and B.C. Winters across southern Canada south to California and Pennsylvania.

NESTING: In conifers at varying heights. Nest of twigs and coarse grass lined with moss and plant fiber. Eggs, 4-6, pale blue dotted and scrawled with black. (Fawcett, May 28.)

REMARKS: The bohemian waxwing nests in the dense mixed-wood and coniferous forests of northern and western Alberta south to about the Athabasca river. In most settled areas, however, it is known only as a winter visitor.

Late in the fall large flocks of bohemian waxwings descend upon our cities and towns to feast on the fruits of ornamental shrubs and trees, and if the supply is good they remain all winter. Settling on some well laden mountain ash they make short work of its crimson berry clusters. Then, after much twittering conversation, they rise in a flock and swirl over the rooftops before settling into the thick evergreens to spend the night. In rural areas their habits are similar although they are dependent on native berries for food. Their soft voices, trim appearance, and beautiful colors endear them to rural and urban dwellers alike.

348

SPRAGUE'S PIPIT   C. HAMPSON

BOHEMIAN WAXWING   KAY HODGES

CEDAR WAXWING
Bombycilla cedrorum

Common Summer Resident.
Length 7 in.

DESCRIPTION: Ads.—Head with long, pointed crest. General color soft grayish-brown shading to cinnamon on head and yellow on abdomen; throat and line from beak over eye black; wings slaty-gray, secondaries usually with 'sealing wax' appendages; tail gray darkening towards tip but with yellow terminal band; under tail coverts white. Im.—Crest small. Above olive brown becoming dull white below and streaked with dusky; black line from beak to eye; usually white line behind eye; tail as in adult.

IDENTIFICATION: Similar only to bohemian waxwing. Smaller size, lack of white markings on wings, and white under tail coverts will identify this species at any age.

RANGE: North and Central America. Breeds from tree line in northern Canada south to California and Georgia. Winters from southern B.C. and northern United States to Central America.

NESTING: In trees at varying heights. Nest, a compact cup of grass, moss and bark, lined with finer fibers. Eggs, 3-5, pale bluish-gray sparsely dotted and scrawled with black. (Calgary, July 1.)

REMARKS: Although the cedar waxwing occurs throughout Alberta it is relatively scarce in the northern half of the province. In the southern half it nests commonly even in urban areas.

Weeks after the bohemian waxwings have retired to their northerly nesting areas cedar waxwings begin to arrive in Alberta. They are among the last of the spring migrants and always the last to start nesting. Early in July while most birds have young able to fly, cedar waxwings may still be incubating fresh eggs in the caragana hedges along the street. Nor do they linger long once their family duties are over; by the end of August all but a few stragglers have left the province. In recent years small numbers of cedar waxwings have stayed in Alberta beyond their usual time of departure; a few have been observed in Lethbridge as late as the end of November. At Edmonton cedar waxwings stayed over the winters of 1963-64 and 1964-65. Single birds or small groups usually moved about with the flocks of bohemian waxwings yet they were inclined to stay to themselves as a unit within the flock. Larger groups of up to twenty-five remained apart from the bohemians.

Hillsides thick with berry bushes, willowy borders of streams, and bushy edges of forest clearings are favorite haunts of the cedar waxwing. It perches openly on saskatoon boughs while picking off the purple berries, or sallies out to catch an insect in flight. Quiet in voice and manner, yet not at all wary, it is often overlooked in rural areas; in cities its friendly unsuspicious nature attracts attention.

SHRIKES — Family Laniidae

Although they are true songbirds shrikes have developed carnivorous habits. Their beaks are strong and hooked but their feet are weak and lack the sharp talons usually found on carnivorous birds. Since they cannot hold their prey in their feet they impale it on thorns or barb wire, thus earning the name 'butcher-birds'. The two American species are clothed in soft gray boldly marked with black and white.

NORTHERN SHRIKE
Lanius excubitor subsp. (p. 496)

Scarce Winter Visitor.
Length 10 in.

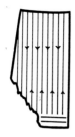

DESCRIPTION: Ads.—Above plain light bluish-gray becoming white on rump; white line over eye; dark line from base of beak becoming black under eye and over ear; wings black except white at base of primaries and tips of secondaries; tail black, the outer feathers tipped with white; underparts white with fine gray pencillings on breast. Im.—Similar but colors of upperparts clouded with brown and underparts more heavily barred.

IDENTIFICATION: A bluish-gray bird with black and white wings, heavy dark patch behind eye and hooked beak. Larger than the loggerhead shrike and black in front of eye does not meet over the beak. Occurs in Alberta from late fall to early spring. Often hovers like a sparrow hawk.

RANGE: North America. Breeds in north from Alaska to northern Quebec. Winters in southern Canada and United States.

NESTING: In conifers. Nest of twigs, grass, feathers, and hair. Eggs, 4-6, grayish-white heavily spotted with browns.

REMARKS: The northern shrike passes through Alberta in October as a southbound migrant and returns northward in April. A few individuals may spend the winter in the central part of the province but normally extreme southern Alberta is the northern limit of the wintering range. It has been found nesting only in the Lake Athabasca region.

From a perch on a telephone wire the northern shrike watches the fields for the movement of a vole or the passage of a flock of English sparrows or snowbirds. Dashing out on rapidly beating wings it overtakes a small bird and kills it with a blow of its beak or, hovering for a moment over thick stubble, plummets onto an unsuspecting mouse. While in Alberta the northern shrike has little opportunity to indulge its taste for insects but when available they form nearly half of its food. Solitary by nature northern shrikes are never abundant and their food habits have no great effect on any species of prey.

CEDAR WAXWING

NORTHERN SHRIKE

C. HAMPSON

LOGGERHEAD SHRIKE

KAY HODGES

STARLING

SHRIKES — Family Laniidae

LOGGERHEAD SHRIKE
Lanius ludovicianus subsp. (p. 496)

Common Summer Resident.
Length 9 in.

DESCRIPTION: Ads.—Upperparts plain light bluish-gray becoming white on rump; wide black streak from base of beak, around eye and over ear; wings black except white at base of primaries and tips of secondaries; tail black, the outer feathers tipped with white; underparts white tinged with gray on sides. Im.—Similar to adult but colors duller, more or less overwashed with buffy, and with much dusky wavy-barring above and below.

IDENTIFICATION: Similar to northern shrike but smaller and with heavier black face stripes which meet over the beak. The only shrike likely to be seen in settled areas of Alberta during the summer.

RANGE: North America. Breeds from southern Canada through United States to Mexico. Winters in southern parts of its range.

NESTING: In thickly branched trees and bushes, at heights of 8-12 ft. Nest, a bulky mass of twigs, grass, feathers, wool, and rags. Eggs, 4-6, dull white, spotted with gray and brown. (Delia, May 30.)

REMARKS: The loggerhead shrike nests in the lightly wooded river valleys and coulees of the prairies and the copse-studded meadows of the parklands. With the clearing of forests for cultivation it has extended its range northward in recent years. In 1952 it was first recorded at Falher; by 1954 it had reached Fairview.

Although the hooked beak and black mask of the loggerhead shrike give it the look of a brigand it has not the ferocious nature of its larger relative, the northern shrike. In summer it lives mainly on grasshoppers, crickets, beetles, and other large insects. Only when this type of food is unavailable does it take mice or small birds. Various species of small birds nest unmolested in farm shelter belts which may also be tenanted by a family of loggerhead shrikes. Perched on a high branch or a telephone wire the loggerhead shrike sits motionless for long periods on bright days. In changing this vantage point it shows the peculiar flight habit characteristic of both species of shrikes; dropping suddenly with rapid wing strokes it flies off within a few feet of the ground rising abruptly only as it nears a new perch.

Loggerhead shrikes arrive in Alberta during the last week of April only a short time after the northern shrikes have left for the north. They usually move southward before the end of August at least a month before northern shrikes return from the north. Shrikes seen during April and September might be laggards or early arrivals of either species; they should be identified carefully.

STARLINGS — Family Sturnidae

No representative of this Old World family is native to North America but two species have been recently introduced: the crested mynah, an Asiatic species, is now established in southern B.C. and the common starling, a European immigrant, has now invaded most of the temperate regions of this continent.

STARLING   Common Summer Resident.
Sturnus vulgaris subsp. (p. 496)   Length 8½ in.

DESCRIPTION: Breeding ads.—Entire head and body jet black with purplish reflections on head and neck and greenish iridescence elsewhere; the feathers of hindneck, back, sides, and abdomen tipped with small triangles of buffy-brown; wings and tail dull brownish - black the feathers edged with buffy; beak, long, yellow; legs reddish-brown; iris brown. Winter ads.—Similar but with more light feather edges and beak black. Im.—Grayish-brown with white throat and face and many feathers edged with grayish-white.

IDENTIFICATION: A black bird with stumpy tail and long beak, yellow in spring. Most commonly confused with Brewer's blackbird but, sitting, the stumpy tail hangs down giving hunchbacked appearance; flight is direct and wing-strokes rapid.

RANGE: Europe, Asia, North America. Introduced into New York in 1890; now spread over most of temperate North America. Resident except in extreme north of its range.

NESTING: In holes in trees or buildings. Nest an untidy mass of grass, straw, feathers, etc. Eggs, 5-7, white or pale blue. (Beynon, May 10.)

REMARKS: The starling was first recorded in Alberta in 1934. Ten years later it had spread over the southern part of the province and west as far as the mountains. By 1952 it was nesting in the Peace River district and at Ft. Chipewyan. Most starlings migrate southward during October but small numbers have been observed wintering at various places from about Clyde south. Spring migrants return early in March.

Most of our native birds cannot compete with this hardy bully. Woodpeckers, bluebirds, small owls, buffleheads, and other species which nest in trees are most affected by this competition and there is no doubt that their numbers will be reduced as starlings increase. Retreat into the wilderness does not solve their problem for already the starling has usurped nesting sites in northern muskeg areas. It is unfortunate that Albertans were not alerted to the dangers of the introduction of this undesirable alien before it gained such a strong foothold in the province.

SOLITARY VIREO

RED-EYED VIREOS

VIREOS — Family Vireonidae

Vireos are small, non-gregarious, arboreal birds lacking distinctive markings and distinctive habits. They most closely resemble warblers but are less active, moving along the branches rather than flitting about. The tip of the upper mandible is bent downward to form a small hook.

SOLITARY VIREO　　　　　　　　　　　Scarce Summer Resident.
Vireo solitarius subsp. (p. 496)　　　　　　　　Length 5½ in.

DESCRIPTION: Sides of head, crown, and hindneck slate-gray; a broad white line from base of bill goes completely around eye forming a white eye-ring; back olive-green; wings and tail blackish with olive tinge; two yellowish wing bars; underparts white; sides yellow with indistinct dusky stripes; iris brown.

IDENTIFICATION: A small olive and white bird with bluish-gray head. Similar to other small vireos and to Tennessee warbler but distinguished from all by very evident white eye-ring and two light wing bars.

RANGE: North and Central America. Breeds from southern N.W.T. across to Nova Scotia and south to Mexico. Winters in southern states south to Nicaragua.

NESTING: In trees, usually coniferous. Nest, a cup made of bark, moss, lichens, and plant down, suspended from a branch by its upper rim. Eggs, 3-5, white with brown spots. (Glenevis, June 3).

REMARKS: As a breeding bird the solitary vireo is found mainly in the mixed-wood forests of central and northern Alberta. In the mountains it has been recorded at Banff and at the Gorge Creek Biological Station where singing males have been seen during the nesting season. On migration it is more widespread occurring even in the wooded coulees of the southern prairies.

The solitary vireo, although it frequents mixed stands of deciduous and evergreen trees during the summer, usually chooses a coniferous tree on the edge of a clearing for its nesting site. It is not a very active bird; the male may sit motionless in one spot for long periods of time, merely raising its head to sing every few moments. He shares with the female the duty of incubation. Incubating birds are very tame and may allow themselves to be touched on the nest. Yet solitary vireos rarely seek out human company, preferring the solitudes of the forest to the bustle of the city park. Nor are they any more sociable with their own kind; as their name indicates they remain pretty much by themselves. On migration they more often associate with warblers than with other vireos. Migrants pass northward through central Alberta shortly after the middle of May and move southward again in the latter half of August.

VIREOS — Family Vireonidae

RED-EYED VIREO

Vireo olivaceus

Common Summer Resident.

Length 6 in.

DESCRIPTION: Crown slate-gray bordered with black on sides; rest of upperparts and tail grayish olive-green; broad white line over eye bordered above by black edges of crown and below by dusky streak from base of bill through eye and over ear; cheeks, sides of neck, and sides grayish-olive; rest of underparts white; iris red. Immature birds are similar but the iris is brown.

IDENTIFICATION: A grayish-olive and dull white bird likely to be confused only with other vireos. Lack of wing bars distinguishes from solitary, lack of yellow from Philadelphia; larger size, greener color, and better defined stripe over eye from warbling. Red eye of adults is distinctive.

RANGE: North and South America. Breeds from northern B.C. and Newfoundland south to Oregon and Florida. Winters in northern half of South America.

NESTING: In trees or shrubs. Nest, a well woven structure of grass, rootlets, and birch bark, suspended from a branch with spider web and strands of bark. Eggs, 3-5, white with a few brown dots. (Edmonton, June 29.)

REMARKS: The red-eyed vireo is never found far from poplar groves. Along the river valleys of the southern prairies and the mountains, in the parklands, and in the mixed-wood forests of the north, wherever there is a dense stand of poplar the red-eyed vireo will be found. It spends a great deal of time in one tree slowly and deliberately moving along the branches searching every spider web and every leaf for food. Insects comprise most of its food but in late summer soft berries are added to the diet. Slow movement and dull color combine to make it inconspicuous and if it were not for its song it would usually go unnoticed. However, few birds are more vocal than the red-eyed vireo; it sings throughout the day interrupting its ordinary occupations every few seconds to pour out a series of pleasing but rather monotonous phrases each ending on a rising inflection. On migration late in May, the song may be heard anywhere in the province even in farm shelter belts well out on the prairies. Late in August, as red-eyed vireos move southward through the trees with the warblers, an occasional ebullient individual may pause between mouthfuls of caterpillars and aphids to practise a few bars of song, as though fearful that he might forget the melody.

VIREOS — Family Vireonidae

PHILADELPHIA VIREO   Fairly Common Summer Resident.
Vireo philadelphicus   Length 5 in.

DESCRIPTION: Crown and hindneck slate-gray; back grayish-olive; wings and tail brownish-olive; white line over eye and dusky streak through eye; eyelids white forming indistinct and incomplete eye-ring; cheeks grayish; underparts pale yellow becoming almost white on abdomen.

IDENTIFICATION: A small grayish-olive bird with pale lemon-yellow tinge on underparts. Resembles the other vireos but differs in smaller size and yellowish underparts.

RANGE: North and Central America. Breeds from northern Alberta and Newfoundland south to northern United States east of the Rockies. Winters in Central America.

NESTING: In trees or bushes, often alders. Nest, a cup made of birch bark, grass, and spider web hung below a branch. Eggs, 3-5, white with a few brown spots.

REMARKS: The range of the Philadelphia vireo in Alberta is imperfectly known. It breeds in the parklands southwest to Sundre and in the mixed-wood forests north of Edmonton probably as far as the sixtieth parallel for it has been recorded at Ft. Chipewyan. It has been reported in the Peace River district and on the prairies but its distribution in these regions has yet to be ascertained.

The Philadelphia vireo is probably more common in Alberta than is generally believed for its song is easily mistaken for that of the red-eyed vireo. It frequents second-growth poplar and alder - willow thickets, especially those close to rivers and lakes. Never very active it easily escapes notice in such dense growth but close scrutiny of the region from which the song comes is sometimes rewarded by a view of the singer whose pale yellow breast and olive back blend well with the leaves.

During the last half of August when the migration of insectivorous birds is at its height Philadelphia vireos migrate in small numbers through central Alberta. At this time, as in the summer, they keep largely to leafy brush bordering the woods. In the seclusion of the willows they go sedately about the business of gathering insects, apparently unperturbed by the hustle and bustle of the warblers and flycatchers which may be moving southward with them.

VIREOS — Family Vireonidae

WARBLING VIREO
Vireo gilvus subsp. (p. 497)

Fairly Common Summer Resident.
Length 5½ in.

DESCRIPTION: Upperparts dull gray tinged, mainly on lower back, with olive-green; light line over eye; cheeks and sides of neck gray; underparts white lightly tinged with olive on sides; iris brown.

IDENTIFICATION: A small bird light gray above and dull white below. Similar to red-eyed and Philadelphia vireos but much grayer; smaller than former and lacking black-bordered crown and red eye; lacks yellowish underparts of latter.

RANGE: North and Central America. Breeds across Canada and northern half of United States. Winters in Mexico and Central America.

NESTING: In trees, usually deciduous. Nest, a cup woven of grass, inner bark, and cobwebs, attached beneath a branch. Eggs, 3-5, white with a few spots of brown. (Glenevis, June 7.)

REMARKS: The warbling vireo is widely distributed in the province occurring in poplar groves along the southern rivers, in the parklands, and in the mixed-wood forests of western and northern Alberta. In the mountains it is found in the poplar and aspen thickets of the lower levels.

The warbling vireo is an inconspicuous inhabitant of high bushes and deciduous trees. It is not afraid of noise and other disturbances for it often nests in tall trees along roads, in public parks, and along shady streets of cities and towns; in fact it seems to show a preference for such places. It is more often heard than seen for like a true vireo it sings incessantly until well on in the summer. Even in the middle of a hot afternoon when most birds are still and silent it may be heard in the leafy canopies overhead. The song is a continuous series of notes gradually increasing in pitch and intensity to the last which is always highest and loudest.

Like all vireos, male and female warbling vireos share the duties of incubation. The male, however, cannot keep silent even at this task and, seated on the nest, he pours out his liquid song until the female comes to relieve him. In twelve days the eggs hatch. The young grow rapidly on a diet of soft insects and sixteen days later they are ready to leave the nest. They are dependent upon the parents for several weeks but before the fall migration starts in mid-August they are quite capable of looking after themselves.

PHILADELPHIA VIREO

WARBLING VIREO

T. M. SHORTT

WOOD WARBLERS — Family Parulidae

Wood warblers are small arboreal birds whose thin sharp beaks are well adapted for capturing insects. They are very active birds, rarely remaining still longer than is necessary for a burst of song. Males of many species are very brightly colored; females usually have a distinct plumage duller than that of the males. There are also seasonal differences in plumage to complicate the problem of identification.

BLACK AND WHITE WARBLER   Fairly Common Summer Resident.
Mniotilta varia   Length 5 in.

DESCRIPTION: Ad. m.—Crown and hindneck black with broad white medial stripe; white line over eye; black under eye and over cheeks; throat black separated from black cheeks by white line; rest of upperparts black with irregular streaks of white; two broad white wing bars; rest of underparts white with broad streaks of black on upper breast and sides; tail black, outer two feathers tipped with white. Ad.f.—Same as male above but lighter below with white throat and fewer black streaks. Im.— Similar to female but less distinctly marked and black tinged with brown.

IDENTIFICATION: A small black and white striped bird. Differs from blackpoll warbler in having broad white stripe through crown and lack of olive-green on back.

RANGE: North and South America. Breeds in United States and most of Canada except arctic. Winters in southern states south to northern South America.

NESTING: On the ground. Nest of bark, grass, and rootlets usually under some overhanging object. Eggs, 4-5, white, spotted with brown and lavender.

REMARKS: The breeding range of the black and white warbler coincides closely with the mixed-wood forest zone of northern and western Alberta. The species has been observed in the Cypress Hills in July and may nest there. It has not been recorded in the mountains. Over the rest of the province it occurs only as a migrant.

Deciduous or mixed woods bordering lakes and streams are the home of this strikingly marked warbler. Although it is quite at home among leafy boughs the black and white warbler keeps mainly to the larger trees creeping about on their trunks and larger branches and probing crevices in the bark after the manner of a nuthatch. Yet it is a true warbler ready to capture in flight any insect which passes by. Its song is a high pitched *tsee*, repeated seven or eight times in about two seconds and often decreasing somewhat in intensity towards the end.

WOOD WARBLERS — Family Parulidae

TENNESSEE WARBLER
Vermivora peregrina

Common Summer Resident.
Length 5 in.

DESCRIPTION: Ad. m.—Crown, hindneck, and cheeks bluish-gray, except white eye-lids and black spot in front of eye; rest of upperparts yellowish-green, except grayish-brown flight feathers and tail; underparts dull white; small white patch on outer tail feather. Ad.f.—Similar but head greenish and underparts tinged with yellow. In the fall both sexes show less gray on head and more yellowish below.

IDENTIFICATION: A small warbler with grayish head and greenish back. Under tail coverts white and white patch only on outermost tail feather. Young birds lack white on tail and are yellowish below but always have white under tail.

RANGE: North America east of Rockies. Breeds in northern states and in Canada north to tree-limit. Winters in Central and northern South America.

NESTING: On the ground in woods, often in muskegs or swamps. Nest, of grass, hair, and rootlets, covered by overhanging vegetation. Eggs, 5-7, white marked mainly at large end with brown and lilac. (Glenevis, June 15.)

REMARKS: The Tennessee warbler breeds commonly in the deciduous and mixed-wood forests of central, northern, and western Alberta including the lower mountain valleys from Crowsnest Pass northward. On migration it travels over the prairies keeping mainly to the river valleys and coulees.

After the middle of May small groups of Tennessee warblers move gradually through the upper levels of the woods busily garnering the newly-hatched crop of small insects. There is considerable bickering and fighting when individuals find themselves on adjacent branches, which may indicate that some of them have reached their nesting grounds and are establishing territorial rights. The edges of muskegs or mixed woods near water are preferred locations for nesting territories. Here the male chooses a number of singing posts at various heights while the female sits very close on her nest below. Tennessee warblers are more often found in deciduous trees and bushes than in conifers and, since they are about the same color and size as a leaf, they are not easy to spot even when singing. The song is a loud clear, *ten-ten-ten-ten — tenna-tenna-tenna-tenna — ten-ten-ten-ten — seeseeseeseeseesee,* the first series of notes being slow and deliberate while the last are rapidly repeated to form a sort of trill. In August mixed flocks of warblers and vireos, including both adult and immature Tennessees swarm southward through the poplars and willows severely trying the skill of the observer who is bent on identifying them.

363

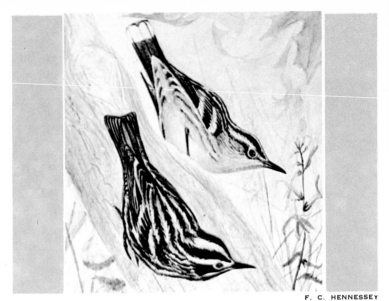

F. C. HENNESSEY

BLACK AND WHITE WARBLER
male   *female*

RAY SALT

TENNESSEE WARBLER

ORANGE-CROWNED WARBLER

YELLOW WARBLER
male   *female*

ORANGE-CROWNED WARBLER   Fairly Common Summer Resident.
Vermivora celata subsp. (p. 497)   Length 5 in.

DESCRIPTION: Upperparts greenish-olive, brightest green on rump; a concealed crown patch of orange-brown; faint light eye-ring and line over eye; underparts grayish-yellow, grayest on sides and indistinctly streaked with dusky on breast; under tail coverts yellow. Females and young are similar; the crown patch may be obscure but the bases of the feathers are always brownish.

IDENTIFICATION: A dull olive-green warbler with no distinct markings, no bars on wings, no light spots on tail; streaks on breast very faint. Differs from Tennessee warbler in having yellow instead of white under tail. Orange crown is not a good field mark but is distinctive in the hand.

RANGE: North America. Breeds from Alaska and northern Canada to Lower California. Winters in southern states and Mexico.

NESTING: On the ground in the woods. Nest of bark and grass lined with fine grass and fur. Eggs, 4-6, white speckled with brown. (Banff, June 9.)

REMARKS: The orange-crowned warbler nests in suitable habitat from the Cypress Hills to the northern boundary of the province and westward into the mountains. It is rather local in distribution and is nowhere abundant. On migration it may occur almost anywhere even in small groves of trees on the prairies.

Early in May before leaves have burst from their buds small green forms appear in the crowns of cottonwoods and aspen bordering southern Alberta streams. They are orange-crowned warblers feeding on small insects attracted to unfolding leaf-buds and catkins. Some of them continue on their journey to nest in the parklands and in the deciduous forests farther north but a few remain to raise their young in the valleys of the Red Deer and the Bow. Although they are not particularly wary they avoid human habitations and one must search the tangled thickets of remote coulee sides to find the nest. Late in August family groups move southward in company with other species of warblers, still keeping to deciduous trees among whose leaves they find shade, security, and food. Lacking any distinctive markings orange-crowned warblers are likely to be overlooked among the fall migrants but in spring, when other warblers are resplendent in blues, blacks, and yellows, orange-crowns are noticeable in their more sombre colors. On migration they rarely sing but once established on their nesting grounds they produce a weak, rapid trill, mainly a monotone, although both pitch and speed may drop somewhat towards the end.

PARULA WARBLER, *Parula americana*   see page 485

WOOD WARBLERS — Family Parulidae

YELLOW WARBLER   Common Summer Resident.
Dendroica petechia   subsp. (p. 497)   Length 5 in.

DESCRIPTION: Ad. m.—Forehead, sides of head, and underparts bright yellow streaked on breast and sides with reddish; rest of upperparts yellowish-green; flight feathers brownish edged with yellow, central tail feathers brownish, rest mainly yellow. Ad. f.—Similar but more olive-green above, lemon-yellow elsewhere, and lacking reddish streaks below. Young like female.

IDENTIFICATION: In sunlight both sexes appear almost completely yellow. Most likely to be confused with Wilson's warbler but larger and no black on crown. At any age the large amount of yellow in the tail is distinctive; Wilson's warblers have a dark tail.

RANGE: North and South America. Breeds throughout most of United States and Canada north to tree limit. Winters in Central America, Brazil and Peru.

NESTING: In bushes. Nest of grass and plant fibers lined with hair, wool, and feathers. Eggs, 4-5, white speckled with brown. (Calgary, June 10.)

REMARKS: The most familiar of the wood warblers to residents of town and country alike is the yellow warbler, or wild canary as it is commonly but incorrectly called. It breeds throughout the province in mountain valleys, northern forests, parkland copses, and prairie coulees; even solitary tangles of caragana near isolated prairie farms are acceptable nesting sites.

Shortly after the middle of May the yellow warbler announces his arrival with a song unequalled in the warbler family, and soon there is not a city park nor a bit of undergrowth in the wilds which lacks a pair of these colorful birds. They prefer ornamental hedges, or willow, saskatoon, and chokecherry patches where sunlight penetrates the foliage, rather than the darkness of the woods. They are true warblers, pert, active, and inquisitive, but their curiosity must be satisfied from behind a leafy screen for they rarely venture into the open. A diet of aphids, caterpillars, and other insect pests makes them friends of the gardener and at the same time shows their lack of relationship to the seed-eating domestic canary.

The rapidity of development of many species of small birds is well illustrated by the yellow warbler. About ten days after the eggs are laid they hatch; eleven days later the young are out of the nest and testing their wings. Few animals can match this rate of growth.

MAGNOLIA WARBLER
male   *female*

CAPE MAY WARBLER

WOOD WARBLERS — Family Parulidae

MAGNOLIA WARBLER Scarce Summer Resident.
Dendroica magnolia Length 5 in.

DESCRIPTION: Ad. m.—Crown and hindneck gray; rest of upperparts black, the feathers near base of wings tinged with green and rump yellow; broad patch on wing and band across middle of tail white; broad mark across forehead over cheeks black; white line over eye; underparts except abdomen yellow with black band across upper breast and black streaks on sides; abdomen white. Ad. f.—Upperparts olive-gray streaked on back with black; rump yellow; two white wing bars; underparts pale yellow streaked with black on sides. Im. and fall ads.. — Like spring adults but duller due to grayish feather edges.

IDENTIFICATION: Adults are distinctively marked in the spring. Streaked yellow underparts and grayish upperparts distinguish them from most warblers in the fall; the large amount of white near base of tail is distinctive at all seasons.

RANGE: Eastern North America. Breeds from southern Mackenzie to Newfoundland south to northeastern states. Winters in Mexico and Central America.

NESTING: In small evergreens. Nest, a poorly built structure of small twigs and coarse grass lined with fine black rootlets. Eggs, 3-5, white variably marked with browns.

REMARKS: Although the magnolia warbler is a fairly common migrant through north-central Alberta it has been found breeding only north of a line through Jasper, Edson, and Edmonton. Evidence of nesting has come from Jasper, Rock Lake, Christina Lake, Calling Lake, Lesser Slave Lake, Lac la Biche, and Chipewyan. It is quite local in distribution. In the mountains it has been seen as far south as Banff and Gorge Creek.

Rather open coniferous woods are the usual summer haunts of the magnolia warbler. Second growth spruce and pine only six or eight feet tall makes ideal nesting territory if not too dense. If there are marshy spots or a lake nearby so much the better. In such surroundings the male magnolia warbler is a beautiful sight as he spreads his tail and droops his wings to show off his markings with full effect. However, most observers see magnolia warblers only on migration late in May and August. At such times they frequent mixed woods showing no particular preference for conifers and often accompanying warblers of other species. On a warm sunny day in spring the members of such an assemblage may burst into song and magnolia warblers show themselves to be good performers, sweet of voice although not too strong.

WOOD WARBLERS — Family Parulidae

CAPE MAY WARBLER
Dendroica tigrina

Scarce Summer Resident.
Length 5 in.

DESCRIPTION: Ad. m.—Crown black; rest of upper-parts olive-green streaked with black; cheeks and line over eye chestnut; sides of neck yellow; underparts yellow heavily streaked with black; patch on front of wing and tips of three outer tail feathers white. Fall males are similar but duller. Ad. f.—Upperparts grayish-olive streaked with black; rump yellow; no chestnut ear patches and yellow on sides of neck indistinct; underparts white tinged with yellow on breast and streaked indistinctly with black; one white wing bar. Im.—Similar to female but even duller.

IDENTIFICATION: The male is distinctively marked. Fall adults and young have heavily streaked whitish or yellowish underparts and a yellow patch on rump.

RANGE: Eastern North America. Breeds from southern Mackenzie and northern Alberta to Quebec and the northeastern states. Winters in West Indies.

NESTING: In conifers usually near the top. Nest of grass and moss lined with feathers and hair. Eggs, 6-7, white blotched with browns.

REMARKS: The Cape May warbler is an uncommon species throughout its entire range. In Alberta males have been heard singing at Jasper, Lesser Slave Lake, Ft. Assiniboine, Glenevis, Chipewyan, and Wood Buffalo Park, and it may be assumed, therefore, that the species will be found nesting in parts of this northern area as more field work is done. On migration the Cape May warbler is not uncommonly found in central Alberta particularly in late August. At this season specimens have been taken as far south as Rosebud.

During the nesting season Cape May warblers frequent the edges of heavy stands of spruce in either coniferous or mixed-wood forests. Recognition of their thin, insect-like song, *tsee-tsee-tsee* . . . , repeated seven or eight times on an extremely high note, is essential if they are to be located. Even with the song to direct attention the singer is difficult to find for he keeps to the crowns of the trees and his tiny form is inconspicuous among the green needles. On migration Cape May warblers desert the conifers for deciduous trees and bushes. Here they feed at any level picking up insects from leaves and branches, from the air and even from the ground. They are usually found in mixed company, their companions being other species of warblers and usually a few chickadees. In the fall the chickadees are the noisiest members of the group and the observer who enters the late August woods to look for warblers would do well to heed the call of the chickadees.

BLACK-THROATED BLUE WARBLER   Status Unknown.
Dendroica caerulescens subsp. (p. 497)   Length 5 in.

DESCRIPTION: Ad. m.—Upperparts plain dark blue; large white mark on wing at base of primaries; throat and sides of head and body black; rest of underparts white; large white patch on outer tail feathers. Ad. f.—Upperparts olive-green slightly tinged with blue only on tail; white mark at base of primaries; underparts yellowish; tail unmarked or only faintly marked with white.

IDENTIFICATION: Males are unmistakable. Females are plainly colored birds difficult to identify in the field; the light mark at the base of the primaries is distinctive.

RANGE: Eastern North and South America. Breeds in eastern Canada and northeastern states west to western Ontario and Minnesota. Winters in West Indies and northern South America.

NESTING: Within three feet of ground in bushes or small trees. Nest of fine bark, straw, and leaves, lined with fine rootlets and hair. Eggs, 3-4, white speckled with browns.

REMARKS: The black-throated blue warbler is an eastern species which has been recorded in Alberta on only four occasions: an adult male was taken in Edmonton on May 17, 1917, and another specimen was collected at Tofield in the fall of 1928. In recent years the species has been recorded with increasing frequency in Manitoba and Saskatchewan west of its usual range and it is not surprising, therefore, that two specimens were recorded in Alberta in 1957. On June 3rd, 1957, an adult male black-throated blue warbler was taken near Rosebud, and on October 22nd, 1957, an immature male flew into a cabin near Windy Point about 12 miles southwest of Nordegg and died during the night. Observers should be alert to the possibility of further appearances of the species in Alberta.

In the east where it is relatively common the black-throated blue warbler inhabits dense undergrowth in mixed-wood forests. In such surroundings it appears to be somewhat retiring but it is actually one of the tamest of the warblers and takes little notice of human intruders. It is not a very active species; after sitting in one place for some time it darts to another spot remaining there for a few minutes before moving again. While sitting it has the habit of lowering its wings and partially spreading its tail thus exposing to view the white patches on these appendages.

371

WOOD WARBLERS — Family Parulidae

MYRTLE WARBLER   Common Summer Resident.
Dendroica coronata   subsp. (p. 497)   Length 5½ in.

DESCRIPTION: Spring m. — Upperparts bluish-gray streaked with black except golden yellow patch in middle of crown and another on rump; two white wing bars; white line over eye; face and ears black; throat and underparts white except a band of black streaks across upper breast and down sides and a patch of yellow on side near bend of wing; outer three tail feathers with white areas. Ad. f.—Similar but paler; back tinged with brownish; face gray instead of black and black feathers on breast edged with white. Im.—Browner above than adults and yellow marks present but paler; face brownish-gray shading to buffy-white on throat and underparts; black streaks and yellow patch on sides very faint.

IDENTIFICATION: Yellow patches on crown, rump, and sides are sufficiently distinct in all plumages to separate from all other species except Audubon's warbler. The myrtle warbler has a white throat and a white line over the eye; Audubon's has a yellow throat and lacks the white line.

RANGE: North America. Breeds across continent from tree limit south to central parts of western provinces and northeastern states. Winters in southwestern states and Central America, also southeastern states and West Indies.

NESTING: In evergreen trees at varying heights. Nest of twigs and grass lined with plant fibers and hair. Eggs, 4-5, creamy-white spotted and blotched with browns and lilac. (St. Albert, June 5.)

REMARKS: The myrtle warbler breeds in the mixed-wood forests of northern and western Alberta south to about the Bow River and west to the eastern margin of the Rockies where it is replaced by Audubon's warbler. It migrates through the rest of the province.

In the river valleys of southern Alberta myrtle warblers often arrive before the trees have burst into leaf. They travel in groups through the tree tops hanging from catkins like chickadees, creeping along branches like creepers, or flitting out after passing insects like flycatchers. Never still for a minute they show their four golden identification marks at every opportunity. On their nesting grounds they inhabit mixed-wood forests well sprinkled with spruce and jack-pine and in one of these conifers the family is raised. In summer the myrtle warbler is largely insectivorous but in winter it eats fruits and berries, in fact it got its name from a fondness for the berries of the waxmyrtle. Common enough in the spring migration myrtle warblers travel southwards in hordes during September and early October, some still keeping to the tree tops but others overflowing into low bushes along roads and streams and many entering residential districts to garner the insect wealth around shrubbery and buildings.

BLACK-THROATED BLUE WARBLER

MYRTLE WARBLER
male *female*

373

WOOD WARBLERS — Family Parulidae

AUDUBON'S WARBLER
Dendroica auduboni subsp. (p. 497)

Common Summer Resident.
Length 5½ in.

DESCRIPTION: Spring m. — Upperparts bluish-gray streaked with black; golden yellow patch on crown and another on rump; two broad white wing bars; white eyelids; black of face becomes bluish on ears; throat yellow; underparts white very heavily streaked with black across breast and down sides; yellow patch on side at bend of wing; white mark on outer four tail feathers. Ad. f.—Similar but colors subdued; no black on face and band across breast grayish instead of black. Im.—Like female but browner above.

IDENTIFICATION: Golden yellow patches on crown, throat, rump, and sides distinguish Audubon's from all other warblers; myrtle warbler is similar but has a white throat. Hybrids show a mixture of the color characteristics of the two species.

RANGE: Western North America. Breeds mainly in mountain and coastal areas from northern B.C. and Alberta south to California and Arizona. Winters at lower altitudes from southern B.C. to Guatemala.

NESTING: In evergreens at varying heights. Nest of twigs, grass, and rootlets lined with fine rootlets, hair, and feathers. Eggs, 3-5, creamy-white spotted and blotched with browns and gray. (Banff, June 25.)

REMARKS: Audubon's warbler is a western species whose breeding range extends into Alberta along the eastern slopes of the Rockies and their foothills. It also nests in the Cypress Hills. On migration it has been observed or collected at widely scattered points including Calgary, Rosebud, Camrose, Clyde, and Egremont.

In habits as well as in color Audubon's warbler is an almost exact replica of the myrtle warbler but it is rarely found far from the mountains. It frequents coniferous woods on mountain slopes and mixed woods in the valleys. Few warblers are more active than Audubon's. In the dense foliage of evergreens one catches an occasional glimpse of blue, black, or yellow, flashing from branch to branch; only when the male perches on top of a tree to sing is it still long enough to afford a good view. In the fall Audubon's warbler migrates to lower altitudes as well as lower latitudes. Forsaking the mountain slopes where it spent the summer it passes the winter comfortably in warm coastal valleys.

374

TOWNSEND'S WARBLER
Dendroica townsendi

Scarce Summer Resident.
Length 5 in.

DESCRIPTION: Ad. m.—Crown black; rest of upperparts green spotted with black; two white wing bars; tail black with much white on outer three feathers; cheeks, throat, and streaks on sides black; line over eye, sides of throat and neck, and breast yellow; rest of underparts white. Ad. f.—Similar to male but black areas of face and underparts much broken up by yellow feathers. Im.—Similar to female but duller.

IDENTIFICATION: Most likely to be confused with black-throated green warbler but with black crown and striking black and yellow face markings. Some suggestion of face markings is usually present in the fall to distinguish this from other warblers.

RANGE: Western North America. Breeds from Alaska south to Wyoming in Rockies and westward. Winters in California and in Mexico and Central America.

NESTING: In conifers. Nest, a rather large mass of shredded bark and moss lined with moss or hair. Eggs, 3-5, white speckled with browns.

REMARKS: Townsend's warbler is a typical mountain species whose range in Alberta is restricted to the Rocky Mountains from the international boundary to north of Jasper. It is known to breed in Banff National Park along the Banff-Windermere highway but there are no definite nesting records from the Waterton Lakes or Jasper Parks. In both of these regions, however, it has been seen during the breeding season. It occasionally wanders eastward; a male in full plumage was taken at Rosebud on May 18, 1935.

The favorite habitat of Townsend's warblers is coniferous forests, particularly thick stands of tall firs. During the nesting season they remain almost constantly in the tree tops where their small size and green color help to make them inconspicuous. Only their sibilant song, a gentle, *weazy* repeated four or five times, indicates their presence. The observer who cannot recognize this song has little chance of finding the species during the summer. On migration, however, Townsend's warblers often come down to lower levels and even feed in deciduous bushes with flocks of other warblers and chickadees.

ALLAN BROOKS

AUDUBON'S WARBLER
female   *male*

ALLAN BROOKS

TOWNSEND'S WARBLER
male   *female*

ALLAN BROOKS

BLACK-THROATED GREEN WARBLER
male   *female*

ALLAN BROOKS

BLACKBURNIAN WARBLER
female   *male*

WOOD WARBLERS — Family Parulidae

BLACK-THROATED GREEN WARBLER   Scarce Summer Resident.
Dendroica virens subsp. (p. 497)   Length 5 in.

DESCRIPTION: Ad.. m.—Upperparts yellowish-green; wings black with two white bars; tail black, outer feathers largely white; forehead, sides of head and neck yellow; throat, upper breast, and sides black; rest of underparts white. Ad. f.—Similar but black of underparts partly obscured by yellow feather edges. Im.—Similar above to adults but with dark streaks on feathers; below yellow on breast becoming white on abdomen; obscure black streaks mainly confined to sides.

IDENTIFICATION: Adults similar to Townsend's warbler but more black below and lack black crown. In the fall the combination of yellow cheeks, yellow underparts streaked with black, and two white wing bars is distinctive..

RANGE: Eastern North America. Breeds from northern Alberta to Newfoundland southeast to northeastern states. Winters in Mexico and Central America.

NESTING: In trees, usually evergreens. Nest of fine twigs and shredded bark lined with fine grass and rootlets. Eggs, 4-5, creamy-white spotted and blotched with browns. (Glenevis, June 15.)

REMARKS: During the breeding season the black-throated green warbler is found in the coniferous and mixed-wood forest areas of northern Alberta including the Peace River District and south to Glenevis, Belvedere and Athabasca. A male was seen near Cameron Lake in Waterton Lakes Park on July 1, 1959. On migration the species is more widely distributed; it has been seen or collected at Edmonton, Camrose, Red Deer, Pigeon Lake, Calgary, Waterton Lakes and Medicine Hat.

High in the tree-tops the black-throated green warbler may easily be overlooked unless one watches for a small green form which is constantly on the move. Occasionally, if one remains motionless, the beautifully marked male may come to lower levels to inspect the observer for it is full of curiosity and not at all timid. In the mixed flocks of warblers which pass through central Alberta about the middle of May a few black-throated green warblers are usually found. They feed upon the insects attracted to catkins of poplar and willow and, since leaves may not yet be opened, they are easily seen. During the nesting season black-throated green warblers frequent stands of evergreens or mixed clumps of conifers and deciduous trees but, while they always nest in the former, they feed anywhere. Late in August when myriads of warblers in their dull fall plumage move southward through the woods, black-throated greens add a touch of color to the parade. At this time they are often found at low levels picking up aphids from the leaves and investigating every spider web for possibility of bounty.

378

WOOD WARBLERS — Family Parulidae

BLACKBURNIAN WARBLER
Dendroica fusca

Scarce Wanderer.
Length 5 in.

DESCRIPTION: Ad. m.—Upperparts black with orange patch on crown, some white streaking on back, and a very wide white wing bar; outer four tail feathers white with black tips; orange stripe over eye extending onto neck; black patch behind eye extending to neck; throat and upper breast orange; rest of underparts pale yellow streaked with black on sides. Ad. f.—Similar but the orange largely replaced by yellow and the black by brownish-gray; two white wing bars.

IDENTIFICATION: No other warbler has such striking black and orange markings on the head; females usually show enough orange to be recognizable.

RANGE: Eastern North America and South America. Breeds from southern Manitoba and Minnesota east to the Atlantic states. Winters in central South America.

NESTING: High in coniferous trees. Nest of twigs lined with grasses and horsehair. Eggs, 4-5, white spotted with browns.

REMARKS: Specimens of Blackburnian warblers have been taken only at High River, Edmonton and Grand Center, near Cold Lake but the species has been seen during migration periods in various parts of central Alberta. Singing males of this species have been observed at Glenevis, Skeleton Lake and Cold Lake and there is little doubt that Blackburnian warblers nest, or have nested, in these regions. In the Skeleton Lake area during recent years Blackburnian warblers have been present in fair numbers throughout the breeding season and there is every evidence of nesting although no nests have yet been found. More intensive investigation of the northeastern section of Alberta will be necessary before the breeding range of this species can be accurately outlined.

In eastern Canada Blackburnian warblers inhabit both deciduous and coniferous forests but show a preference for spruce woods, especially during the nesting season. In Alberta Blackburnian warblers show similar preferences during the summer; they are usually found in thick stands of evergreens in mixed-wood forests. Since the males choose singing posts high in a spruce and the females build their nests at a considerable height, the birds spend most of their time in the crowns of conifers where they are difficult to see. They are best located by recognition of their song, a high note repeated four or five times followed by a more rapidly repeated series an octave or more higher and almost at the limit of audibility. On migration Blackburnian warblers are less likely to confine themselves to conifers although they still feed mainly in the tops of trees. Among the colorful array of migrant warblers which move through the province about the time leaf-buds are bursting the Blackburnian is a beautiful rarity well worth looking for.

CHESTNUT-SIDED WARBLER
immature   *male*

BAY-BREASTED WARBLER
male   *female*

CHESTNUT-SIDED WARBLER   Scarce Summer Resident.
Dendroica pensylvanica   Length 5 in.

DESCRIPTION: Spring m. — Forehead and crown yellow; ear and side of neck white; black line through eye and across nape; back black, the feathers edged with white or green; two yellowish wing bars; throat and underparts white, the throat bordered with black and sides heavily streaked with chestnut; white marks on two outer tail feathers. Spring f. – Similar but duller and less chestnut on sides. Im.—Yellowish-olive above faintly streaked with dusky; face and underparts grayish-white with light eye-ring and suggestion of chestnut on sides.

IDENTIFICATION: Black, white, and yellow head of adults is distinctive. Immatures similar to certain plumages of black-poll and bay-breasted warblers but may be distinguished by grayer underparts, gray face and eye-ring.

RANGE: Eastern North America. Breeds from northern Alberta and Newfoundland southeast to Georgia. Winters in Central America.

NESTING: In small trees or bushes about 2-3 feet from ground. Nest of grass and plant fibers lined with horsehair and rootlets. Eggs, 3-5, creamy-white marked with browns. (Boyle, July 4, young.)

REMARKS: The chestnut-sided warbler is an eastern species which may not occur regularly in Alberta for there are very few records. On May 20, 1934, the species was observed near Boyle and on July 4th a nest containing young was found. Early in May, 1935, five chestnut-sided warblers were seen near Fawcett. On August 8, 1938, 'a small flock' was seen in the city of Red Deer. These are all the known records for the province.

The chestnut-sided warbler prefers second-growth deciduous woods of medium height in whose leafy confines it can forage for insects. It is an active bird and does not hesitate to dart out after an insect which tries to escape in flight. Its search for food apparently occupies most of its attention for it is not particularly wary and will usually allow a fairly close approach.

The observer who lacks binoculars may miss completely the wave of colorful warblers which passes through central Alberta during May. A good view of such beautiful and unusual species as the chestnut-sided warbler is ample return for the small financial outlay involved in securing visual aid.

381

BAY-BREASTED WARBLER Scarce Summer Resident.
Dendroica castanea Length 5½ in.

DESCRIPTION: Spring m.—Crown chestnut; forehead and face black; large buffy-white spot on side of neck; rest of upperparts greenish-gray streaked with black; two white wing bars; white patches on outer two tail feathers; throat, foreneck, and sides chestnut; rest of underparts white. Ad. f.—Upperparts olive-gray streaked with black sometimes with a little chestnut in crown; two white wing bars; underparts buffy-white lightly streaked with chestnut on sides. Im.—Like female but greener above with less streaking and only faint suggestions of chestnut on sides. Fall adults lose their bright coloring and are more like immatures.

IDENTIFICATION: Adult males are distinctively marked. In other plumages this species may be similar to young blackpoll or chestnut-sided warblers; brownish sides distinguish it from former, darker face and lack of eye-ring from latter.

RANGE: Eastern North America. Breeds from northern Alberta to Labrador south to southern Manitoba and New York. Winters in Central and South America.

NESTING: In evergreen trees. Nest, a bulky structure of twigs and grasses lined with rootlets and hair. Eggs, 4-6, creamy white blotched with browns.

REMARKS: The bay-breasted warbler nests locally and in small numbers from the northern boundary of the province south to Jasper, Peers, Athabasca and Boyle. A pair nesting near Skeleton Lake were photographed in 1965. Singing males have been seen about fifty miles west of Edmonton. On migration bay-breasted warblers have been observed at many places in southern Alberta and specimens have been taken at Edmonton, Rosebud and Medicine Hat.

For its breeding territory the bay-breasted warbler selects a spruce grove in a coniferous or mixed-wood forest and spends much of its time in, or at the edge of, the shadowy confines of the conifers. Its song, a sibilant *seesy-seesy* - -, repeated four or five times on one note, is so high pitched and weak that it does not carry far enough to be of much help in locating the singer. Like most of the warblers the bay-breasted is quite active; it moves about at any levels in the maze of evergreens giving an observer only fleeting glimpses. On migration bay-breasted warblers are often found in deciduous trees with other warblers. They are most abundant in the fall when young birds swell the flocks but they are not as colorful at this time and it takes careful scrutiny to pick out the rusty markings which identify them.

WOOD WARBLERS — Family Parulidae

BLACKPOLL WARBLER
Dendroica striata

Scarce Summer Resident.
Length 5½ in.

DESCRIPTION: Spring m.—Top of head from lower edge of eye upward black; face and entire underparts white except a narrow row of black streaks starting at middle of beak and becoming heavier and broader as it extends down sides of breast and along sides; rest of upperparts olive-gray streaked with black; two white wing bars; two outer tail feathers tipped with white. In fall male resembles female. Ad. f.—Similar but more olive above and the crown yellowish-green streaked with black; underparts washed with yellow and markings indistinct. Im.—Olive-green above streaked with black on back; wings and tail as in adult; throat, breast, and sides washed with yellowish-green and very faintly streaked with dusky; middle of abdomen and under tail white.

IDENTIFICATION: Males are most likely to be confused with black-and-white warbler but entire top of head is black and there is little white on back. Fall adults and immatures are similar to immature chestnut-sided and bay-breasted warblers but lack the gray face of former and suggestion of chestnut on sides of latter.

RANGE: North and South America. Breeds from tree limit across continent south to northern B.C. and prairie provinces across to Maine. Winters in northern South America.

NESTING: In evergreens at height of 10 ft. or less. Nest of grass, lichens, and rootlets lined with fine grass and feathers. Eggs, 3-5, creamy-white speckled with browns and lilac.

REMARKS: The blackpoll warbler nests in the coniferous woods of northern Alberta south to about Athabasca. It also breeds in small numbers in the mountains and foothills, where nests have been recorded at Banff and Bragg Creek. In central and southern Alberta it occurs only as a migrant.

Blackpoll warblers migrate through southern Alberta in late May keeping to the wooded coulees where trees have just burst into leaf. Instead of creeping about on the trunk and branches like black-and-white warblers they search the catkins of willow and poplar for small insects or flit about among the spruce boughs inspecting spider webs. Usually they occur singly or in twos or threes; often a male and a female travel together. On their nesting grounds blackpoll warblers frequent dense spruce woods in whose stillness their thin sibilant song carries far. On the southward migration small flocks, now in the greenish plumage, often migrate together. For a few days late in August the species is well represented in the mixed flocks of warblers which frequent the upper branches of coniferous and deciduous woods; then they are gone, leaving the abundant insect life to myrtle warblers and other laggards.

WOOD WARBLERS — Family Parulidae

PINE WARBLER   Scarce Summer Resident.
Dendroica pinus   subsp. (p. 497)   Length 5 in.

DESCRIPTION: Ads. — Upperparts yellowish-olive; face and sides of neck olive-green; line over eye and mark under eye yellow; throat, breast, and sides yellow, indistinctly streaked with gray; rest of underparts white; two white wing bars; two outer tail feathers tipped with white. Females are browner above than males. Im.—Brownish-olive above; two white wing bars; underparts dull white streaked with gray on breast and sides and sometimes tinged with yellow.

IDENTIFICATION: Adults may be confused with orange-crowned warblers but have two white wing bars, white spots on outer tail feathers, and white under tail coverts. Young birds appear something like young palm warblers but have two white wing bars and white instead of yellow under tail coverts.

RANGE: Eastern North America. Breeds from central Alberta and southern Quebec south to Texas and Florida. Winters in southern states.

NESTING: In conifers, usually pines. Nest of twigs, strips of bark, and pine needles bound with spider webs and lined with hair and feathers. Eggs, 3-5, dull white speckled with browns.

REMARKS: The only specimen of the pine warbler taken in Alberta is a male collected at Castor in June, 1924. During the summer of 1928 several pairs of pine warblers were observed near the town of Athabasca. They appeared to have established territories but no direct evidence of nesting was found. There are also sight records of pine warblers at Glenevis and in the Cypress Hills. These scanty records constitute our present knowledge of the distribution of this species in Alberta.

Pine warblers, as their name indicates, usually frequent coniferous forests. Those which were observed near Athabasca remained in several isolated stands of mature spruce east of the town. They often creep about on the trunks and limbs of trees after the manner of black and white warblers but they also fly about actively and catch insects on the wing. They are not very wary but they are such inconspicuous birds that it is possible they are being overlooked in some parts of Alberta. Any unusual trill coming from coniferous woods should be investigated carefully. The pine warbler repeats the same note rapidly about twenty times, *chi, chi, chi, chi, chi,* — —, producing a liquid trill somewhat reminiscent of the song of the chipping sparrow.

384

BLACKPOLL WARBLER
male   *female*

PINE WARBLER

WOOD WARBLERS — Family Parulidae

PALM WARBLER   Scarce Summer Resident.
Dendroica palmarum   subsp. (p. 497)   Length 5 in.

DESCRIPTION: Ads.—Crown chestnut; rest of upper-parts and face grayish-brown tinged with green on rump; line over eye, throat, breast, and under tail coverts yellow, but the sides of throat, breast, and sides streaked with chestnut; abdomen white; outer two tail feathers with white spots at tip. Sexes alike. Im.—Upperparts grayish-brown tinged with yellowish-green on rump; buffy line over eye; underparts buffy indistinctly streaked on sides of throat, breast, and sides with grayish-brown; under tail coverts yellow; tail as in adult.

IDENTIFICATION: A rather colorless warbler dull brown above and dull yellow below; chestnut cap and yellow throat and under tail coverts are best field marks. In the fall the general brownish color with yellow only under the tail is distinctive.

RANGE: North America. Breeds from southern Mackenzie to Newfoundland south to central Alberta and Maine. Winters in southeastern states and West Indies.

NESTING: On the ground in the moss of dry muskegs. Nest of grass and moss lined with fine grass and feathers. Eggs, 4-5, white speckled with browns. (Belvedere, June 12.)

REMARKS: The palm warbler breeds in the heavily wooded areas of northeastern Alberta south as far as Elk Island Park and Glenevis and west to Wood Buffalo Park, Grouard and Whitecourt. It has not been found in the Peace River District or in the mountains. On migration it has been observed in many places in southern Alberta mostly east of a line through Edmonton and Calgary.

The borders of dry muskegs are favorite haunts of the palm warbler during the nesting season. Here, at the foot of a dwarfed tree in dry sphagnum moss shaded by blueberry and bearberry, the female builds her nest, while her mate nearby sings an unmusical song, *zee, zee, zee, zee,* — —, a series of six or seven sibilant notes all on the same pitch. Palm warblers spend as much time on the ground as they do in bushes and trees. Wherever they are their habit of nervously pumping the tail up and down every few seconds helps to identify them. Palm warblers are neither shy nor wary and may usually be approached closely for observation. During the fall migration they often accompany other species of warblers through the bushes and tree tops feeding on the abundant insect life. At this time they occasionally appear in wooded river valleys on the prairies and in shade trees along city streets.

WOOD WARBLERS — Family Parulidae

OVENBIRD Fairly Common Summer Resident.
Seiurus aurocapillus   subsp. (p. 497) Length 5½ in.

DESCRIPTION: Ads. — Upperparts olive-green except orange-brown stripe down middle of crown bordered on each side with black; underparts white streaked with black on sides of throat and more heavily across breast and down sides. Sexes alike. Immature birds are similar but browner above and somewhat buffy below.

IDENTIFICATION: Looks much like a small thrush with a warbler's beak. The two black crown stripes with orange between are distinctive.

RANGE: North and South America. Breeds from southern Mackenzie and Newfoundland south to Colorado and Georgia. Winters in southeastern states, central, and northern South America.

NESTING: On the ground in woods. Nest, a domed structure of leaves, moss, and grass, lined with fine rootlets and hair; entrance at side. Eggs, 3-6, white speckled with brown and gray. (Glenevis, June 27, 2 eggs and one of cowbird.)

REMARKS: The ovenbird nests in the deciduous and mixed-wood forests of Alberta from near Edmonton north to the provincial boundary. It also nests commonly in the Cypress Hills. In the mountains and foothills it is a scarce summer resident having been seen near Jasper and west of Turner Valley. In the parklands and on the prairies the ovenbird occurs only as a migrant.

Ovenbirds avoid coniferous forests showing a decided preference for aspen and other deciduous woods where the undergrowth is not too dense. They spend most of their time on the ground scratching among the dead leaves for small insects. Instead of hopping like most other warblers they walk about with a peculiar springy gait. Ovenbirds are very shy. Usually they disappear among the lower branches when disturbed and, since they are not as active as most other warblers, they are difficult to find. However, their presence in any locality is never left in doubt for their song is quite distinctive. It consists of a single note repeated twelve or thirteen times, starting softly and gradually becoming louder and louder, *teach-teach-Teach-Teach-TEACH-TEACH* — — —. Occasionally a two-note phrase, *teacher,* is repeated but most ovenbirds whose voices have been recorded in Alberta use the single note.

The nest is usually built in the dead leaves on the woodland floor where the undergrowth is sparse enough to allow the female to walk to it from any direction. From its resemblance to an old dutch oven, covered and with the opening in the side, comes the name ovenbird. Both male and female are solicitous in care of the young.

387

PALM WARBLER

C. HAMPSON

OVENBIRDS
female   *male*

NORTHERN WATER-THRUSH

R. CHANDLER

CONNECTICUT WARBLER

RAY SALT

WOOD WARBLERS — Family Parulidae

NORTHERN WATERTHRUSH Fairly Common Summer Resident.
Seiurus noveboracensis subsp. (p. 497) Length 5½ in.

DESCRIPTION: Ads. — Upperparts dark olive-brown; pale buffy line over eye extending back over ear; underparts white faintly tinged with yellow on breast and abdomen, and streaked with dark brown everywhere except on abdomen. Sexes alike. Immature birds are similar but browner.

IDENTIFICATION: A small thrush-like bird with beak of warbler. Light line over eye and small size distinguish it from thrushes. Most likely to be confused with ovenbird but has line over eye and lacks any markings on crown.

RANGE: North and South America. Breeds from Alaska and Newfoundland south to southern B.C. and North Carolina. Winters from Mexico to northern South America.

NESTING: On the ground at the foot of a stump or on bank of stream. Nest of moss, leaves, and twigs, lined with fine grass and hair. Eggs, 4-5, creamy-white spotted with browns.

REMARKS: The waterthrush is widely distributed as a breeding bird in the heavily forested regions of northern and western Alberta entering the mountains along the lower valleys. In the parklands and prairies it occurs only as a migrant although a recent record indicates that it may nest in the Cypress Hills.

As its name indicates the waterthrush looks and acts something like a thrush and is usually found near water. Yet it is a true warbler. Deciduous growth with heavy underbrush along the shores of lakes and streams is the favorite habitat. If the water has flooded the forest floor so much the better. In such damp places the waterthrush spends most of its time on or near the ground searching along logs or turning over wet leaves to get at the insects beneath. Like the ovenbird it walks instead of hopping but with each step its legs bend, producing a teetering gait accentuated by repeated flirtings of the tail. Waterthrushes are solitary in habit. For this reason and because their haunts are relatively inaccessible many observers fail to find them. However, they have a robust song which may be sung from the ground, from the bushes or from the top of a tall spruce. It is a beautiful song — one of the finest musical performances of the warblers — and during the mid-May migration a chorus of five or six northern waterthrushes may produce a never-to-be-forgotten symphony. During the third week of August northern waterthrushes move southward through the dense woods usually keeping near the ground and not far from water. The observer who stands still and waits for the birds to come to him is most likely to see such species as the waterthrush.

WOOD WARBLERS — Family Parulidae

CONNECTICUT WARBLER Fairly Common Summer Resident.
Oporornis agilis Length 5½ in.

DESCRIPTION: Ads.—Head, throat, and upper breast bluish-gray, lighter on throat; complete white eye-ring; rest of upperparts olive-green; rest of underparts yellow tinged with olive on sides; no white on tail. Females are lighter than males. Im.—Upperparts brownish-olive; pale buffy eye-ring; throat and breast olive-brown, sides olive; rest of underparts yellow.

IDENTIFICATION: Similar to mourning and MacGillivray's warblers. White eye-ring and lack of black on throat and breast distinguish from former; complete eye-ring and lack of black in front of eye from latter. The complete light eye-ring is the best identification mark of females and immature birds.

RANGE: North and South America. Breeds from northern B.C. and Ontario south to Minnesota and Michigan. Winters in Brazil and Venezuela.

NESTING: On the ground. Nest of grass and plant fibers. Eggs, 4-5, creamy white speckled with browns. (Belvedere, June 19.)

REMARKS: The Connecticut, mourning, and MacGillivray's warblers and the yellowthroat belong to a group known as ground warblers because they spend most of their time either on the ground or in low shrubbery. As a breeding bird the Connecticut warbler is widely but locally distributed in the forest regions of Alberta from Edmonton north at least to Ft. McMurray and the Peace River district. Nothing is known of its distribution farther north. In the southern half of the province it occurs rarely on migration.

The Connecticut warbler is a late migrant, never arriving on its nesting grounds before the first of June. Open poplar bluffs on ridges above rivers and lakes or mixed woods along their shores are its haunts. In the grass under a small tree the female builds her nest and in the surrounding underbrush the family is raised. Never very shy the male may sit motionless on a limb of a tree singing in full view of an observer, yet he is difficult to see for his colors blend well with the foliage. The song, *wheecha — wheecha — wheecha — wheecha — wheech,* accented on the first syllable, or *MacMurchy — MacMurchy — MacMurchy — MacMurchy,* accented on the second syllable, is very loud and clear, as loud as that of the ovenbird. It carries quite a distance; a few miles from Edmonton it is possible to hear from one spot, two males singing lustily, and each producing a different type of song.

MOURNING WARBLER

RAY SALT

ALLAN BROOKS

MACGILLIVRAY'S WARBLER
female   *male*

WOOD WARBLERS — Family Parulidae

MOURNING WARBLER
Oporornis philadelphia

Fairly Common Summer Resident.
Length 5 in.

DESCRIPTION: Ads.—Head and neck bluish-gray except black stripe in front of eye which may form eye-ring; throat and upper breast black; rest of upperparts olive-green; rest of underparts yellow washed with olive on sides; no white on tail. Female lacks black on throat and breast which are pale bluish-gray. Im.—Upperparts olive-green; throat and breast buffy, often marked with black; sides grayish-olive; rest of underparts yellow.

IDENTIFICATION: Similar to Connecticut and MacGillivray's warblers but no light marks around eye and male has black throat and breast. In the fall females and young are brownish-olive birds with yellow underparts; immatures may have light eye-ring.

RANGE: North and South America. Breeds from northern B.C. to Newfoundland south to North Dakota and Virginia. Winters in Central and northern South America.

NESTING: On or near the ground. Nest, a bulky mass of dead leaves, weeds, and grass often in low bushes. Eggs, 3-5, creamy-white speckled with browns. (Edmonton, June 6.)

REMARKS: The mourning warbler breeds in the heavily wooded regions of northern Alberta north as far as Chipewyan. Southward it ranges into the parklands along wooded river valleys as far as Red Deer. Elsewhere in southern Alberta it occurs mainly as a migrant. It has not been recorded from the mountains or the foothills. Here its place is taken by MacGillivray's warbler which is similar in appearance, behavior, song and choice of habitat. In an area west of Edmonton and approaching the mountains specimens have been taken which show characters of both MacGillivray's and the mourning warbler. These intermediate forms are at present the subject of a taxonomic study.

In the northern regions the mourning warbler is generally found in poplar woods where windfall and dense undergrowth provide heavy cover near the forest floor. In the parklands it chooses dense thickets which form a similar type of habitat. Although it is quite active the mourning warbler is very shy and prefers to remain in the seclusion of the dense foliage of the underbrush. The male sings from the top of a bush but at the first sign of danger he drops into the shrubbery where, not far away, his mate is incubating her eggs. The observer who wishes to see the mourning warbler must be a master at the art of 'squeaking' for if his imitation of the cry of a young bird in distress is sufficiently realistic even this shy warbler will approach his hiding place to investigate the cause of the trouble.

393

WOOD WARBLERS — Family Parulidae

MACGILLIVRAY'S WARBLER   Fairly Common Summer Resident..
Oporornis tolmiei subsp. (p. 498)   Length 5 in.

DESCRIPTION: Ads.—Head, neck, and upper breast bluish-gray with some black feathers on throat and breast; black mark in front of eye; eyelids white forming incomplete eye-ring; rest of upperparts olive-green; rest of underparts yellow washed with olive on sides; no white on tail. Females are similar but lack black markings of head and breast. Im.—Upperparts brownish-olive; throat and upper breast grayish-olive; sides brownish-olive; rest of underparts yellow.

IDENTIFICATION: Similar to Connecticut and mourning warblers; incomplete eye-ring is best identification mark in all plumages.

RANGE: Western North and South America. Breeds from Alaska and Saskatchewan south to California and New Mexico. Winters from Mexico to northern South America.

NESTING: In bushes, within five feet of ground.. Nest of grass and shreds of bark. Eggs, 3-5, creamy-white speckled with browns. (Cypress Hills, June 21.)

REMARKS: MacGillivray's warbler might be called the western mourning warbler for its range begins where that of the mourning warbler stops. In Alberta there is some overlapping of their ranges. MacGillivray's warbler nests in the Rocky Mountains and their foothills. It also nests in the Cypress Hills and in the brush-covered slopes of the coulees which run into the Red Deer River valley. Records of its occurrence in the Edmonton and Peace River districts during the breeding season require further substantiation particularly since specimens intermediate between mourning and MacGillivray's warblers have been collected not far from these areas.

MacGillivray's warblers frequent thick bushy growth not far from water. Tangles of saskatoon, chokecherry, willow, and alder, with undergrowth of gooseberry, currant, and rose are favorite haunts in the prairie coulees. In habitat of this sort only the loud cheerful song of the male coming first from this place then from that is evidence of his activity. If the female is disturbed from her nest he may join her in scolding the intruder; when the young have hatched both birds show themselves openly and become quite agitated until they have lured him away from the family. On the southward migration when most warblers travel through the trees MacGillivray's warblers may easily be overlooked since they still keep largely to the underbrush.

394

WOOD WARBLERS — Family Parulidae

YELLOWTHROAT Common Summer Resident.
Geothlypis trichas subsp. (p. 498) Length 5 in.

DESCRIPTION: Ad. m. — Forehead and face black forming a broad mask over eyes edged behind by white; rest of upperparts greenish-olive, unmarked; throat, breast and under tail coverts yellow; abdomen white; sides washed with brownish-olive. Ad. f.—Upperparts grayish-olive unmarked; no black mask; throat, breast, and under tail coverts pale yellow; sides brownish-olive; abdomen whitish. Im.—Like female; young males often show suggestion of black mask.

IDENTIFICATION: The black mask of the male is distinctive. Females are similar to female mourning and MacGillivray's warblers but are browner above and on the sides; there is no eye-ring and the throat is always yellowish.

RANGE: North and Central America. Breeds throughout most of Canada and the U.S.A. Winters in southern states and Central America.

NESTING: On or near the ground, usually near water. Nest, a bulky mass of grass, weeds, and leaves lined with finer grass and hair. Eggs, 3-5, creamy-white speckled with brown, black, and gray. (Cooking Lake, June 26.)

REMARKS: The yellowthroat breeds in all parts of Alberta including the mountains and foothills but it is quite locally distributed in the heavily forested areas and on the prairies. On migration its distribution is much wider.

The yellowthroat frequents bushes rather than trees and is rarely found close to human habitation or far from water. The nesting site may be in low buck brush near a prairie brook, in willow tangles along a stream, or in cat-tail beds or the underbrush bordering swamps and lakes. From such places comes a loud *witchity — witchity — witchity* which may be the only indication of the presence of yellowthroats for they are secretive birds seldom seen in the open. Like all warblers they are very active but they usually remain in dense growth close to the ground. Fortunately they are not particularly wary and an observer who can stand in their haunts long enough will catch many glimpses of the black-masked male whose activities may be followed by his bursts of song when they are lost to view. In the fall yellowthroats still stay close to water. Flushed from the reeds they make a quick dash for the nearest brushy cover. Apparently they migrate chiefly at night for many are picked up dead around lighthouses and well-illuminated city buildings after foggy or stormy nights.

YELLOW-BREASTED CHAT Scarce Summer Resident.
Icteria virens subsp. (p. 498) Length 7½ in.

DESCRIPTION: Ad. m.—Upperparts entirely plain olive-brown darkest on crown; line from base of beak to cheeks black; line over eye, eyelids, and stripe on side of throat white; throat and breast bright yellow; abdomen white; flanks olive-brown. Ad. f.—Similar but markings of head less distinct and yellow paler. In the fall young are like adults.

IDENTIFICATION: A greenish-brown bird with bright yellow throat and breast and strong decurved beak. The largest of the warblers.

RANGE: North America. Breeds from extreme southern Canada through United States to northern Mexico. Winters in Mexico and Central America.

NESTING: In low bushes. Nest of coarse grass and leaves lined with fine grasses. Eggs, 3-5, white spotted with browns. (Empress, July 23, young about a week old.)

REMARKS: The chat was first discovered in Alberta at Rosebud where an adult female was collected on June 6, 1941. It has since been found at various places along the Milk and South Saskatchewan rivers and along the Red Deer river north as far as the Trochu ferry. It occurs regularly near Steveville and Empress. It is not known for sure whether the chat was overlooked in southern Alberta for many years or whether it has recently extended its range northward but the latter is probably the case.

Dense shrubbery such as the tangles of willow, hawthorn, saskatoon, and chokecherry which border our southern rivers are the usual haunts of the chat. It is a great skulker and in this habitat such a shy bird could easily be overlooked if the males were not inveterate singers. From the top of a bush or tree they pour out a long series of loud whistles, squawks, and trills which is quite unlike the song of any other bird. The order and arrangement of these sounds are constantly varied so that no two songs are quite alike yet the quality of the tones and the mixture of cackles and squeals with pure notes produces an easily identified song. Sometimes, particularly during courtship, the male rises above the bushes on erratically beating wings and, with legs dangling and head thrown back, lets out his exuberant song. But whether in the air or in the bushes at the first sign of danger the singer drops into the safety of the thicket where he sings again as soon as the coast is clear. On migration in the fall chats are silent and furtive; only rarely are they seen.

RAY SALT

YELLOWTHROAT
male

C. HAMPSON

YELLOW-BREASTED CHAT

WOOD WARBLERS — Family Parulidae

WILSON'S WARBLER Common Summer Resident.
Wilsonia pusilla subsp. (p. 498) Length 5 in.

DESCRIPTION: Ad. m.—Crown black, rest of head and all underparts yellow; upperparts olive-green. Ad. f. —Similar but the black crown may be obscured by greenish feather edges. Adults do not change color in the fall. Im.—Similar to adults; the black crown may or may not be evident.

IDENTIFICATION: Like a yellow warbler but smaller and usually with black cap; the tail of Wilson's warbler is olive, that of the yellow warbler is largely yellow.

RANGE: North America. Breeds from Alaska to Newfoundland south to Vermont and California. Winters in Mexico and Central America.

NESTING: On the ground in wet places. Nest of grass and moss near alder thickets bordering streams and lakes. Eggs, 4-6, white speckled with browns.

REMARKS: During the breeding season Wilson's warbler is quite locally distributed in the wooded areas of northern and western Alberta being most abundant in the Rocky Mountains and their foothills. It has recently been recorded in the Peace River District. On migration the species is widely spread throughout the parklands and prairies.

In summer Wilson's warbler frequents willow-alder thickets on river flats and beaver meadows or similar bushy tangles along lake-shores and woodland streams. It may be found in this type of habitat along the Vermilion Lakes only a few miles west of Banff. Dense, mountain-side thickets and dwarfed, wind-swept clumps of conifers near tree-line also provide nesting sites. They may be found in this type of habitat on Whistlers Mountain near Jasper. Like flycatchers Wilson's warblers catch much of their food on the wing darting out from a leafy maze to snap gnats, mosquitoes and small flies from the air. But unlike flycatchers they are not content to sit on a perch until another insect comes along. They bustle about among the low branches bursting occasionally into a loud hurried song which well reflects their impetuous nature. They are one of the tamest of the warblers; anyone who has the fortitude to get to their haunts will have no trouble in getting acquainted with them.

Wilson's warblers are not uncommon members of the mixed bands of migrating warblers which can be found feeding in wooded valleys of the prairies and parklands in May and August. At these times they do not restrict themselves to the undergrowth but may be found at any height in various types of vegetation although they still show a preference for deciduous trees. One of their common names, the black-capped warbler, is most appropriate for these little golden sprites crowned with black.

398

CANADA WARBLER Fairly Common Summer Resident.
Wilsonia canadensis Length 5¼ in.

DESCRIPTION: Ad. m. — Upperparts bluish - gray spotted with black on crown; face and sides of neck black; yellow line in front of eye continuous with yellow eye-ring; underparts yellow with a row of short black streaks across upper breast. Ad. f.—Similar but lacks black on face and neck and necklace on breast fainter. Im.—Similar to female but tinged with brown above.

IDENTIFICATION: Grayish upperparts and yellow underparts broken by dark necklace on upper breast are distinctive; yellow eye-ring and mark in front of eye are good field marks.

RANGE: Eastern North America and South America. Breeds in southern Canada and northern states east of the Rockies. Winters in Central America and northern South America.

NESTING: On or near the ground. Nest, a bulky structure of leaves lined with shredded bark and fine rootlets. Eggs, 3-5, creamy-white spotted with browns and gray.

REMARKS: The Canada warbler breeds in Alberta from the Beaver River area south of Cold Lake, north to Wood Buffalo Park and west to the Peace River District, Lesser Slave Lake and Belvedere. It is locally distributed throughout its range and is more abundant in the eastern than in the western sections. On migration the Canada warbler has been observed in various parts of central Alberta but there are no records from the south nor from the mountains.

The redstart, Wilson's and the Canada warbler are flycatching warblers characterized not only by their habits but by a somewhat flattened beak bordered at its base by long bristles. The Canada warbler has the agility and the nervous activity common to the members of this group. Its favorite habitat is willow-alder thickets near streams and underbrush bordering mixed-wood or deciduous forests. It flits about from twig to twig usually remaining at low levels and often alighting on the ground. In such places it finds caterpillars, grubs, and spiders but much of its food consists of insects captured on the wing. Like Wilson's warbler and the redstart it is constantly darting into the air to snap up passing flies and mosquitoes. The observer will find that the Canada warbler shows no concern at his approach but goes about its usual business with such energy that it may be difficult to follow.

ALLAN BROOKS

WILSON'S WARBLER

CANADA WARBLER

RAY SALT

AMERICAN REDSTART
female   male

KAY HODGES

HOUSE SPARROW

WOOD WARBLERS — Family Parulidae

AMERICAN REDSTART
Setophaga ruticilla   subsp. (p. 498)

Common Summer Resident.
Length 5 in.

DESCRIPTION: Ad. m.—Entirely jet black except white abdomen and large salmon red patches on sides, wings, and basal half of tail. Ad. f.—Head gray; rest of upperparts greenish-gray with large yellow patch on wing and basal half of tail; underparts white with yellow patch on sides. Im.—Like female. Males are a full year of age before they acquire the black plumage; a few black feathers and a reddish tinge may appear before then.

IDENTIFICATION: Males cannot be confused with any other species. Females and young show a large amount of yellow in the wing, and the tail appears yellow basally and dark at the tip. The most active of the warblers.

RANGE: North and South America. Breeds across Canada and the northern states. Winters from central Mexico to northern South America.

NESTING: In bushes or small trees. Nest of shredded bark matted together and lined with finer plant fibers and hair. Eggs, 4, grayish-white blotched with browns and gray. (Lake Wabamun, July 2.)

REMARKS: From the outer fringes of the parklands to the northern and western boundaries of the province the redstart is one of the more common breeding warblers. In the mountains it is confined to the valleys. It nests in the Cypress Hills but elsewhere in southern Alberta it occurs only as migrant.

Redstarts usually nest along the edges of deciduous woods or in bushes near clearings such as those bordering lakes, rivers, and roads. They are not at all wary nor are they averse to nesting near human habitations. Whether in the leafy maze of the willows or in the canopies of the poplars they are constantly on the move. Some warblers may pause for a moment's rest but not the redstart. Spreading its tail to show the beautiful orange-red marks it flits from twig to twig or hovers momentarily to snatch a dangling caterpillar from its thread. Most of its insect food is captured on the wing with all the aplomb of a flycatcher but with much more grace.

Redstarts sing a variety of songs some of which resemble those of the yellow warbler but the notes are more sibilant. Because redstarts in the gray and yellow plumage may often be seen singing in the spring there is a false belief that females sing as well as males. Male redstarts do not assume the black and red plumage until the second fall moult yet they set up territories and sing their appeal for a mate after their first spring migration. These are the redstarts which sing in the gray and yellow plumage.

WEAVER FINCHES — Family Ploceidae

All members of this family are native to the Old World but two species have been introduced into North America. One of these, the European tree sparrow, has not increased its range since establishing itself near St. Louis, Missouri, but the other, the English or house sparrow, since its original introductions at New York in 1850 and 1852, has spread over most of North America. Members of this family build a spherical woven nest with an opening in one side.

ENGLISH (HOUSE) SPARROW   Common Resident.
Passer domesticus subsp. (p. 498)   Length 6½ in.

DESCRIPTION: Ad. m.—Crown, lower back, cheeks, and sides olive-gray; line back of eye across neck chestnut; line through eye black; back and wings chestnut streaked with black and with one white wing bar; tail brownish-black; throat and breast black; sides and abdomen grayish-white, darkest on sides. Ad.f.—Upperparts brownish-gray, streaked on back and wings with black and buffy; underparts pale brownish-gray becoming almost white on abdomen; buffy line back of eye over ear.

IDENTIFICATION: The black throat and bib and chestnut markings of the male are distinctive. The female is a dull gray sparrow lacking distinctive markings. The stocky build and raucous notes of the English sparrow help to identify it.

RANGE: Europe, Asia, Africa; introduced into North America. Resident wherever found.

NESTING: In buildings, bird boxes, hollow trees, etc.; occasionally builds in branches of trees. Nest, a bulky mass of grass, cloth, hair, feathers, etc., with opening in side when built in trees. Eggs, 4-7, white thickly speckled with grayish-brown. More than one brood is raised each year.

REMARKS: The house sparrow is an introduced pest which has not endeared itself to bird lovers in its new home. It fouls buildings in both city and country; it usurps the nesting places of more welcome and beneficial species; it is boisterous, rowdy, and belligerent at all times. Yet when sparrows flock to the back door for a hand-out in below zero weather, few people can resist the temptation to play the benefactor and most house sparrows winter well. House sparrows have followed the advance of human settlement in the province and the species now occurs in all but the most remote areas. Around farmsteads and grain elevators it finds an easy living but around some of the small northern settlements its existence is more precarious.

403

BOBOLINK

WESTERN MEADOWLARK

MEADOWLARKS, BLACKBIRDS, ORIOLES — Family Icteridae

Members of this family vary greatly in habits, behavior, and color. Most of them are medium-sized birds with long beaks which start well up on the forehead and gradually taper to a point. Two Alberta species, the bobolink and the cowbird, have sparrow-like beaks.

BOBOLINK   Scarce Summer Resident.
Dolichonyx oryzivorus   Length 7 in.

DESCRIPTION: Spring m.—All black except following: broad white or pale buff collar on hindneck, white stripe down sides· of back extending to white rump and tail coverts, feathers of back and some on wings margined with white or buffy; central tail feathers pointed. In fall male resembles female. Ad. f.—Crown with buffy-yellow median stripe, the rest buffy heavily streaked with grayish-brown; upperparts buffy-yellow heavily streaked with grayish-brown; wings and tail grayish-brown; face buffy-yellow with dark streak through eye; underparts buffy-yellow streaked on sides with dusky.

IDENTIFICATION: Black males with light collar and rump are distinctive. Females are similar to some sparrows but larger and have a generally buffy color not found in most sparrows.

RANGE: North and South America. Breeds in northern states and southern Canada mostly east of the Rockies. Winters in central South America.

NESTING: On the ground. Nest, a deep depression lined with grasses and covered by surrounding vegetation. Eggs, 4-7, white heavily marked with browns and lilac. (Calgary, June 20.)

REMARKS: The bobolink is a fairly recent immigrant to Alberta which is apparently slowly extending its range. It has been found nesting at many places in that part of the province extending from near Waterton and the Cypress Hills north to Wainwright, Athabasca and Whitecourt. In some parts of this area bobolinks nest fairly regularly; in others they make sporadic appearances, nesting for a few years, sometimes in fair numbers, and then deserting the locality completely for no apparent reason. There are numerous isolated sightings of bobolinks outside this breeding range; the most westerly are from Gorge Creek and near Jasper. These are probably wide-ranging males which try to set up territories in new areas and, being unable to attract a mate, then move on.

Bobolinks are birds of open meadows and pasture lands where the grass grows to a length of several inches. The short 'prairie wool' of our semi-arid plains is not to their liking. The showy males attract attention in the spring not only with their contrasting colors but with their spectacular flight song. Rising into the air fifteen or twenty feet they slowly settle to earth on quivering wings like longspurs, all the while burbling a rapturous song. Meanwhile female bobolinks go about their business of building a nest ignored and unobserved. Perhaps the display of the males serves a useful purpose in detracting attention from the females.

MEADOWLARKS, BLACKBIRDS, ORIOLES — Family Icteridae

WESTERN MEADOWLARK   Common Summer Resident.
Sturnella neglecta subsp. (p. 498)   Length 9-10 in.

DESCRIPTION: Ad. m.—Crown brownish-gray streaked with black and with white medial stripe; feathers of upperparts brownish-gray edged with gray and barred with black; outer two tail feathers mostly white; face brownish-gray with yellow streak near beak, becoming white over eye and ear; throat and middle of underparts bright yellow with black V across upper breast; sides white streaked with brown. Ad. f.—Similar but duller, the yellow paler and the black V much reduced; about an inch shorter in length.

IDENTIFICATION: A   grayish-brown,   medium-sized bird with short tail, long pointed beak and black V on yellow breast. Color and song are both distinctive.

RANGE: Western North America. Breeds in southern parts of western provinces and in states west of Mississippi south to Texas. Winters from southern B.C. south to Mexico.

NESTING: On the ground. Nest, of grasses usually with an arched cover and entrance at side. Eggs, 4-6, white lightly spotted with brown and purple. Often raises two broods. (Calgary, May 20—July 24.)

REMARKS: Originally confined to the southern prairies the western meadowlark is slowly extending its breeding range in Alberta. It was first noted in Red Deer in 1892 and in Edmonton in 1897. Today it is reasonably common in the Athabasca area and in the Peace River District. Westward it is found in the foothills and even in the lower mountain valleys.

On the short-grass prairies of southern Alberta spring arrives with the return of the meadowlark about the end of March. There is never any doubt about the date for it is proclaimed in a rich loud voice which carries for almost half a mile. By the middle of April females have arrived and territories have been established not without some quarrelling largely vocal in nature. Meadowlarks spend most of their time on the ground walking about instead of hopping like sparrows, but some vantage point such as a fence-post or telephone pole is selected as a look-out perch or for singing. They have adapted well to agricultural encroachment and may often be seen picking up insects and seeds among the sprouting grain or in the stubble. For nesting sites, however, they still prefer the unturned sod. Meadowlarks are late migrants in the fall usually remaining well into October. Individuals occasionally winter in southern Alberta.

MEADOWLARKS, BLACKBIRDS, ORIOLES — Family Icteridae

YELLOW-HEADED BLACKBIRD   Fairly Common Summer Resident.
Xanthocephalus xanthocephalus   Length 10 in.

DESCRIPTION: Ad. m.—Head, neck, and upper breast yellowish-orange; black space around eye and chin black; rest of body, wings, and tail black except large white patch on wing. Ad. f.—Crown, upperparts, and wings dusky-brown; no white on wings; face, sides of neck, throat, and upper breast pale yellow or whitish; rest of underparts dusky-brown with much white streaking on lower breast. Fall adults have the yellow somewhat washed with brown. Im.—Similar to female but paler and the yellow replaced by buffy or buffy-yellow.

IDENTIFICATION: Adults are distinctively marked. Young birds are buffy especially about head and neck; plumage varies a lot but usually there is enough evidence of yellow around the head to identify.

RANGE: Western North America. Breeds from southern Mackenzie to the east side of Hudson Bay south to Mexico, mainly west of the Mississippi. Winters southwestern states and Mexico.

NESTING: In rushes or reeds over water, usually in small colonies. Nest of grasses and reeds woven securely to stems of cat-tails or reeds. Eggs, 3-6, dull white or olive, heavily marked with browns and gray. (Chestermere Lake, June 10.)

REMARKS: Beds of cat-tails on the margins of lakes or tall thick reeds in deep sloughs form nesting places for colonies of yellow-headed blackbirds. Unlike other species of blackbirds they will not nest in bushes or over dry land. Perched on swaying stems the males fill the air with discordant grating sounds which cannot be dignified with the name of song, or else fly about over the reed tops showing off their golden heads and white wing patches. Females, building or incubating at lower levels in the reed-bed, are less noisy and less conspicuous. After the family has been raised to maturity yellow-headed blackbirds are less restricted in their choice of habitat. On migration they may be found in the fields gleaning grain, weed-seeds, and insects from the stubble. Often they travel in company with Brewer's blackbirds or redwings retiring with them to spend the night in the reeds.

The yellow-headed blackbird occurs as a breeding bird throughout Alberta but owing to its restrictive habitat requirements its distribution is extremely local. It is scarce on the prairies and in the mountains. On migration it is more widely distributed.

REDWINGED BLACKBIRD　　　　　　Common Summer Resident.
Agelaius phoeniceus subsp. (p. 498)　　　　　　Length 9½ in.

DESCRIPTION: Ad. m.—Entirely black except a patch of red bordered behind with buffy on the bend of the wing. Ad. f.—Above brownish-black heavily streaked with white, gray, and rust; similar below but the lighter colors predominating; light line over eye and usually a light median stripe on crown; usually a few reddish feathers on bend of wing. Im.—Much like the adult female. There is much variation in plumages and although males usually show some red on the shoulder at an early age, it takes two years to acquire the full adult plumage.

IDENTIFICATION: Males are unmistakable. Females and young are heavily streaked brownish birds unlike any other species of blackbird.

RANGE: North America. Breeds throughout Canada and the U.S. Winters in southern States and Mexico.

NESTING: In bushes or reeds over or near water. Nest of coarse grass and reeds lined with fine grass. Eggs, 3-6, bluish-white scrawled with purplish and black. (Strathmore, May 25–June 23.)

REMARKS: The redwinged blackbird is found in suitable habitat throughout all of Alberta. Favorite haunts are reed-beds in marshes and sloughs or cat-tails along the margins of lakes but bushes close to water are occasionally used as nesting sites. Redwings are early spring migrants, the males appearing in central Alberta early in April followed by the females a few days later, but they do not start to nest until reeds and rushes have grown several inches above the surface of the sloughs. Usually many pairs form a loose colony. Swaying on thin stems the males display their scarlet epaulettes and chorus *oka-lee-a*, in a harsh yet musical voice. There are many quarrels among the owners of adjacent territories but no harm is done and the disputants unite to drive away any crow or marsh hawk which may wander by. Enemies do not take a large toll of young, apparently, for by early summer the reeds are swarming with drab streaked young redwings.

When harvesting is in full swing flocks of redwings swarm into the grainfields to feed among the swaths. They may be accompanied by other species of blackbirds and by starlings but the redwings are usually in the majority. Towards dusk they return to the marsh or to a thick bed of rushes bordering a lake and there they spend the night. As migration time approaches they gather by thousands at a favorite roosting spot, each flock settling among the earlier arrivals with much chatter and commotion until darkness falls and brings a hush. During October the flocks gradually diminish in size and by the end of the month redwings have moved on.

408

YELLOW-HEADED BLACKBIRD
male *female*

RED-WINGED BLACKBIRD
male

409

BALTIMORE ORIOLE Common Summer Resident.
Icterus galbula Length 8 in.

DESCRIPTION: Ad. m.—Head, neck, upper back, and central tail feathers jet black; wing black except orange shoulder and one white wing bar; rest of plumage reddish-orange becoming yellowish-orange on abdomen and tail. Ad. f.—Upperparts yellowish-olive streaked with black on head and back and becoming yellow on rump and tail; wings dusky-brown with two white bars; underparts yellowish-orange tinged with olive on sides and usually with some black feathers on throat. Im.—Similar to female but browner.

IDENTIFICATION: May be confused only with Bullock's oriole. Completely black head and small amount of white on wing distinguishes male Baltimore; female Baltimore has dark head and face and never has yellow line over eye.

RANGE: North and South America. Breeds in southern Canada and most of the states east of the Rockies. Winters in Mexico and northern South America.

NESTING: Usually high in trees. Nest, a deep pouch of grass, string, and hair suspended a few inches below a branch by cords of similar fibers. Eggs, 4-6, white scrawled with brown and black. (Drumheller, June 15.)

REMARKS: In Alberta the Baltimore oriole breeds most abundantly in the parklands but it ranges northward into newly settled farming country as far as Cold Lake in the east and the Peace River district to the west. It was formerly a scarce breeding bird on the prairies but the growth of shade trees around farmsteads has attracted this as well as other species of birds. It has not been reported from the foothills or the mountains although it approaches the foothills closely southwest of Calgary.

The Baltimore oriole is a bird of open deciduous woods such as are found in the parklands and along rivers and coulees on the prairies. Tall stands of poplar are favorite nesting sites in Alberta but the oriole often nests in ornamental trees in city parks, along village streets, or around farmsteads. Baltimore orioles keep largely to the upper levels of the trees; only rarely do they descend into the lower branches or into bushes. They are rather wary of human beings but in other respects they are not at all timid; in fact they seem to have quite a bump of curiosity. The male calls loudly from the treetops and is easily decoyed into view by a whistled imitation of his loud clear call, *Pet-er, Pet-er*, the second note higher than the first. His song is merely a repetition of these notes, any variations being in tempo rather than tone.

MEADOWLARKS, BLACKBIRDS, ORIOLES — Family Icteridae

BULLOCK'S ORIOLE   Scarce Summer Resident.
Icterus bullockii subsp. (p. 498)   Length 8½ in.

DESCRIPTION: Ad. m.—Crown, hindneck, and upper back jet black; wing black with very broad white bar; rump and tail yellowish-orange except central tail feathers black and remainder tipped with black; line from forehead over eye orange; line from beak through eye to neck black; throat black; face and breast reddish-orange fading to yellowish-orange on rest of underparts. Ad. f. — Upperparts yellowish-olive shading to grayish-olive on rump; line over eye, sides of head and neck, throat and breast dull yellowish; rest of underparts pale buff tinged with yellow; wings dusky-brown with distinct white bar; tail yellow.

IDENTIFICATION: Somewhat similar to Baltimore oriole but with yellowish line over eye in both sexes. Male Bullock's orioles have orange face and large amount of white on wing; females have yellowish face and distinct wing bar.

RANGE: Western North America. Breeds from southern B.C. and Alberta south to Mexico. Winters in southwestern states and Mexico.

NESTING: Usually high in trees. Nest, a pendant pouch of plant fibers, string, and hair suspended from a branch. Eggs, bluish-white pencilled with brown and black.

REMARKS: Bullock's oriole nests only in extreme southern Alberta. It is found regularly along the Milk River and less commonly along the most southerly parts of the South Saskatchewan and its tributaries. It nested commonly around Medicine Hat in 1894 and still occurs in that area in small numbers. Specimens taken along the lower reaches of the Red Deer River in August, 1917, constitute the most northerly record of the species. More information is needed on the range of Bullock's oriole and observers in the south of the province would do well to identify all orioles carefully.

Bullock's oriole is similar to the Baltimore oriole in both habits and habitat. It frequents groves of deciduous trees particularly the tall cottonwoods along river valleys. Much of its time is spent in the topmost branches where the female builds her nest and the male feeds and sings. Despite their brilliant colors Bullock's orioles are not conspicuous among the foliage; in fact, it takes a good eye to spot a bird unless it moves. The song of Bullock's oriole is similar to that of the Baltimore oriole but it is not as robust or rich.

BALTIMORE ORIOLE
male   female

BULLOCK'S ORIOLE
male above   female below

412

RUSTY BLACKBIRD
male

BREWER'S BLACKBIRD
male   *female*

413

MEADOWLARKS, BLACKBIRDS, ORIOLES — Family Icteridae

RUSTY BLACKBIRD　　　　　Fairly Common Summer Resident.
Euphagus carolinus　subsp. (p. 498)　　　　Length 8½-9½ in.

DESCRIPTION: Spring m.—Entirely glossy black with bluish-green reflections; no difference in color of iridescence on head and body; some feathers may have rusty tips; iris pale yellow. Spring f.—Dull grayish-black darkest on back, wings, and tail; some feathers may have rusty tips; iris pale yellow. Fall ads. and im.—Similar but most of the feathers edged with rusty-brown; head, neck, back, and breast are quite brownish but a light buffy line is left over eye.

IDENTIFICATION: Most likely to be confused with Brewer's blackbird. Yellow eye of female distinguishes rusty; male rusty does not show any difference in sheen of head and body; in autumn rusty markings are distinctive.

RANGE: North America. Breeds from Alaska to Newfoundland south to central B.C. and across to Maine. Winters in southeastern states.

NESTING: In trees or bushes usually near water. Nest, a bulky structure of leaves, grass, and mud. Eggs, 3-5, so heavily marked with brown and black that whitish ground color is almost concealed. (Fawcett, May 16.)

REMARKS: As Brewer's is the blackbird of the south so the rusty is the blackbird of the northern half of the province but their breeding ranges overlap considerably in central Alberta. The rusty blackbird occurs at Banff and nests have been found at Jasper. In the foothills it may breed fairly far south for a nest has been reported near Okotoks. Blackbirds nesting in the southwest part of the province should be identified carefully.

During the nesting season the rusty blackbird inhabits alder-willow bogs, bushy borders of streams and lakes, and semi-dry muskeg in sparsely settled areas. It is much more of a woodland bird than Brewer's blackbird with little liking for roadside thickets. In the spring rusty blackbirds in small numbers arrive in central Alberta about the middle of April. In the fall large flocks pass southward through the province until about the middle of October. Sometimes they are accompanied by other species of blackbirds and, in recent years, by large numbers of starlings but their rusty plumage identifies them readily. They feed in the stubble, garnering grain, or in bushes picking up berries and the last of the insects. At this season they are to be found throughout southern Alberta but on the prairies they are rarely seen far from a brushy coulee or a farm shelter belt.

MEADOWLARKS, BLACKBIRDS, ORIOLES — Family Icteridae

BREWER'S BLACKBIRD   Common Summer Resident.
Euphagus cyanocephalus   Length 9-10 in.

DESCRIPTION: Ad. m.—Entirely glossy black, the head and neck with purplish iridescence, the rest of the body with greenish-blue reflections; iris pale yellow. Ad. f. —Very dark grayish-brown palest on throat and becoming dull black on back, wings and tail; iris light brown; about an inch shorter than male.

IDENTIFICATION: The male is an entirely black bird smaller, and with shorter tail, than bronzed grackle; lacks light feather edges and has tail longer than starling; larger than cowbird and has purplish instead of brown head; almost indistinguishable from rusty blackbird which usually lacks purplish iridescence on head and has a few feathers tipped with brown. Females distinguished from rusty females by brown instead of yellow iris; from cowbird by larger size, darker color, and longer beak.

RANGE: Western North America. Breeds from central parts of western provinces south to California and Wisconsin. Winters from southern B.C. to Central America.

NESTING: On the ground or in low bushes, usually in loose colonies. Nest of twigs and coarse grass lined with finer grasses. Eggs, 4-6; brown and black markings almost obscure the white ground color. (Claresholm, May 19.)

REMARKS: Brewer's blackbird is the common blackbird of the prairies and the parklands. It is steadily extending its range westward and northward. It occurs at Waterton Lake, Banff and Jasper in the mountains and has been found nesting as far north as Calling Lake north of Athabasca, and along the Meikle River north of Peace River. Occasionally the species winters in the province; a small flock spent the winter of 1937-38 around the stockyards at Camrose.

Brewer's blackbird shows a preference for thick bushy tangles near large open areas. Hedges around farmsteads, bushes along roadsides, and brushy thickets bordering irrigation ditches and prairie streams are favorite haunts. The cultivated parts of the parklands form ideal habitat; in these areas it is one of the most common birds.

Although not particularly timid Brewer's blackbird looks upon man with suspicion and is always on the alert around the farmstead. It is less wary of animals and, like the cowbird, is often found around domestic stock. None of its mannerisms are unusually interesting or endearing and none of its notes could properly be called a song. But while there is no air of charm about its personality there is very little to be said against its character. In some regions it shows a fondness for cultivated fruits but while with us its food is berries and weedseeds and the insects of field and garden. In autumn large flocks assemble, feeding in the fields and roosting in the woods at night or in the rushes with redwings, but moving southward a little each day before the onset of winter.

415

COMMON GRACKLE
male

BROWN-HEADED COWBIRD
male   female

416

MEADOWLARKS, BLACKBIRDS, ORIOLES — Family Icteridae

COMMON GRACKLE　　　　Fairly Common Summer Resident.
Quiscalus quiscula subsp. (p. 498)　　　　Length 11-12½ in.

DESCRIPTION: Male—Entirely black; head, neck, upper breast, and flight feathers with purplish reflections; rest of body with bronze-green reflections; tail long, the short outer feathers always held higher than the long central ones, forming a trough; beak black, long, heavy, and slightly decurved at tip; iris pale yellow. Fem. — Similar but duller and with less iridescence; about an inch shorter than male. Immature birds similar to adults.

IDENTIFICATION: A black bird larger than Brewer's blackbird but smaller than a crow. Heavy beak and long tail forming a trough in flight are good field marks.

RANGE: North America east of the Rockies. Breeds from Great Slave Lake and Newfoundland south to Colorado and Florida. Winters in southeastern states.

NESTING: Often in colonies, usually in trees but also in bushes, in cavities in trees or buildings, or in rushes. Nest, a bulky mass of weeds, grass, twine, etc., bound with mud. Eggs, 4-6, greenish-white, heavily speckled and scrawled with browns and black. (Hay Lakes, June 22.)

REMARKS: The common, or bronzed, grackle is widely distributed throughout Alberta but it is local and rather scarce in the northern forested regions and on the prairies. In the mountains it has been recorded at Banff and Jasper.

Bronzed grackles are rather tame birds which make themselves quite at home around farm homes and lake-side summer resorts, inspecting the buildings, sitting in the trees, or walking about on the lawns with heads erect and tails held well off the ground. In recent years small numbers may be found in the cities especially where a thick stand of spruce provides nesting sites. No matter where they are their mannerisms are a little too cocky and self-assured to be endearing; in fact they are typical bullies, somewhat timid when alone, but ready as a group to pick on anything smaller than themselves. Nor can grackles be said to sing, yet the male gives the impression that he considers his medley of squeaks, cackles and squawks to be a first-class performance for he delivers it with the air of an operatic tenor.

In the farmyard grackles often feed with the poultry; around summer cottages they pick up scraps near the kitchen door or catch insects on the roof; in the wilds they often forage among the debris thrown up by the waves along the lake shore. Unfortunately their food habits are not always harmless; during the nesting season they seek out the nests of other birds and rob them of eggs and nestlings.

417

MEADOWLARKS, BLACKBIRDS, ORIOLES — Family Icteridae

BROWN-HEADED COWBIRD Fairly Common Summer Resident.
Molothrus ater subsp. (p. 498) Length 7½ in.

DESCRIPTION: Ad. m.—Head and neck plain dark brown; rest of plumage black with purplish and greenish reflections; iris brown. Ad. f.—Entirely dark grayish-brown paler on throat and upper breast; most feathers have dark shafts; iris brown. Im.—Similar to female but with light feather edges and some streaking below.

IDENTIFICATION: Much like Brewer's and rusty blackbirds but head brown in male; females may be difficult to distinguish except by shape of beak; at all seasons the beak of the cowbird is short and stout like that of a sparrow.

RANGE: North America. Breeds across Canada except in extreme north and in most of U.S.A. Winters in southern states and Mexico.

NESTING: A parasite; lays its eggs in nests of other birds usually those smaller than itself. Eggs, white, speckled with brown and gray; the number laid is not known.

REMARKS: The cowbird may be found in all parts of the province but is more common in the parklands during the nesting season than it is in the heavily wooded areas of the north and west and the semi-arid plains of the south.

Cowbirds received their name from a habit of associating with cattle. Small groups may be seen perched on the backs of farm stock or walking on the ground nearby feeding on insects attracted to the animals. Years ago they had a similar association with buffalo. The cowbird is the only parasitic species of bird in North America. While the rightful owner is away the female cowbird slips onto the nest of a warbler or sparrow and lays her egg there. Yellow warblers, redstarts, and yellowthroats are commonly victimized. Sometimes the smaller bird deserts her nest and builds a new one; sometimes she relines it burying the cowbird egg beneath the new lining; but sometimes she incubates the egg with her own. When it hatches the young cowbird monopolizes the attention of its foster-parents whose natural offspring become weak from lack of food and are easily pushed from the nest by the imposter. The fact that the foster-parents continue to give solicitous care to this parasite until it is several times their own size and the fact that cowbirds are not nearly as numerous as many of the species which they parasitize gives cause for reflection to the bird student who is prepared to think about bird behavior as well as observe it.

418

TANAGERS — Family Thraupidae

Tanagers are brightly colored arboreal birds of medium size. The beak curves gradually downward towards its tip giving a suggestion of a hook and the edges of the upper mandible have a slight projection about half-way from the base. Most members of the family are tropical in distribution.

WESTERN TANAGER   Fairly Common Summer Resident.
Piranga ludoviciana   Length 7 in.

DESCRIPTION: Ad. m.—Entire head red; hindneck, rump, and all underparts lemon-yellow; back, wings, and tail black, the wings with two wide bars, the front one yellow, the other dull white; beak dull yellow. In fall plumage the head may be largely yellow with some feathers showing red. Ad. f.—Upperparts yellowish-green darkest on middle of back; wings and tail olive-brown, the wing with two yellowish bars and some feathers edged with white; entire underparts lemon-yellow.

IDENTIFICATION: Males with reddish heads are distinctive. Females are about same size as female orioles but are yellow instead of orange below and not nearly as dark above.

RANGE: Western North America. Breeds from Mackenzie valley to California mainly from Rockies westward. Winters in Mexico and Central America.

NESTING: In trees or bushes. Nest, a flat structure of twigs, rootlets, and grass. Eggs, 3-4, pale bluish-green lightly spotted with browns and lilac.

REMARKS: The western tanager breeds in the mixed-wood forests of western and northern Alberta. It occurs in the mountain valleys and the foothills from the international boundary north as far as Jasper. Less frequently it is found along the northern and western fringes of the parklands.

A loud clear song somewhat reminiscent of the robin's notes but repeated more frequently suggests the presence of a western tanager. It usually comes from high in the tree tops for the tanager prefers the leafy canopies of deciduous trees. Here it may remain in one spot for long periods of time often escaping attention through its inactivity. It is not particularly shy but its preference for the shade of the foliage makes it seem retiring.

During summer the western tanager feeds largely on caterpillars and slow-moving insects which may easily be caught among the leaves but when berries begin to ripen they are added to the diet. The western tanager remains in Alberta only about three months. Migrants pass through the Calgary area about May 24th and southbound birds may be found in the same area about the middle of August.

SCARLET TANAGER, *Piranga olivacea*   see page 485

GROSBEAKS, BUNTINGS, FINCHES, SPARROWS — Family Fringillidae

This is the largest family of birds in North America. All its members are relatively small in size the largest being the grosbeaks. The beak is short, stout, and conical in shape being especially adapted for picking up and cracking seeds. It reaches its highest development in the grosbeaks and its most peculiar modification in the crossbills. As would be expected in such a large family the different species inhabit a great diversity of habitats.

ROSE-BREASTED GROSBEAK   Fairly Common Summer Resident.
Pheucticus ludovicianus   Length 7½ in.

DESCRIPTION: Ad. m.—Head, neck, and all upper-parts black except white rump, two broad white wing bars, and three outer tail feathers with white patches near tips; large triangular patch of red on upper breast; rest of underparts white; beak very stout, dull white. Ad. f.— Upperparts streaked with dull black and olive-gray darkest on crown which has an indistinct median stripe; wing with two narrow light bars; white stripe over eye; cheeks grayish-brown bordered below and behind by buffy-white line; underparts white tinged with yellowish and streaked with brown on breast and sides; beak dull white.. Im.— Similar to female.

IDENTIFICATION: Males are unmistakable. Females are large, streaked, sparrow-like birds best identified by large, whitish beak.

RANGE: Eastern North America and South America. Breeds in southern Canada and northern states east of the Rockies. Winters in Mexico, Central America, and northern South America.

NESTING: In trees and bushes. Nest a flat structure, loosely built of twigs and rootlets. Eggs, 3-5, pale blue spotted with brown. (Edmonton, June 5.)

REMARKS: The rose-breasted grosbeak breeds in small numbers along the northern and western fringes of the parklands and more commonly in the forested areas of the province from Edmonton to the northern boundary. It occurs in the southern half of the province on migration but is rarely seen in the mountains.

Light deciduous woods such as aspen groves and stands of balsam poplar are favorite haunts of the rose-breasted grosbeak. Arriving in central Alberta during the third week of May it feeds on catkins hanging heavy in the cottonwoods or picks off beetles and other slow-moving insects in the bushes of the undergrowth. Compared with the warblers which bustle around it the movements of the rose-breasted grosbeak appear slow and deliberate but it is active in defence of its territory and is a vigorous singer. The song is similar to that of the robin but sweeter in tone and more prolonged. The nest is so frail that the eggs can often be seen through its floor. As though to make up for their shortcomings in nest building both birds are devoted parents sharing the duties of incubation and caring solicitously for the young.

WESTERN TANAGER
female   *male*

ROSE-BREASTED GROSBEAK
male   *female*
immature

GROSBEAKS, BUNTINGS, FINCHES, SPARROWS — Family Fringillidae

BLACK-HEADED GROSBEAK Scarce Summer Resident.
Pheucticus melanocephalus subsp. (p. 498) Length 8 in.

DESCRIPTION: Ad. m.—Head black; underparts, collar around neck, and rump buffy-orange; lemon-yellow down middle of abdomen; back black streaked with cinnamon, wings black with white patch at base of primaries and smaller white marks elsewhere; tail black, outer two feathers with white spots at tip; beak very large. Ad. f.—Upperparts streaked with dull black and buffy-gray leaving an indistinct median stripe on crown and two light wing bars; white stripe over eye and under cheeks; cheeks dark gray; underparts white tinged with yellowish on abdomen and suffused with buffy on breast; brown streaks on sides.

IDENTIFICATION: The black and orange male is unmistakable. Females are almost impossible to separate in the field from female rose-breasted grosbeaks; black-headed females are more buffy below and less distinctly streaked on sides.

RANGE: Western North America. Breeds from southern B.C. and Alberta south to central Mexico. Winters in Mexico.

NESTING: In trees or shrubs. Nest, a frail structure of twigs, grass, and rootlets. Eggs, 3-4, bluish-green speckled with brown.

REMARKS: In the early 1900s black-headed grosbeaks occurred as far north as High River but in recent years they have not been recorded north of the South Saskatchewan River. No nests have been found but adults with young have been seen near Medicine Hat and Taber. The species is not uncommon in the poplar groves along the Oldman River near Lethbridge where it apparently nests for males sing lustily during the month of June. Black-headed grosbeaks should be watched for in the wooded valleys of extreme southern Alberta. Records of their occurrence and abundance are of value.

Like other grosbeaks black-headed grosbeaks are arboreal birds of rather sedentary habits. They frequent poplar and cottonwood stands feeding on insects and on saskatoons, chokecherries, and other wild fruits produced by the bushes of the undergrowth. In one of these bushes, usually a tall alder or birch near water, the nest is built and the family raised. The male shares in the duties of incubation and assists in feeding the young but he still finds time to sing a cheerful song. It is so much like that of the rose-breasted grosbeak that it takes a keen ear to detect any difference. Since rose-breasted grosbeaks do not occur in the range of the black-headed grosbeak during the breeding season any grosbeak song in extreme southern Alberta should come from the latter species. The song of the black-headed grosbeak has varied phrases similar to those of the robin but the tones are sweeter.

GROSBEAKS, BUNTINGS, FINCHES, SPARROWS — Family Fringillidae

INDIGO BUNTING Scarce Summer Resident.
Passerina cyanea Length 5½ in.

DESCRIPTION: Ad. m.—Entirely indigo-blue darkest on crown; flight feathers are black broadly margined with blue. Ad. f.—Upperparts dull brown; throat and abdomen dull white; rest of underparts grayish-buff indistinctly streaked with dusky; a greenish-blue tinge is usually evident on crown, sides of head, wings, rump, and tail. Im.—Similar to female.

IDENTIFICATION: Males are much smaller than mountain bluebirds and a deeper blue.. Females are plain brownish above, lighter below; much like female lazuli buntings but lacking wing bars.

RANGE: Eastern North America. Breeds in southern Canada and U.S.A. mainly east of the prairies. Winters in Central America and West Indies.

NESTING: In bushes, within three feet of ground. Nest of grass and strips of bark lined with fine grass and hair. Eggs, 3-4, plain bluish-white.

REMARKS: The indigo bunting is rarely found west of Manitoba. There are few records of its occurrence in Alberta: a male in full plumage was taken at Lac La Nonne on June 3, 1926, and specimens have been taken more recently at Gorge Creek. A male was seen near Elkwater Lake in the Cypress Hills on June 26, 1952. In 1958 and 1959 indigo buntings, apparently nesting, were found near the Biological Station at Gorge Creek in the foothills west of Turner Valley. Although ornithologists had been working in this area for several years the species had not previously been observed. Indigo buntings were seen on several occasions in clumps of poplar with thick undergrowth. This is the same type of habitat used by lazuli buntings; in fact lazuli buntings were nesting in the vicinity. Males of both species could be heard singing at the same time but the songs were so much alike that it was found impossible to separate the species by voice. These recent observations of indigo buntings in the Cypress Hills and in the foothills suggest that they may be gradually extending their range into southern Alberta and that further occurrences in the province might be expected.

In the east indigo buntings inhabit thick scrubby growth along roadsides or at the edge of deciduous forests. This is the type of habitat in prairie coulees and river valleys which lazuli buntings inhabit in south-central Alberta. It is possible that indigo buntings might show up in this part of the province.

BLACK-HEADED GROSBEAK
male   *female*

INDIGO BUNTING

LAZULI BUNTING
male above   female below

DICKCISSEL
male   female

GROSBEAKS, BUNTINGS, FINCHES, SPARROWS — Family Fringillidae

LAZULI BUNTING
Passerina amoena

Fairly Common Summer Resident.
Length 5½ in.

DESCRIPTION: Ad. m.—Entire head, neck, and back bright blue, darker across shoulders; wings and tail dark gray, each feather edged with blue; two white wing bars, the front one quite broad; upper breast buffy-orange contrasting with blue of throat in front and with white of abdomen behind. Ad. f.—Grayish-brown above; buffy-brown below; wings and tail dusky-gray tinged with blue; rump often tinged with blue. Im.—Like female.

IDENTIFICATION: Males are distinctively colored; the blue is similar to that of the larger mountain bluebird but much lighter than that of the indigo bunting. Females are much like female indigo buntings but are not striped underneath.

RANGE: Western North America. Breeds in southern B.C., Alberta, and Saskatchewan south to Lower California and Texas. Winters in Mexico.

NESTING: In bushes. Nest of grass, leaves, and rootlets, lined with fine grass and hair. Eggs, 3-4, bluish-white, unmarked. (Gorge Creek, July 1.)

REMARKS: The lazuli bunting breeds in the mountains and the foothills of Alberta from Jasper south to Waterton Lakes. It has also been found nesting locally as far east as Castor, Beynon, and Brooks. In these latter areas its appearances are inclined to be sporadic.

In the mountains lazuli buntings frequent the leafy crowns of poplar and aspen stands and other deciduous growths. The singing perch is usually a dead twig well up towards the top of a tree. Away from the mountains they occur in the same type of habitat where it is present but more usually they are found in thickets of saskatoon, chokecherry, black birch and willow on the side of a coulee and not necessarily near water. Several pairs often nest in a relatively small area forming a loosely associated colony. In the dense undergrowth the females are rarely seen but the males show themselves quite openly singing from the topmost twig of one of the bushes. They are not as shy as the brown thrashers and towhees which may be singing nearby yet they are rather wary and usually drop into thick cover when approached. When all is quiet, however, they soon reappear for they are persistent singers. The song is a pleasing warble somewhat similar to that of the yellow warbler but sufficiently harsher in quality to be recognizable. Lazuli buntings may best be studied by an observer who has the patience to station himself quietly in a territory and remain motionless until the birds lose their apprehension. Under these circumstances he may be treated to many unusual sights and sounds.

GROSBEAKS, BUNTINGS, FINCHES, SPARROWS — Family Fringillidae

DICKCISSEL
Scarce Wanderer.
Spiza americana
Length 6½ in.

DESCRIPTION: Ad. m.—Crown, hindneck, and sides of head gray; yellow stripe over eye; rest of upperparts olive-gray with broad streaks of black on back and a cinnamon-brown patch on shoulders; throat white bordered by black which continues across breast to form a broad V; breast yellow; sides pale olive-gray; abdomen white. Ad. f.—Similar to male but black V on breast reduced or absent and yellow over eye and on breast very pale; breast and sides may have fine dusky streaks.

IDENTIFICATION: The male dickcissel looks like a small meadowlark but is not so extensively yellow below. The female looks like many small gray sparrows but is never heavily streaked below and always shows some yellow on breast.

RANGE: North and South America. Breeds from southern Manitoba and Ontario south to Gulf states. Winters from Mexico to northern South America.

NESTING: On the ground or in bushes. Nest, a large structure of weeds and leaves lined with fine grass and hair. Eggs, 3-5, pale blue.

REMARKS: The dickcissel has been recorded only once in Alberta. On June 24, 1940, a singing male was collected a few miles north of Walsh and not far from the Saskatchewan boundary.

Most species of birds return to the same nesting area year after year but the dickcissel is noted for its irregularity of appearance in any locality. In an area where dickcissels nest in abundance one year they may be entirely absent for several years following, after which they may suddenly again become abundant. Apparently no strong ties bind them to any particular locality and their northward migration often ends as fancy dictates. One migrant travelled farther northwest than usual in 1940 and established his territory in southeastern Alberta. It is possible that this may occur again. Dickcissels frequent prairies, pasture lands, and grassy meadows partly overgrown with short brush. Their name is derived from their song, an unmusical *dick — dick — cissell-cissel-cissel*, with the first two notes much louder than the rest.

EVENING GROSBEAK

PURPLE FINCH
male　　*female*

428

GROSBEAKS, BUNTINGS, FINCHES, SPARROWS — Family Fringillidae

EVENING GROSBEAK   Fairly Common Resident or Winter Resident.
Hesperiphona vespertina subsp. (p. 498)   Length 8 in.

DESCRIPTION: Ad. m.—Beak yellow, very thick; forehead and line over eye yellow; rest of head, upper breast and back dark brown becoming black on crown; wings black with large patch of white on secondaries; tail black; rest of plumage lemon-yellow gradually shading into brown of back and breast. Ad. f. and im.—Entire body pale gray tinged with yellow around neck, on back and on sides; wings black with several patches of yellowish-white and gray; tail black with white spots near tip; beak dull yellow, very thick.

IDENTIFICATION: A heavy-set bird with thick yellow beak; females are rather colorless but the males show much black, white, and yellow, especially in flight. Usually seen in settled regions only in winter.

RANGE: Western North America. Breeds from central B.C. to Michigan south in the Rockies to Mexico. Winters in southern Canada and northern states.

NESTING: High in trees, usually conifers. Nest loosely made of twigs, grass, and moss. Eggs, 3-4, pale greenish-blue speckled with brown and gray.

REMARKS: During the breeding season the evening grosbeak has a wide distribution in the forested regions of northern and western Alberta but its numbers at this time are never great. The only definite record of nesting in the province is from Dunvegan in the Peace River district where a pair of adults with young just able to fly were observed on July 26, 1903. Since that time evening grosbeaks have been seen in June and July, the height of the nesting season, at Banff, Jasper, Belvedere, Glenevis, Lesser Slave Lake, the Swan Hills, and Wood Buffalo Park. In winter the species occurs in fair numbers throughout southern Alberta.

Each winter shortly after flocks of bohemian waxwings and pine grosbeaks have invaded the cities of central Alberta evening grosbeaks in their showy black, white, and yellow coats arrive to add a touch of color to the drab scene. Rather quiet in habit and not the least bit shy or wary small flocks sit about in the ornamental trees showing little concern for the traffic below. Green ash and manitoba maple are popular resorts for the winged seeds of these trees are favorite food. A single clip with their strong beaks removes the seed and allows the wings to float gently down to the snow. In the wilds poplar buds and berries form a major part of the diet. Here as in the cities evening grosbeaks are quiet and not too active; perhaps for that reason they are often overlooked.

GROSBEAKS, BUNTINGS, FINCHES, SPARROWS — Family Fringillidae

PURPLE FINCH Fairly Common Summer Resident.
Carpodacus purpureus subsp. (p. 498) Length 6 in.

DESCRIPTION: Ad. m.—General color purplish-red becoming white on abdomen; wings and tail dark grayish-brown, most feathers edged with red; back and flanks may be indistinctly streaked with brown; beak quite thick. Ad. f. and im.—Brownish-gray above streaked with white; below white streaked with brownish-gray; the dark color may be tinged with olive.

IDENTIFICATION: The rosy male is easily separated from all other species except the darker Cassin's purple finch; the rosy plumage is not assumed until males are over one year of age. Females, young, and immature males are heavily streaked dusky-brown birds with heavy beaks; the tail is slightly forked.

RANGE: North America. Breeds from northern B.C. and California east to Newfoundland and Maryland. Winters in southern part of its range and in Mexico.

NESTING: In coniferous trees. Nest of twigs and grasses lined with hair and fine rootlets. Eggs, 4-6, blue spotted with brown, black, and lavender. (Edmonton, June 5.)

REMARKS: The purple finch breeds locally in the wooded areas of central and northern Alberta. In the mountains it ranges south through Jasper and Banff National Parks but in Waterton Lakes Park its place is taken by Cassin's purple finch. Where the ranges of these two species meet or overlap is not known at present. The purple finch occurs on the southern prairies only on migration.

Mixed-wood forests are favorite haunts of purple finches for while they prefer evergreens as nesting sites they like to feed in deciduous trees. In many towns and cities of central Alberta purple finches nest commonly in shade trees in residential districts. They arrive about the end of April before the leaves have burst on the trees. At this time they are most conspicuous as they feed upon newly opened catkins and the insects attracted to them. At this time too their beautiful, half-whispered song is heard to best advantage. It is a soft melodious warble with a quality unusual in the song of finches. It is sometimes claimed that females sing but since first-year males have gray plumage like females this is a case of mistaken identity. Purple finches are fond of buds and newly opened blossoms from which they eat the centres. Later in the year they add fruit, seeds and insects to their diet. In late September purple finches may be found among the bands of migrant sparrows moving southward through the trees; they are hardy birds and some may stay until early October.

GROSBEAKS, BUNTINGS, FINCHES, SPARROWS — Family Fringillidae

CASSIN'S FINCH Fairly Common Summer Resident.
Carpodacus cassinii Length 6 in.

DESCRIPTION: Ad. m.—Square patch on crown bright red; rump grayish-red; rest of upperparts dull pinkish-brown streaked with dark brown; wings and tail dusky-brown, the feathers edged with pink; underparts pale pink fading to white on abdomen. Ad. f.—Upperparts brownish-gray streaked with dusky-brown; underparts dull white conspicuously streaked with grayish-brown except on abdomen.

IDENTIFICATION: Much like the purple finch but the red crown of the male Cassin's finch contrasts sharply with the rest of the upperparts; female Cassin's show less olive tinge above and have finer, sharper streaking below than the purple finch.

RANGE: Western North America. Breeds from southern B.C. and Alberta south to California, Arizona and New Mexico. Winters in southern parts of range and Mexico.

NESTING: In coniferous trees. Nest of twigs and weed stems lined with grass, rootlets, and wool. Eggs, 4-5, greenish-blue, lightly spotted with brown, black, and lavender.

REMARKS: Cassin's finch breeds in Waterton Lakes National Park but the exact extent of its breeding range in Alberta is not known. It has not been seen in Banff National Park where the common purple finch occurs. Ornithologists working at Gorge Creek on the edge of the mountains west of Turner Valley have not recorded either Cassin's or the purple finch. Nor has either of these finches been reported as yet along the Kananaskis-Coleman road. In the area opened up by this road the ranges of the two species might be expected to meet.

Cassin's finch inhabits coniferous and mixed-wood forests in mountainous regions. Its feeding habits, its song, and its general behavior are similar to those of the common purple finch. Despite its color Cassin's finch is not a conspicuous bird for it usually keeps to the upper branches of the trees. It sits in one place for minutes at a time feeding on poplar catkins and the insects attracted to them and occasionally bursting into song. It is not very active and an observer must scan the branches from which the song comes for a long time before catching a movement which locates the singer. Even then identification is difficult for Cassin's finch resembles the purple finch as much in color as it does in song.

GROSBEAKS, BUNTINGS, FINCHES, SPARROWS — Family Fringillidae

HOUSE FINCH   Scarce Wanderer.
Carpodacus mexicanus   subsp. (p. 499)   Length 5½ in.

DESCRIPTION: Ad. m.—Forehead, throat, upper breast, and rump vermilion; rest of upperparts gray streaked with dusky brown; rest of underparts white heavily streaked with dusky brown; beak thick. Ad. f. and im. —Like male but without any red; this replaced by same colors as adjacent areas.

IDENTIFICATION: Males are somewhat like purple finches and redpolls but less extensively red than former and more than latter. Females are heavily streaked gray sparrows with thick beaks; smaller than purple finch and more heavily and evenly streaked below than either female purple finch or redpoll; they lack any distinctive markings.

RANGE: Western North America. Breeds throughout western United States and northern Mexico; casual in southern B.C.. Winters in all except northern part of its range.

NESTING: Like the English sparrow nests almost anywhere. Nest of any handy materials such as straw, grass, paper, rags, hair, etc. Eggs, 3-6, bluish-white spotted and lined with brown and black.

REMARKS: The house finch is one of the commonest birds of the western states and has recently extended its range northward into British Columbia. There are two records of .its occurrence in Alberta. A specimen was collected at Topaz Lake in Jasper Park on May 29, 1944 and a house finch was observed in Waterton Lakes Park in June, 1964. A photograph of this latter bird forms the illustration on page 433.

In the western states house finches make themselves at home in urban areas just as house sparrows do in Alberta. They nest in ornamental bushes and shade trees and feed on seeds and insects. Unfortunately in fruit growing areas a fondness for fruit has caused them to become a serious pest. Large flocks congregate in orchards and do great damage by pecking indiscriminately at ripening cherries, peaches, and pears. Elsewhere, however, their food habits attract no particular attention and they are accepted as ordinary members of the bird community.

Normally it is only when large numbers of birds congregate in small areas that they come into conflict with man's interests. Under such circumstances almost any species can become a pest. Robins, bobolinks, grosbeaks, house finches, and even game birds such as pheasants and ducks, can menace crops of fruit and grain when they flock into one locality. One of the problems of wildlife management yet to be solved is how to disperse these aggregations without endangering the species.

432

CASSIN'S FINCH
male   *female*

HOUSE FINCH

H. SIVYER

GROSBEAKS, BUNTINGS, FINCHES, SPARROWS — Family Fringillidae

PINE GROSBEAK   Fairly Common Resident or Winter Resident.
Pinicola enucleator   subsp. (p. 499)   Length 9 in.

DESCRIPTION: Ad. m.—Beak black, very thick at base; wings, tail, and abdomen gray; two white wing bars; rest of plumage dull red, darkest on back and brightest on head and rump. Ad. f. and im.—Top of head and rump orange; rest of plumage gray, lightly tinged with orange on breast; two white wing bars.

IDENTIFICATION: Males are distinctive although they are often called robins in winter; their rose red color is unlike the reddish-orange of the robin. Females and immature males are gray birds with much orange on head, breast and rump.

RANGE: Northern parts of northern hemisphere. In North America breeds in northern coniferous forests across continent, south in the Rockies to California. Winters in southern Canada and northern states.

NESTING: In conifers at height of 6-10 ft. Nest, poorly constructed of twigs lined with fine grasses. Eggs, 4, pale greenish-blue speckled with brown and black. (Moraine Lake, June 22.)

REMARKS: In Alberta the pine grosbeak has been found nesting only in Banff National Park although it occurs in Jasper National Park during the nesting season. There are no actual nesting records from northern Alberta but a pair were seen in Wood Buffalo Park on May 27, 1933, and a female was seen at Salt Prairie, north of Grouard, on June 24, 1964. In winter the pine grosbeak is found throughout the province being most abundant in the more heavily wooded areas including the Cypress Hills.

Few people see pine grosbeaks in summer but a visitor to our mountain parks may find a pair inspecting his camp from the closest evergreen tree if he is lucky. They are slow and deliberate in their movements and attract attention more with their musical whistle than by their actions. They are not easily alarmed and will allow close approach. At this season they are usually seen singly or in pairs but later on they often form small flocks. Descending from their mountain haunts they move eastward to spend the winter in the mixed-wood and coniferous forests at lower altitudes. Their favorite food is the seeds of conifers but they also eat other seeds and berries. The generous food supply provided by ornamental trees and shrubs often attracts them to the residential districts of cities where they feed side by side with bohemian waxwings and evening grosbeaks. As in summer they are not at all wary and will allow close observation through a window or from the sidewalk unless startled into flight by sudden movement.

GROSBEAKS, BUNTINGS, FINCHES, SPARROWS — Family Fringillidae

GRAY-CROWNED ROSY FINCH   Fairly Common Resident.
Leucosticte tephrocotis subsp. (p. 499)   Length 6½ in.

DESCRIPTION: Ads.—Crown black bordered by broad band of pale gray over eye and across nape; wings and tail dark grayish-brown, except a patch of light rose on bend of wing; rest of plumage seal brown washed with light rose on rump, flanks, and abdomen. Female slightly paler than male. Im.—Similar to adults but most feathers edged with buffy.

IDENTIFICATION: General color of chocolate-brown with pink shoulders and rump and gray-bordered black crown identifies rosy finch from all other species.

RANGE: Mountains of western North America. Breeds at high altitudes from Alaska to New Mexico. Largely resident throughout range but usually descends to lower altitudes in winter.

NESTING: In crevices or under rocks. Nest of grass lined with fine grass and feathers. Eggs, 3-5, white, unmarked. (Banff, June 9.)

REMARKS: Since the gray-crowned rosy finch nests only at high altitudes it is confined to the Rocky Mountain region in Alberta during the nesting season. It is somewhat local in distribution but occurs throughout the mountains. To see the rosy finch in summer the observer must be willing to leave his car and climb above tree-line where roads rarely penetrate. In winter, however, gray-crowned rosy finches descend to lower altitudes in the mountains and foothills and occasionally wander farther eastward. At this season they have been seen as far east as Elk Island Park and Brooks.

On cliffs and scree slopes well above tree line in the mountains rosy finches build their nests and raise their young. At such elevations it is surprising that there is enough food to keep them alive but they apparently find a good supply of insects and seeds among the lichens and rocks, and even on the snow. Of necessity they are largely terrestrial for the wind-swept slopes support little vegetation. For protection from wind, rain, and snow they crouch in a crevice or in the lee of a boulder. During the fall and winter flocks of several dozen rosy finches often appear around foothill ranches to feed in the hay pawed up by cattle. Showing little fear of man they also visit mountain towns where their rose-tinged brown plumage is displayed to perfection against the white snow. At this season they may have to find their food in tall weeds protruding above the snow or in the trees but they prefer to feed on the ground. A bare spot in the backyard swept clear of snow and spread with a bit of straw, grain, or other small seeds forms an attraction which they cannot resist.

PINE GROSBEAK
male

S. MACDONALD

GRAY-CROWNED ROSY FINCH
female   *male*

T. M. SHORTT

436

ALLAN BROOKS

COMMON REDPOLL
female   *male*

T. M. SHORTT

PINE SISKIN

GROSBEAKS, BUNTINGS, FINCHES, SPARROWS — Family Fringillidae

HOARY REDPOLL   Fairly Common Winter Resident.
Acanthis hornemanni subsp. (p. 499)   Length 5 in.

COMMON REDPOLL   Common Winter Resident.
Acanthis flammea subsp. (p. 499)   Length 5 in.

DESCRIPTION: Common redpoll. Ad. m.—Throat and area around base of beak black; crown crimson; rest of upperparts buffy streaked heavily with dark brown and lightly with white, palest on rump which is tinged with red; two pale wing bars; sides of head, neck, and body pale buffy streaked with grayish-brown; foreneck and breast washed with rosy pink; abdomen white; beak yellow tipped with black. Ad. f. and im.—Similar but no red on rump and pink underparts replaced by white. Hoary redpoll — Like the common redpoll but lighter in all plumages; rump white; streaks on sides less distinct; breast of male pale pink.

IDENTIFICATION: Small, streaked, dark brown or grayish-brown birds with dark crimson patch on crown in all plumages; not easily confused with any other winter species.

RANGE: Northern parts of northern hemisphere. In North America breeds in arctic regions. Winters in southern Canada and occasionally south as far as Alabama and California.

NESTING: On the ground or in low bushes. Eggs, 3-6, pale green spotted with brown.

REMARKS: The common and the hoary redpoll associate freely and are so similar in habits and appearance that they are treated together here. They are winter visitors in all parts of Alberta including the mountains, arriving about mid-October and leaving towards the middle of April. In some winters redpolls are extremely abundant; other winters may pass with very few putting in an appearance. Their erratic occurrence does not seem to be related to variations in temperature, snowfall, or food supply.

In years of abundance hundreds of redpolls rise from the weedy roadside as a car passes, quickly settling back again when the disturbance is over. Balancing gracefully on thin stems they chitter excitedly as they extract the tiny seeds. When snow covers the short vegetation they resort to the birch trees whose seeds are a favorite food. In cities redpolls soon learn to come to a feeding shelf supplied with crumbs and small seeds especially if it is near trees or shrubbery. Some of the visitors may appear to be frosted with white; these are the hoary redpolls less numerous than their common brethren but just as bright and cheerful on a cold winter day.

GROSBEAKS, BUNTINGS, FINCHES, SPARROWS — Family Fringillidae

PINE SISKIN   Common Summer Resident.
Spinus pinus subsp. (p. 499)   Length 5 in.

DESCRIPTION: Upperparts heavily streaked with gray-ish-buff and dark grayish-brown; underparts similar but the lighter color predominating; wings dark grayish-brown, the primaries with yellow at bases forming yellow wing bars; tail dark grayish-brown, yellow at base; sometimes yellow on rump.

IDENTIFICATION: A small gray, heavily streaked bird with no very distinct markings; the yellow on wings and tail is not too obvious when the siskin is at rest. Much like a dark redpoll but without red cap.

RANGE: North America. Breeds in coniferous forests of North America except in southeastern states. Winters from southern Canada to Mexico.

NESTING: In trees, usually conifers. Nest of fine twigs and rootlets lined with plant down. Eggs, 4-6, pale bluish-white lightly spotted with black and brown.

REMARKS: There are few birds more erratic in their movements within the province than the pine siskin. It is extremely local in distribution appearing in certain areas in large numbers for short periods and then disappearing completely. It breeds regularly, however, in the foothills of western Alberta and probably breeds locally and sporadically in the heavily forested areas of the north. Pine siskins have been seen in the Cypress Hills in summer but no nests have been found. Normally they migrate from the province in winter but a few have been reported at Canmore, Red Deer, and in the Cypress Hills during this season.

As their name implies pine siskins are commonly associated with conifers. In the mixed-wood forests and in the mountains they are more likely to be found in the crowns of pines and spruces than in deciduous trees yet they also frequent the latter. They are quiet, unobtrusive birds unlikely to attract attention while they are feeding but when the flock leaves a tree-top they set up a twitter which is very similar to that of red-polls. In the conifers they feed on seeds from cones and on insects hidden in crevices of the bark. In mid-summer pine siskins are fond of feeding on the seeds of dandelions and thistles. Their quietness, their economy of movement, and their color usually cause them to go unnoticed until almost stepped upon. They are not at all wary; no more wary than the butterflies attracted to the blossoms. But when thoroughly alarmed they head for the nearest trees or bushes. In flight as well as in color and voice they resemble redpolls and it is easy to confuse the two species.

439

KAY HODGES

AMERICAN GOLDFINCH
female   *male*

T. M. SHORTT

RED CROSSBILL
male   *female*   *male*

GROSBEAKS, BUNTINGS, FINCHES, SPARROWS — Family Fringillidae

AMERICAN GOLDFINCH
Spinus tristis subsp. (p. 499)

Common Summer Resident.
Length 5 in.

DESCRIPTION: Ad. m.—Over-all color lemon-yellow with black cap, wings, and tail; most feathers of wing edged with white; inner webs of tail feathers mostly white. Ad. f.—Upperparts brownish-olive; wings and tail brownish-black; two white wing bars; white patches on inner webs of tail feathers; underparts greenish-yellow washed with buffy on sides. Fall m. and im.—Similar to female; males always have darker wings than females.

IDENTIFICATION: The male in summer is unmistakable; females, young, and fall males are greenish birds with dark wings and pale yellow underparts. Undulating flight and call note are best field marks.

RANGE: North America. Breeds across southern Canada south to California and Georgia. Winters from extreme southern Canada south to Mexico.

NESTING: In bushes or trees. Nest of grass and plant down usually lined with thistle floss. Eggs, 3-6, very pale blue, unmarked. (Calgary, August 3.)

REMARKS: In the southern half of the province including the foothills the goldfinch has a wide distribution but in the mountains it has been seen only at Waterton Lake and Canmore. It also ranges as far north as the Peace River District but is rarely seen in the densely forested areas of northern Alberta. One of the last of the spring migrants the goldfinch arrives towards the end of May.

Weedy fields and roadsides are favorite feeding grounds of goldfinches. They eat any small seeds but are especially fond of dandelions and thistles whose seeds provide fiber for nest building as well as food. In the heat of the day they spend much time in willows and poplars seeking shade and insects. Occasionally they visit city gardens and parks where their black and yellow livery is a match for the brightest flower. Here they can be admired at leisure for they are rather confiding little birds. The flight of the goldfinch consists of a series of wing beats followed by a glide. As it opens its wings at the bottom of each glide it bounces sharply upward like a badminton bird hit by a racket. The alternating sharp rise and gradual fall produces a characteristic undulating flight which identifies the goldfinch at quite a distance. In flight or at rest it utters periodically a distinctive four-syllable call, *per — chick — o — pee*. The song is a longer, more musical performance.

GROSBEAKS, BUNTINGS, FINCHES, SPARROWS — Family Fringillidae

RED CROSSBILL Scarce Resident.
Loxia curvirostra subsp. (p. 499) Length 6 in.

DESCRIPTION: Ad. m.—Entire body plumage brick-red or dull orange-red, brightest on rump; wings and tail brownish-black; tail slightly forked; mandibles of beak crossed near tip. Ad. f. and im.—Body color dull grayish-olive tinged with yellow on head, back, and breast; rump dull yellow; wings and tail dusky-brown; beak as in male.

IDENTIFICATION: Much smaller than pine grosbeaks, the brick-red males may be confused only with white-winged crossbills but lack white on wings. Females and young are also distinguished from white-winged crossbills by lack of white on wings.

RANGE: Northern parts of North America, Europe, and Asia. Breeds in coniferous forests of northern North America south in the mountains to Mexico and Georgia. Winters throughout its range but wanders widely at this season.

NESTING: In conifers. Nest of twigs and rootlets lined with moss, hair, and feathers. Eggs, 3-4, greenish-white speckled with brown and lavender. Nests irregularly from January to June.

REMARKS: In the Rocky Mountains and their foothills and in the Cypress Hills the red crossbill occurs fairly regularly throughout the year but elsewhere in the province its occurrences are irregular and erratic. A pair or a flock may appear in a region, stay for a few days or a few months, and then disappear as suddenly as they came. They are almost invariably found in conifers. In 1963 a pair of red crossbills nested in a spruce on the Edmonton University campus while at the same time a flock of forty or more frequented a muskeg only fifteen miles away, apparently without a care in the world. The irregularity of nesting habits of the crossbills is a physiological phenomenon which has long puzzled the experts.

There are many unusual adaptations of the beak of birds and not the least peculiar is the crossing of the mandibles in crossbills. In some individuals the lower mandible crosses to the left side of the upper and in others to the right. In either case the crossbill is adept at removing seeds from their husks and particularly in extracting seeds from between the scales of cones. When a flock is feeding in the crown of a conifer the shower of scales dropping to the ground produces as much noise as the birds themselves.

There is a pretty legend which tells that when our Lord was suffering crucifixion a small gray bird alighted upon the cross and attempted to pull the nails from his hands and feet. So vigorous were its efforts that its beak was badly twisted and its plumage covered with blood. That bird, which carries to this day the evidence of its compassion, was a crossbill.

GROSBEAKS, BUNTINGS, FINCHES, SPARROWS — Family Fringillidae

WHITE-WINGED CROSSBILL   Fairly Common Resident.
Loxia leucoptera subsp. (p. 499)   Length 6 in.

DESCRIPTION: Ad. m.—Body plumage entirely rosy-red, somewhat grayed on underparts especially on abdomen where gray predominates; wings black with two broad white wing bars; tail black, slightly forked; mandibles of beak distinctly crossed at tip. Ad. f. and im.—Entire body plumage dusky-gray or grayish-olive tinged with yellow on head, back, and breast; rump yellow; wings dull black with two broad white wing bars; tail dull black; beak as in male.

IDENTIFICATION: The crossed mandibles are not a good field mark. Red and black males with two obvious bars of white on wings are easily identified. Usually found in flocks, the females can be identified by the males they accompany; they are olive-gray birds with two white wing bars easily seen at rest or in flight.

RANGE: Northern North America. Breeds in northern coniferous forests across Canada south to northern parts of northeastern states. Winters in same areas occasionally wandering south to central states.

NESTING: In conifers. Nest of twigs, rootlets and shredded bark lined with moss, feathers, and hair. Eggs, 3-4, pale bluish-green spotted with brown and lavender. Very irregular in nesting habits; nests with eggs may be found from January to August.

REMARKS: Of the two species of crossbills the white-winged is much more common in Alberta. It occurs throughout the province, erratically it is true, but that is the nature of crossbills; here one season, gone the next; sometimes in small numbers, more often in large flocks. During the breeding season white-winged crossbills range through northern Alberta south to the edge of the parklands, and through the Rocky Mountain regions. In winter they may appear anywhere, even in the wooded coulees of the prairies.

Since they nest in evergreens, and since their favorite food is seeds removed from cones, white-winged crossbills are rarely found far from coniferous woods. They are gregarious birds usually travelling in flocks of several dozen. At tree-top level the twittering flock flies swiftly over the woods seeking the well-laden crown of a spruce in which to alight. There, clambering about like miniature parrots, they soon make the scales fly as they start to feed. White-winged crossbills occasionally visit winter feeding stations in urban areas if there are evergreens in the vicinity; whole sunflower heads are an attraction which they find hard to resist.

GROSBEAKS, BUNTINGS, FINCHES, SPARROWS — Family Fringillidae

RUFOUS-SIDED TOWHEE Fairly Common Summer Resident.
Pipilo erythrophthalmus subsp. (p. 499) Length 8 in.

DESCRIPTION: Ad. m. — Entire head, neck, and upperparts jet black, the wings with numerous white spots; tail black, the outer three feathers broadly tipped with white; broad band down sides to under tail coverts reddish-brown; remainder of underparts white; iris red. Ad. f.—Similar but black replaced by dark grayish-brown.

IDENTIFICATION: A black, or dark gray, sparrow-like bird with white breast sharply contrasting with black neck and reddish sides; tail almost as long as rest of body; red eye is distinctive.

RANGE: North America. Breeds from southern Canada through most of United States to Mexico. Winters in B.C. and southern states.

NESTING: On or very close to the ground, in thick bushes. Nest of grass, leaves, and rootlets lined with fine grass and rootlets. Eggs, 4-5, pale greenish-white spotted with reddish-brown and lavender. (Rosebud, June 6.)

REMARKS: The towhee breeds in Alberta mainly along the river valleys and brushy coulees of the prairies but its range extends north into the parklands as far as Scollard, Coronation, and Wainwright. It has been found nesting at Calgary and has been seen in the Crow's Nest Pass near Lundbreck.

Thick tangles of rose, saskatoon, hawthorn and willow which cover the slopes of prairie coulees are favorite haunts of the towhee but dense undergrowth in poplar stands along streams also provides suitable habitat. Towhees feed most commonly on the ground scratching about like hens as they search for seeds and insects among the fallen leaves. They rarely appear in the open except to flash from one covert to another. Quiet, seclusive, and solitary in habit, they are easily overlooked except during the nesting season. At this time the males expose themselves openly on the top of a bush and proclaim their ardor with a loud, metallic, *chink — chink — chink — churr-rrr-rrr*, which cannot be confused with the song of any other bird. Once the young are hatched, however, there is little time for singing and towhees retreat into the seclusion of the thick tangles where the family is raised.

Rufous-sided towhees arrive in the Lethbridge area during the third week of May and in the northern part of their range about a week later. Most have left the province by early September although occasional laggards may remain until early October.

444

WHITE-WINGED CROSSBILL

ALLAN BROOKS

RUFOUS-SIDED TOWHEE

445

LARK BUNTING
Calamospiza melanocorys

Common Summer Resident.
Length 7 in.

DESCRIPTION: Ad. m.—Entirely black except a large white patch on wing and small white tips on all tail feathers except middle pair; under tail coverts tipped with white; some birds show more or less white feather edging on abdomen. Ad. f. and im.—Upperparts pale grayish-brown streaked with dusky brown; large buffy-white patch on wing; tail grayish-brown, all but middle feathers tipped with white; underparts white streaked with dusky brown except on throat and abdomen; sides tinged with buffy.

IDENTIFICATION: The black and white male is unmistakable. Females are much like vesper sparrows but lack cinnamon on shoulder and have pale buffy patch farther back; pale wing patch and tail tips show best in flight.

RANGE: North America. Breeds on plains region from prairie provinces south to Texas. Winters in southwestern states and Mexico.

NESTING: On the ground. Nest a depression under a tuft of grass lined with grass. Eggs, 4-5, light blue, unmarked. (Burdett, June 3.)

REMARKS: The lark bunting is a typical prairie bird which breeds locally in southeastern Alberta north to about Sibbald and Youngstown and west to Calgary and Ft. Macleod. There are records of casual occurrences in Waterton Lakes and Banff parks and from several places north of its usual range.

Lark buntings select grassy plains for their nesting grounds, preferably those where the grass is thick and interspersed with sage. Usually several pairs occupy one field forming a loose colony with the chestnut-collared and McCown's longspurs which may nest in the same area. Like the latter species the males have a beautiful flight song uttered as they flutter to the ground with wings raised and tail spread. From this performance which resembles that of the larks, comes their name; from the black plumage with contrasting white wing patch comes another local name, the white-winged blackbird. The lark bunting is neither a lark nor a blackbird but a true bunting or sparrow.

On the short-grass prairies of southern Alberta lark buntings spend the summer close to the ground, perhaps finding that the monotony of their surroundings is their greatest protection. A rock, a sage-bush or an occasional fence-post is a convenient vantage point from which they can overlook their territory; rarely do they ascend higher; even their short flights are made at low level. Their young thrive in these surroundings, the abundant insect life providing their food until they are old enough to add seeds and berries to their diet.

SAVANNAH SPARROW Common Summer Resident.
Passerculus sandwichensis subsp. (p. 499) Length 5½ in.

DESCRIPTION: Ads. — Crown brownish-black lightly streaked with buffy-gray and with narrow median stripe of buffy-gray; pale yellow line over eye; cheeks and rest of upperparts grayish-brown streaked with dark brown; four indistinct grayish lines down back; tail grayish-brown; throat white bordered with dark brown; underparts white streaked with dark brown across breast and down sides; legs flesh pink. Im.—Similar but darker above and somewhat buffy below.

IDENTIFICATION: A small sparrow with short tail and yellow stripe over eye. Darker than vesper sparrow and no white in tail; similar to song sparrow but smaller and with shorter tail. Yellow line over eye is distinctive.

RANGE: North America. Breeds from California and Connecticut north to the arctic coast and Aleutian Islands. Winters in southern states.

NESTING: On the ground. Nest of coarse grass lined with fine grass and hair. Eggs, 4-5, grayish-white speckled with reddish-brown. (Indus, June 1.)

REMARKS: As a breeding bird the savannah sparrow is the most widely distributed member of the sparrow family in Alberta. This is not because it accepts a variety of nesting sites but because it will nest in any small grassy or brushy areas no matter whether they be surrounded by forest, rock, bush, prairie or water. Thus suitable habitat can be found in almost any locality including the mountains.

Grassy meadows, especially those with a stream running through or those bordering a slough, are favorite haunts of savannah sparrows during the summer. Whether the surrounding vegetation be forest, light bush, or desert does not matter; in any case savannah sparrows spend most of their time in the grass and weeds of the meadow, rarely making excursions beyond its borders. The males select for their perch a tall grass stem or the top of a snowberry bush all of eighteen inches above the ground and from this they sing a distinctive song, *tsip — tsip — tsip — tsip — you-ree-e-e-e-you.* When approached they prefer to run rather than fly but when hard pressed they take wing and flit away only a few inches above the grass. They rarely go far before dropping into the grass again and continuing their retreat along the ground. Their habitat provides them with an abundance of seeds and insects for food as well as shelter for the nest. In it their neighbors may be Leconte's or Baird's sparrows while on the prairies vesper sparrows and horned larks occupy the short-grass areas nearby.

447

ALLAN BROOKS

LARK BUNTING
female   *male*

C. HAMPSON

SAVANNAH SPARROW

GRASSHOPPER SPARROW

BAIRD'S SPARROW

449

GROSBEAKS, BUNTINGS, FINCHES, SPARROWS – Family Fringillidae

GRASSHOPPER SPARROW   Scarce Summer Resident.
Ammodramus savannarum   subsp. (p. 499)   Length 5 in.

DESCRIPTION: Ads.—Crown brownish-black with light median stripes; hindneck gray streaked with chestnut; rest of upperparts streaked with black, brown, gray, and white; tail grayish-brown, the middle two feathers narrow and pointed; line over eye and sides of head buffy-yellow; dark line back of eye; underparts pale buffy becoming white on abdomen; a few indistinct dusky streaks may be present on sides of breast; beak grayish-pink.

IDENTIFICATION: A small ground sparrow with yellowish stripe over eye. Differs from all other ground sparrows in lacking distinct dark streaks on sides and flanks.

RANGE: North America. Breeds in extreme southern Canada and throughout the United States. Winters from southern states to Guatemala.

NESTING: On the ground. Nest of coarse grass lined with fine grass and hair; usually hidden in a clump of grass and arched over. Eggs, 4-5, white spotted with brown.

REMARKS: Until 1945 there were no authenticated records of the grasshopper sparrow in Alberta. In July of that year a male was collected and another bird seen in the valley of Lost River in extreme southern Alberta. There were indications that the birds were nesting. In 1956 several observers reported a grasshopper sparrow singing in an established territory near Calgary. No nest was found. The habitat was destroyed in 1957 and no grasshopper sparrows have since been seen in that area. More recently there have been sight records from another part of the Calgary district.

Grasshopper sparrows frequent dry fields and meadows. Virgin prairie dotted with clumps of rosebush, snowberry, and wolf willows is a favorite habitat since it provides open grasslands for feeding and bits of taller vegetation for singing and lookout perches. There is nothing conspicuous about grasshopper sparrows; their colors blend well with dry grass and earth and their song is so weak that it is easily overlooked in the chorus of insect sounds. It resembles somewhat the song of the savannah sparrow with the first and last notes lopped off, *sip — sip — sree-e-e-e.* They spend most of their time on the ground. Even when pursued they seek to escape by running among the grass stems like mice; only when hard pressed do they take wing. It is then that the diminutive grasshopper sparrows best identify themselves for their fluttering flight is like that of no other sparrow. As though with great effort their quivering wings keep them above the grass tops for a short distance but they soon drop to the ground again to continue their escape on foot.

450

BAIRD'S SPARROW　　　　　　Fairly Common Summer Resident.
Ammodramus bairdii　　　　　　　　　　　　Length 5½ in.

DESCRIPTION: Ads. — Top of head buffy-brown streaked with black leaving light median stripe; sides of head and neck buffy streaked on cheeks and neck with black; rest of upperparts buffy-gray, most feathers with dark brown centers; rump brown flecked with black; throat white bordered with a row of black spots; rest of underparts white or buffy-white streaked with black across breast and with brown down sides; legs pink.

IDENTIFICATION: A small short-tailed sparrow with streaked buffy crown and face. Similar to savannah sparrow but with buffy head distinctly streaked, and lacking yellow eye-stripe; similar to vesper sparrow but buffy on head and no white in tail; the brown rump is not a good fieldmark but is distinctive in the hand.

RANGE: Western North America. Breeds in the great plains regions of Canada and United States. Winters from Texas south to northern Mexico.

NESTING: On the ground. Nest of grass lined with fine grass and hair and concealed in long grass. Eggs, 4-5, grayish-white blotched and lined with browns.

REMARKS: Baird's sparrow has been found nesting in southern Alberta west to Calgary and north as far as Tofield but it is mainly a bird of the prairies rather than the parklands. It is extremely local in distribution during the nesting season. Preference is shown for meadows and pastures well covered with long grass which provides cover for nests and birds alike. Grassy slough bottoms and alkali flats are favorite haunts in dry years but after a rainy cycle such places become too damp for Baird's sparrow and the species may disappear from a locality which it has occupied for several years.

A rosebush or a tuft of grass only a few inches above the surrounding prairie is the customary singing perch of Baird's sparrow. Like most prairie birds, however, it also utilizes any fence near its territory. Rather shy and wary, it rarely allows close approach. Slipping from its perch it runs away among the grass or else flies off so close to the ground that it is difficult to tell where it drops to earth again. Such behavior challenges the skill of the observer and until he learns to relate its distinctive song with this rather colorless bird Baird's sparrow may elude him.

LECONTES SPARROW

SHARP-TAILED SPARROW

GROSBEAKS, BUNTINGS, FINCHES, SPARROWS — Family Fringillidae

LECONTE'S SPARROW Fairly Common Summer Resident.
Passerherbulus caudacutus Length 5 in.

DESCRIPTION: Ads.—Crown black with broad whitish median stripe and bordered with buffy-orange stripe over eye; collar of pale chestnut; back blackish with four buffy stripes; wings streaked with black, brown, and buffy; tail of narrow, pointed feathers, brown edged with buffy; cheeks gray; black line back of eye; throat, breast, and sides pale buffy-orange; sides streaked with black; abdomen, white; beak slate-blue.

IDENTIFICATION: A small ground sparrow with much buffy-orange on face and underparts; obvious pale median stripe on crown and lack of streaking on breast will separate Leconte's from the savannah and Nelson's sparrows, the only two sparrows likely to be found in its normal habitat.

RANGE: North America. Breeds from Great Slave Lake to southern Alberta east to Manitoba and Minnesota. Winters in southeastern states.

NESTING: On the ground. Nest of coarse grass lined with fine grass and hair; usually well hidden in a tuft of grass. Eggs, 4-5, greenish-white finely spotted with brown. (Fawcett, June 4.)

REMARKS: During the nesting season Leconte's sparrow is widely but locally distributed in Alberta from near Okotoks and Rosebud north to the provincial boundary. Farther south it has been found nesting at Brooks and Lethbridge. In the foothills it breeds from Gorge Creek north at least as far as Cochrane; in the mountains it has been recorded at Jasper.

Leconte's sparrow is a ground sparrow which frequents damp meadows and marshes in the central and northern parts of the province; in the south, where such habitat is scarce, it may occupy tall grass and buck-brush near a creek or slough even though the ground beneath is quite dry. In any case the grass cover must be dense; fields of cultivated grass often attract the species. The male sings a weak, wheezy song from a grass stem which may not protrude above the surface of the vegetation. Sometimes he sings from within a low bush but his singing post is never prominent and the singer is hard to locate. When approached he drops to the ground and scurries off between the maze of stems, allowing only a momentary glimpse here and there. When hard-pressed he flies off haltingly close to the grass tops and soon drops to earth again as though tired by the brief exertion. But like many timid birds Leconte's sparrow soon becomes inquisitive about a motionless object and the observer who can keep still will shortly find himself under scrutiny by a curious, rather beautifully marked bird. In September duck hunters quietly waiting in the cattails often see a variety of migrating sparrows working through the reeds; the most furtive will probably be Leconte's sparrows.

453

GROSBEAKS, BUNTINGS, FINCHES, SPARROWS — Family Fringillidae

NELSON'S (SHARP-TAILED) SPARROW   Scarce Summer Resident.
Ammospiza caudacuta   subsp. (p. 499)   Length 5 in.

DESCRIPTION: Ads.—Crown dark brown with medial stripe of dark gray and bordered by buffy stripe over eye; collar of bluish-gray; back and wings brownish-olive, the back with two broad dark brown stripes narrowly bordered with white; tail of narrow pointed feathers, brown edged with buffy; cheeks gray bordered with buffy; a black streak back of eye; throat either white or buffy; breast and sides buffy streaked indistinctly on breast, distinctly on sides, with brown; abdomen white; beak slate-blue.

IDENTIFICATION: Smaller, darker, and less heavily streaked below than savannah sparrow. Similar to Leconte's sparrow but no light medial crown-stripe and gray instead of brown collar.

RANGE: North America. Breeds from Great Slave Lake south to South Dakota and east to Nova Scotia and Florida. Winters in southeastern states and coast of Gulf of Mexico.

NESTING: On the ground in marshes. Nest of coarse grass in a dry tuft of grass. Eggs, 4-5, grayish or greenish-white speckled with black and brown. (Spruce Grove, June 3.)

REMARKS: The paucity of information about Nelson's sparrow in Alberta may be an indication of its scarcity in the province or it may be merely proof of the secretive nature of the bird. The species is probably more abundant than is supposed for in recent years ornithologists have found it breeding in various localities of northern and central Alberta south to about Red Deer. It has not been reported from the mountains.

Nelson's sparrows inhabit damp marshy spots in the forested areas of Alberta. In northern muskegs they frequent grassy and reedy margins of pools; cattails along the shallow margins of woodland lakes are also favorite haunts. Like Leconte's sparrows which often nest in the same area, Nelson's sparrows are timid and secretive. To find them one must wade extensively in the grassy marsh and flush them from the shorter vegetation into the surrounding bushes; or else, half-hidden in the cattails, one must watch carefully for the asthmatic singer which climbs periodically towards the top of a stem and delivers a few harsh, wheezy notes much coarser and louder than those of Leconte's sparrow. The slightest alarm will send him scurrying to the safety of lower levels along with the long-billed marsh wrens but, while the latter are likely to move farther out over the water, Nelson's sparrow will probably move towards the shore seeking security in the thick grass.

GROSBEAKS, BUNTINGS, FINCHES, SPARROWS — Family Fringillidae

VESPER SPARROW Common Summer Resident.
Pooecetes gramineus subsp. (p. 499) Length 6 in.

DESCRIPTION: Ads.—Upperparts pale buffy-gray each feather with a central streak of dark grayish-brown; bend of wing pale cinnamon; two pale gray wing bars; tail about 2½ in., grayish-brown, the outer feather mainly white; eye ring and line over eye white; cheeks buffy bordered by brown; underparts white lightly streaked with brown on sides of throat, across breast and down flanks; legs pale pink. Sexes alike. Im.—Similar to adults but more buffy and less gray.

IDENTIFICATION: A pale grayish sparrow with light eye ring, brownish cheeks outlined with white, and buffy-brown shoulder patch. In flight the tail shows white margins. Brownish shoulder patch and white outer tail feathers are good field marks.

RANGE: Temperate North America. Breeds across southern Canada south to California and North Carolina. Winters in southern states and Mexico.

NESTING: On the ground. Nest of grass lined with fine grass and hair. Eggs, 4-6, bluish-white speckled with brown. (Drumheller, June 2.)

REMARKS: The breeding range of the vesper sparrow extends across the prairies of southern Alberta north through the open meadows of the parklands to the edge of the northern forest region. Westward it extends into the foothills and lower valleys of the Rocky Mountains. It comes as something of a surprise to hear this prairie bird in the meadows at Canmore competing in song with white-crowned sparrows in the bordering bushes.

On the prairies the vesper sparrow is the most common and the best known member of the sparrow family. The short-grass plains are its original home but it has adapted well to settlement and cultivation of these regions. No patch of grass beside a road, under a fence-line, or in a coulee is too small to provide cover for its nest. Most of its life is spent near the ground. Its highest perch is a fencepost; even in flight it rarely rises higher. Disturbed from the roadside it flits away close to the ground, only the white tail margins breaking its earth-gray color. In the parklands and forest regions it frequents open meadows still keeping close to the earth much of the time although its singing post may be in one of the bordering trees.

The vesper sparrow is not shy nor does it skulk but it blends so well with its surroundings that it is never conspicuous. Vocally, however, it is outstanding. Its song is heard to best advantage in the calm of the evening when vespers of incomparable beauty pour from its vibrant throat to break the silence that ends the day.

GROSBEAKS, BUNTINGS, FINCHES, SPARROWS — Family Fringillidae

LARK SPARROW Fairly Common Summer Resident.
Chondestes grammacus subsp. (p. 499) Length 6¼ in.

DESCRIPTION: Ads.—Two broad chestnut stripes on crown separated by pale buffy stripe; white line over eye; sides of head white except black line through eye, black line bordering white throat, chestnut ear coverts, and black line behind them; rest of upperparts olive-gray streaked with brownish-black; underparts white tinged with olive-gray on breast and sides; black spot in middle of breast; tail brownish-black tipped with white, most broadly on outer feathers. Im.—Similar but browner and head markings less distinct.

IDENTIFICATION: Distinctive head markings and large amount of white on tail tip make the lark sparrow easy to identify.

RANGE: Western North America. Breeds from southern B.C. and Ontario south to West Virginia and northern Mexico. Winters in southwestern states, Mexico, and Central America.

NESTING: On the ground usually under low vegetation. Nest, a depression lined with grass, rootlets, and hair. Eggs, 3-5, white marked with brown and black. (Steveville, June 18.)

REMARKS: The badlands of Alberta yield much of interest to the student of birds and not the least enjoyable of his experiences may be his observations of the lark sparrow. Although it has been recorded as far north as Botha the lark sparrow is most abundant in the badlands of the Red Deer River from near Morrin southward. It may be found in undergrowth along streams, in saskatoon clumps on sloping coulee walls, or in sage brush on the flats but it is always at the edge of the vegetation for it spends as much time in the open as in the shade. Often it may be seen picking up seeds and insects on the crumbling clay cliffs; in these surroundings its colors are remarkably protective. The lark sparrow seems to be fond of human company and frequently nests in the vicinity of farmhouses and villages. It makes itself at home in the yard and in the garden especially if there is a tangle of shrubbery close at hand. Using a fencepost, a building, or occasionally a tree as a singing perch the male sings a beautifuly clear, sweet song. It apparently reminded the early settlers of their favorite European bird and they named the pretty songster the lark sparrow.

As a breeding bird the lark sparrow occurs only in southern Alberta from Lethbridge, Calgary and Big Valley south and east to the provincial boundaries. It is extremely local in distribution within this area. It is most likely to be found in river valleys bounded by steep clay cliffs or in the coulees running into them. The lark sparrow nests regularly in the valleys of the Red Deer, South Saskatchewan, Old Man and Milk Rivers.

ALLAN BROOKS

VESPER SPARROW

RAY SALT

LARK SPARROW

GROSBEAKS, BUNTINGS, FINCHES, SPARROWS — Family Fringillidae

SLATE-COLORED JUNCO   Common Summer Resident.
Junco hyemalis subsp. (p. 499)   Length 6 in.

DESCRIPTION: Ad. m.—Entire head, upper breast, and all upperparts slaty-black, darkest on head; rest of underparts white shaded with pale slate-gray on sides; tail slaty-black except two white outer feathers; beak pale pink. Ad. f.—Similar but the slaty-black paler and lightly tinged with brown. Im.—Similar to adults but more heavily tinged with brown.

IDENTIFICATION: A distinctively marked sparrow with black head and back and sharp line of demarkation between black of upper breast and white of lower. White outer feathers show distinctly against black tail in flight.

RANGE: North America. Breeds from Alaska to Labrador south to central Alberta and Georgia. Winters in extreme southern Canada and throughout the U.S.

NESTING: On the ground in woods. Nest of grass, rootlets, and shredded bark lined with moss and hair. Eggs, 3-5, greenish-white speckled with reddish-brown. (Camrose, May 12.)

REMARKS: The slate-colored junco breeds in the coniferous and mixed-wood forests of northern and western Alberta south to Jasper and the fringes of the parklands. In the mountain regions south of Jasper it hybridizes with the Oregon junco. On migration the slate-colored junco occurs throughout the province. Individuals occasionally winter as far north as Edmonton.

With their dark color, pink beak, a flash of white down the sides of a black tail, and the metallic *tititit* alarm note as they dart for cover, juncoes are perhaps the most easily recognized of all the woodland sparrows. They arrive early in April, and before the end of the month they are in every tangle of undergrowth, in every brush-pile, and along every forest path. They feed most commonly on the ground garnering the wealth of seeds from the forest floor, from roadside ditches, and from the edges of fields bordered by woods. Rather confiding in nature they move along the woodland path just ahead of the observer and when he stops they approach and feed all about him. During the summer slate-colored juncoes usually frequent shady woods containing both evergreen and deciduous trees. From high branches the males assert their territorial rights with a trilling song similar to but more melodious than that of the chipping sparrow. In the fall slate-colored juncoes are late migrants but most have left the province before the end of October.

GROSBEAKS, BUNTINGS, FINCHES, SPARROWS — Family Fringillidae

OREGON JUNCO Common Summer Resident.
Junco oreganus subsp. (p. 499) Length 6 in.

DESCRIPTION: Ad. m.—Entire head, neck, and upper breast black; back rusty brown; wings and lower back slaty-gray. tinged with brown; outer tail feather white, rest brownish-gray; sides pinkish-buff; rest of underparts white; beak pale pink. Ad. f.—Similar but all colors paler and the black tinged with brown. Mearn's junco is a pale Oregon junco in which the black is replaced by slate-gray and the brown by buffy or pinkish-buff.

IDENTIFICATION: A junco with a reddish-brown back and light brown sides.

RANGE: Western North America. Breeds from Alaska south through the mountains to Lower California and Mexico. Winters in southern part of range.

NESTING: On the ground in dense woods. Nest of grass and rootlets lined with fine grass, moss, and rootlets. Eggs, 4-5, greenish-white spotted with brown. (Gorge Creek, May 20.)

REMARKS: The Oregon junco breeds in the Rocky Mountain region of southwestern Alberta from the international boundary to about Banff. Farther north in the Jasper region the slate-colored junco is the main breeding junco although the Oregon junco has been reported nesting there. There is considerable hybridization of the two species; in fact some taxonomists do not recognize the two forms as distinct species. A subspecies, Mearn's junco, much paler in color, breeds in the Cypress Hills region of extreme southeastern Alberta. On migration either subspecies, and many hybrids between the Oregon and slate-colored junco, may be found, often in mixed flocks, well outside their usual breeding ranges. In habits, behavior, and song they are all alike. It is usually a waste of time to attempt field identification of many of these birds.

In the mountains Oregon juncoes spend much of their time on the forest floor or in the undergrowth looking for seeds and insects but when the male feels an urge to sing he rises to the top of a tall spruce to deliver his monotonous but cheerful song. Juncoes are rather friendly little birds. Often the nest is built near a cottage and the fledglings are brought to the back door for a hand-out of crumbs and table scraps. Oregon juncoes are among the first migrants to arrive in the spring and the last to leave in the fall. Occasionally small numbers winter in the province; a few spent the winter of 1956-57 in the vicinity of Banff.

459

SLATE-COLORED JUNCO
male and female at nest

OREGON (PINK-SIDED) JUNCO

TREE SPARROW

CHIPPING SPARROW

461

GROSBEAKS, BUNTINGS, FINCHES, SPARROWS — Family Fringillidae

TREE SPARROW

Common Migrant.

Spizella arborea   subsp. (p. 500)

Length 6 in.

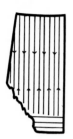

DESCRIPTION: Ads.—Crown chestnut; hindneck gray; back and wings streaked with chestnut, black, and gray; two white wing bars; tail brownish-gray; sides of head and neck and line over eye pale gray; narrow line back from eye chestnut; throat and breast gray fading to white on abdomen and buffy on sides; an indistinct black spot in middle of breast; chestnut spot on side near bend of wing. In the fall slightly paler due to grayish feather edges.

IDENTIFICATION: A medium-sized sparrow with chestnut cap and black spot in middle of breast. Most likely to be confused with chipping sparrow but larger, line over eye gray instead of white, no black on forehead, and black spot on breast. The tree sparrow is never found in Alberta during the nesting season.

RANGE: North America. Breeds from Alaska to Newfoundland south to southern Mackenzie and Quebec. Winters from extreme southern Canada to Texas and South Carolina.

NESTING: On or near the ground. Nest of grasses and fine rootlets. Eggs, 4-5, pale greenish-blue speckled with browns.

REMARKS: Tree sparrows occur in all parts of Alberta during both spring and fall migration periods but they do not breed in the province. Small numbers occasionally winter in Alberta; at this season they have been recorded as far north as Camrose.

Towards the end of March the first spring migrants arrive in Alberta and in the vanguard are the tree sparrows. By the middle of April they are in every shrub and bush. Their weak but pleasing song comes from shelterbelts around the farmstead, from brushy prairie coulees, from thickets along the roadside, and from the edges of the forest. They are easily identified for only juncoes and a few song sparrows share the bushes with them this early in the season; the similar chipping sparrow does not arrive until the beginning of May when most tree sparrows have left the province. Despite their name tree sparrows often feed on the ground picking up seeds uncovered by melting snows but they never get far from a tangle of boughs into which they can fly when alarmed. The trim brown form with fairly long tail shows well in flight but it blends beautifully with the drab vegetation when they choose to hide. Tree sparrows are gone before the buds burst on trees and shrubs. About the middle of September they reappear. Their numbers swelled by the young of the year, they pass gradually southward during the following six weeks occupying the same type of habitat as they did in the spring and feeding on the bountiful crop of weed seeds.

CHIPPING SPARROW Common Summer Resident.
Spizella passerina subsp. (p. 500) Length 5¼ in.

DESCRIPTION: Ads.—Forehead black; crown chestnut; white line over eye; hindneck gray streaked with black; back and wings streaked with black, brown, and buffy; two buffy wing bars; tail brownish-gray; throat dull white; sides of head, neck, and rest of underparts gray fading to white on abdomen. Nestlings are grayish-brown birds heavily streaked above and below with dark gray; in August they assume a plumage similar to that of the adult but browner with chestnut cap concealed.

IDENTIFICATION: A small sparrow with chestnut cap and white line over eye. May be confused with tree sparrow but has no black spot on breast, or with clay-colored sparrow which is paler and never has chestnut cap.

RANGE: North America. Breeds in forested areas from Yukon and Newfoundland south through most of the United States. Winters in southern states.

NESTING: In small trees and bushes, rarely more than 5 ft. from ground. Nest of grass lined with hair. Eggs, 3-5, greenish-blue lightly spotted with browns. (Sylvan Lake, June 15.)

REMARKS: The breeding range of the chipping sparrow includes the wooded regions of northern and western Alberta, the mountains and the foothills, the more heavily wooded river valleys of the parklands and the prairies, and the Cypress Hills. On migration the chipping sparrow occurs throughout the province except on the open prairies.

Chipping sparrows are arboreal birds usually found, during the nesting season, in open deciduous and mixed-wood forests. In central Alberta they occur commonly in shelter belts near farms and in shade trees along city streets, especially if there are a few evergreens which are their favorite nesting sites in these locations. They show little fear of man and his works; in fact, they respond readily to friendly overtures and will make themselves quite at home in a garden hedge. Chipping sparrows received their name from their call note, a sharp *chip*. Their song, delivered from an open singing perch, is a single note so rapidly repeated that it forms a trill. Although far from musical it is not loud enough to be objectionable.

Chipping sparrows arrive in central Alberta about the first of May. They are largely insectivorous during the summer but later seeds and small fruits are added to their diet. The nestlings are fed entirely on insects. In the fall chipping sparrows pass southward in late August and September, moving through the trees with the main migratory wave of sparrows and warblers.

463

CLAY-COLORED SPARROW

C. HAMPSON

BREWER'S SPARROW

CLAY-COLORED SPARROW
Spizella pallida

Common Summer Resident.
Length 5¼ in.

DESCRIPTION: Ads. —— Crown brownish-black with buffy-gray medial stripe; hindneck gray with few streaks of black; back and wings buffy-gray streaked with black; one white wing bar; tail brownish-gray; white line over eye; sides of neck gray; underparts white becoming buffy on sides and flanks.

IDENTIFICATION: A buffy or earth-colored sparrow with light stripe down middle of dark crown, and gray hindneck. Differs from chipping sparrow in having brown face patch and pale gray hindneck, both noticeable at a distance, and in lacking chestnut crown; distinguished from Brewer's sparrow by gray hindneck, white line over eye, and brown face patch.

RANGE: Interior of North America. Breeds from southern Mackenzie and northern Manitoba south to Colorado and Illinois. Winters in southwestern states and Mexico.

NESTING: Within few feet of ground in bushes. Nest of grass lined with fine grass and hair. Eggs, 3-5, greenish-blue spotted with brown. (Tofield, June 2.)

REMARKS: The clay-colored sparrow breeds in suitable habitat in all parts of Alberta including the mountain valleys but it is most common in the parklands and on the prairies. On migration it is widespread.

Late in April or early in May an unmusical, insect-like, *bzzzz — bzzzz — bzzzz — bzzzz*, tells of the arrival of clay-colored sparrows. With this tuneless song the males proclaim territorial rights to a roadside thicket or a bit of buckbrush dotting the prairie. In suitable habitat there may be a pair of clay-colored sparrows every hundred yards along a roadway. Unlike chipping sparrows, however, they rarely nest along city streets or close to houses. For food they find insects in the foliage of the bushes and seeds in the grass along the roadside. They keep out of grainfields during the nesting season but later in the summer when the young are fledged and the grain is ripe they are often found gleaning.

Clay-colored sparrows are small, long-tailed sparrows, trim and neat of form if somewhat drab of voice and color. They are not particularly timid; when approached they retreat into the brush, chipping with alarm, but their curiosity soon brings them into the open and the alarm note changes to the buzzing song. As soon as the young are fledged clay-colored sparrows leave the nesting areas and wander over the countryside. Early in September they move southward feeding in the grainfields and hedgerows with vesper and savannah sparrows and in the trees with chipping sparrows and warblers.

465

GROSBEAKS, BUNTINGS, FINCHES, SPARROWS — Family Fringillidae

BREWER'S SPARROW   Fairly Common Summer Resident.
Spizella breweri   subsp. (p. 500)   Length 5 in.

DESCRIPTION: Ads.—Upperparts buffy-gray streaked with brownish-black except on tail; sides of head and neck and a line over eye buffy-gray; underparts dull white tinged with pale buffy-gray over breast and down sides. Im.—Similar but streaked below as well as above.

IDENTIFICATION: The most colorless of the sparrows. A ground-haunting, earth-colored sparrow heavily streaked above. Most like the clay-colored sparrow but no medial stripe on crown, no definite markings on head and no pale gray hindneck.

RANGE: Western North America. Breeds from southern B.C., Alberta and Saskatchewan, south to California and Texas. Winters in southwestern states and Mexico.

NESTING: Near to or on the ground. Nest of stems, leaves and grass; on the prairies the nest is usually placed low in a sagebush; in the mountains it is placed in a low juniper or scrub pine. Eggs, 3-4, pale greenish-blue spotted with brown.

REMARKS: Two races of this species occur in widely separated parts of Alberta. Brewer's sparrow inhabits the semi-arid plains of the southeastern corner of the province while the timberline sparrow lives near tree limit at high altitudes in the Rocky Mountains. Although reasonably abundant within their range they are not well known since they usually go unrecognized.

Brewer's sparrows are ground sparrows whose drab colors blend so well with the dry earth that they move about inconspicuously among the sparse brown vegetation. They sing from the top of a sage brush but rarely rise any higher even in flight. On migration, however, they are occasionally found in trees with chipping and clay-colored sparrows. Timberline sparrows frequent the clumps of dwarf bushes and trees which dot the grassy slopes where mountain forests give way to talus. They are difficult to find in these out of the way places except during the breeding season when the males sing a rolling song more beautiful than would be expected from such colorless birds. The song starts out with buzzing sounds like those of the clay-colored sparrow but these give way to pure sweet notes which rival in quality those of the vesper and song sparrows. When disturbed the songsters creep away on the ground to find retreat in any bit of tangled brush.

GROSBEAKS, BUNTINGS, FINCHES, SPARROWS — Family Fringillidae

HARRIS' SPARROW
Zonotrichia querula

Scarce Migrant.
Length 7½ in.

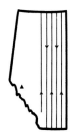

DESCRIPTION: Spring ads.—Top of head, throat, and space in front of eyes black; underparts white tinged with buffy on flanks and with row of black streaks across breast and down sides; line over eye white; face and hindneck gray with black mark behind eye; back and wings olive-brown streaked with black and pale buff; two white wing bars; tail brownish-gray; beak reddish-orange. Im.— Crown black each feather margined with gray; throat white bordered on side with narrow black line and below by row of brownish-black streaks across upper breast; face and neck buffy; remainder similar to adult.

IDENTIFICATION: A large long-tailed sparrow with dark crown lacking medial light stripe. Spring adults are distinctively marked; fall birds have white throat, a necklace of dark brown marks across upper breast, and brown-streaked sides.

RANGE: Interior North America. Breeds along the fringe of northern forest from Mackenzie east to Hudson Bay. Winters from Kansas and Missouri to Texas.

NESTING: On the ground. Nest of coarse grass lined with finer grass. Eggs, 4, pale bluish-green marked with brown.

REMARKS: Although it rarely occurs in Alberta on its northward migration in spring Harris' sparrow migrates southward through the eastern half of the province in fair numbers each fall. The species breeds in most of the heavily forested parts of the Canadian Shield and therefore might be expected to nest in that part of the Shield which cuts through the northeastern corner of the province. However, it has not yet been found nesting in Alberta.

Along the lower valley of the Rosebud river Harris' sparrows occur regularly each fall appearing in late September or early October and passing through the region in about ten days. They feed on the ground like white-crowns picking up weed-seeds close to or under a tangle of willow or hawthorn which will provide cover if a northern shrike should pass by. When alarmed they scurry away among the roots or flit to another thicket, letting their long tails droop occasionally like the white-crowns with which they associate and once safely hidden they express their alarm with loud notes, *peent* or *queenk*, until assured that all danger is past. Yet Harris' sparrows are not difficult to approach. If the observer moves cautiously they will soon hop up into the leafless boughs and stare back curiously at the binoculars focused upon them.

467

GROSBEAKS, BUNTINGS, FINCHES, SPARROWS — Family Fringillidae

WHITE-CROWNED SPARROW Common Summer Resident.
Zonotrichia leucophrys subsp. (p. 500) Length 6½ in.

DESCRIPTION: Ads.—Crown with broad medial white stripe bordered by broad black stripe; white line over eye and black line back of eye to hindneck; face and underparts gray becoming white in middle of abdomen and washed with buffy on flanks; back and wings brownish-gray most feathers with chocolate-brown centers and whitish edges; two white wing bars; tail 2¾ in., grayish-brown. Im.—Similar but medial crown stripe buffy and lateral stripes chestnut.

IDENTIFICATION: A brown long-tailed sparrow with black and white head stripes. Similar to white-throated sparrow but chocolate rather than reddish-brown, medial crown stripe very broad, and no yellow spot in front of eye; throat may be light but is never sharply defined from gray of neck.

RANGE: North America. Breeds in most of northern Canada north to tree limit and in Rocky Mountains and foothills south to California. Winters in southern states and Mexico.

NESTING: On the ground or in low bushes. Nest of grasses and rootlets lined with fine grass and hair. Eggs, 3-5, pale bluish-white or greenish-white spotted with brown and black. (Calgary, June 25.)

REMARKS: Although very common on migration in southern Alberta the white-crowned sparrow breeds there only in the Cypress Hills and in the Rocky Mountains and their foothills east to Calgary and Nordegg. In northern Alberta it breeds only in the Peace River district and in the Lake Athabasca region where the Canadian Shield cuts through the northeastern corner of the province.

White-crowned sparrows appear in central Alberta about the end of April and are abundant during the first two weeks of May. They move southward in large numbers in September. On migration white-crowned sparrows travel in flocks of up to several dozen frequenting roadside thickets or open weedy patches close to bushes into which they can scurry at the approach of danger. As they flit away their tails seem to drop down periodically as though too heavy to hold up. Once in the bushes they are not particularly wary and will often sing in full view of the observer. Much of their food consists of weed seeds picked up from the ground.

For their nesting territory white-crowned sparrows choose thick bushes at the edge of mixed-wood or deciduous forests showing no particular preference for water. The male has a pretty little song, the last three notes of which are in rapidly descending tones.

468

DOUG GILROY

HARRIS' SPARROW

KAY HODGES

WHITE-CROWNED SPARROW

469

GROSBEAKS, BUNTINGS, FINCHES, SPARROWS — Family Fringillidae

GOLDEN-CROWNED SPARROW   Fairly Common Summer Resident.
Zonotrichia atricapilla   Length 7 in.

DESCRIPTION: Ads.—Top of head above eyes and hindneck black with large median patch yellow in front, gray behind; rest of upperparts grayish-brown streaked on back and wings with black, brown, and gray; two white wing bars; rest of head, neck, and breast gray; abdomen white; sides grayish-buff. Im.—Crown yellowish-brown with indistinct lighter patch in middle; rest like adults.

IDENTIFICATION: A large grayish sparrow normally found in the mountains. Similar to white-crowned sparrow in body color but lacking white on head.

RANGE: Western North America. Breeds in south central B.C. and adjacent mountains of Alberta north to Alaska. Winters from Oregon to California.

NESTING: On the ground under bushes. Nest of grass lined with fine rootlets. Eggs, 4-5, pale greenish-blue speckled with browns. (Pipestone Pass, July 8.)

REMARKS: As a breeding bird the golden-crowned sparrow is found only at high altitudes in the mountain regions of western Alberta. It nests in Jasper and Banff National Parks and southward for an undetermined distance. Eastward it has been found nesting as far as Mountain Park. The only known record away from the mountains is of three birds seen at Red Deer in October, 1939, after a heavy snowfall.

In the fringe of juniper, scrub pine, and spruce just above timberline in the mountains the golden-crowned sparrow will be found. In adjacent meadows and scree horned larks, American pipits, and white-tailed ptarmigan nest but the golden-crowned sparrow makes its home in clumps of dwarf conifers which never grow more than three or four feet high at this altitude. From the top of one of these the male sings. He is very wary; at the approach of an intruder he drops into the dense tangle of evergreen boughs under which his mate has built her nest. Like most birds, however, he is inquisitive and a patient observer who can sit quietly nearby for a few minutes will soon be able to add this alpine beauty to his sight list.

In common with, and sometimes in company with his close relatives the white-crowned and fox sparrows, the golden-crowned sparrow feeds on the ground. Where seeds and insects are an inducement he may move out into the open but never more than a few feet from the bushes. Periodically, and for no apparent reason, he beats a hasty retreat into his thicket. Shortly, however, he reappears and again works gradually farther and farther afield until another fancied peril sends him fleeing for cover.

470

GROSBEAKS, BUNTINGS, FINCHES, SPARROWS — Family Fringillidae

WHITE-THROATED SPARROW   Common Summer Resident.
Zonotrichia albicollis   Length 6¾ in.

DESCRIPTION: Ads.—Crown black with narrow medial white stripe; line over eye is yellow in front, white behind; black line back of eye; throat white; face, breast and sides gray streaked with dusky; rest of underparts white; back and wings chestnut, most feathers with black centers; two white wing bars; tail 3 in., grayish-brown. Im.—Similar but crown chestnut with thin medial gray stripe; line over eye yellow in front, buffy behind.

IDENTIFICATION: A long-tailed reddish-brown sparrow with yellow spot in front of eye. Similar to white-crowned sparrow but brown instead of gray, white stripes on head less distinct, white throat, and yellow spot in front of eye.

RANGE: North America. Breeds in forested areas of northern Canada southeast to Minnesota and New York. Winters in southeastern states.

NESTING: On the ground or in low bushes. Nest of grasses and rootlets lined with rootlets and moss. Eggs, 4-5, bluish-white speckled with brown. (Edmonton, June 5.)

REMARKS: The white-throated sparrow breeds in mixed deciduous and coniferous forests in the northern half of Alberta. It also nests in small numbers in the mixed woods along river valleys and lake shores in the parklands. It has not been seen in the mountains south of the Jasper region. In the southern parts of the province including the Cypress Hills it occurs only on migration.

In the undergrowth along a forest path or near a forest stream white-throated sparrows find the seclusion which they prefer. They like to scratch among the dead leaves on the woodland floor well concealed by a maze of boughs and leaves but they do not confine their activities to these lower levels. They work through bushes along roadsides and at the edges of clearings and deeper in the forest they move freely through the lower branches always showing a preference for deciduous rather than coniferous growths.

White-throats are not particularly shy. An observer standing near a brush-pile in a forest clearing will soon find himself being inspected from its latticework. If a nest is in the vicinity he is met more openly with excited chirpings. They will nest near a woodland cabin showing little fear of its occupants but rarely responding to friendly overtures. During the day the song of the white-throated sparrow is just part of the woodland chorus but at dusk his clear sweet whistle stands out in counterpoint against the rich flutings of Swainson's thrushes. And even in the dark stillness of the night his voice may break the silence with *Dear — Canada — Canada — Canada.*

B. & J. MORGAN

GOLDEN-CROWNED SPARROW

C. HAMPSON

WHITE-THROATED SPARROW

FOX SPARROW

LINCOLN'S SPARROW

DOUG GILROY

GROSBEAKS, BUNTINGS, FINCHES, SPARROWS — Family Fringillidae

FOX SPARROW
Passerella iliaca   subsp. (p. 500)

Scarce Summer Resident.
Length 7 in.

DESCRIPTION: Ads.—Upperparts olive-gray more or less streaked with chestnut or rust-red, especially on wings and tail; sides of head rusty; throat white bordered with rusty; underparts white with rust-red streaks on sides and a band of rust-red V's across breast, the V's pointing toward throat. Fox sparrows vary greatly in color; in some the rusty color is almost entirely replaced by olive-gray.

IDENTIFICATION: A large sparrow with fairly long tail. Rusty-red fox sparrows are easily identified; gray ones are best identified by lack of streaking on back and inverted V's on breast.

RANGE: North America. Breeds in Alaska and the forested regions of Canada south in the Rockies to California. Winters in southern states.

NESTING: On the ground or low in bushes. Nest of grass lined with moss, hair, and feathers. Eggs, 4-5, pale bluish-green speckled with brown.

REMARKS: In the mixed-wood forests of northern Alberta south to the edge of the parklands and in the mountains south to the international boundary the fox sparrow breeds locally and in small numbers. It migrates over most of Alberta but is never abundant. Occasionally migrating fox sparrows may visit a city or town in central Alberta during the last week of April or in late September feeding in those gardens where dense shrubbery and extensive tree growth gives them good protection.

Although it inhabits forested areas the fox sparrow is more often found in thickets of willow and alder or in thick underbrush at the edge of a clearing rather than in the open woods. In the mountains it occurs most commonly in the stunted growth near timberline where its neighbors may be golden-crowned sparrows. In general behavior the fox sparrow resembles the song sparrow with which the gray subspecies may easily be confused but it is far more secretive usually disappearing into the thick undergrowth when approached. It spends much time on the ground scratching about in the leaves after the manner of a towhee and making far more noise than would be expected of a bird of its size. For its singing post, however, it chooses a twig near the top of a bush. The song of the fox sparrow is heard at its best against the silence of mountain peaks or the northern wilderness but occasionally in early May a fine chorus may come from a brush pile in the parklands heralding the late passage of fox sparrows through the settled regions of the province.

LINCOLN'S SPARROW
Melospiza lincolnii subsp. (p. 500)

Fairly Common Summer Resident.
Length 5¾ in.

DESCRIPTION: Ads.—Crown dark brown streaked with black and with medial stripe of dark gray and bordering line of dark gray over eye; cheeks and neck dark gray, the cheeks narrowly edged with buffy; rest of upperparts dark olive-gray heavily streaked with black and brown, the black predominating; two faint wing bars; tail about 2¼ in., olive-gray; throat pale gray faintly flecked with black and heavily bordered with black streaks; a buffy band across breast and down sides is streaked with brownish-black; abdomen white. Sexes alike. Im.—Like adults.

IDENTIFICATION: Lincoln's sparrow is similar to the song sparrow but may be distinguished by the buffy band across the breast and the lack of a dark spot in middle of breast.

RANGE: North America. Breeds in the heavily forested areas of Canada south in the mountains to California and New York. Winters in the southern states, Mexico and Central America.

NESTING: On the ground in marshes and muskegs. Nest of coarse grass lined with fine grass and rootlets. Eggs, 4-5, pale greenish-white blotched with brown. (Turner Valley, July 1.)

REMARKS: Lincoln's sparrow nests in the heavily forested areas of northern Alberta south to the edge of the parklands. It also nests in the mountains and foothills south to the international boundary and east as far as Calgary. In migration it is found throughout Alberta.

During the nesting season Lincoln's sparrow inhabits willow and alder thickets which border muskegs, marshes, or woodland streams. This habitat is often shared with yellow-throats and water-thrushes. Shy and secretive Lincoln's sparrow is more often heard than seen. The male sings a beautifully plaintive song from a perch in the bushes or from a low branch of the neighboring trees. When approached he retreats silently into the brush and steals away to a safe distance before singing again. Meanwhile on a dry hummock in the marsh the female builds her nest and incubates the eggs. On migration Lincoln's sparrows frequent brushy forest borders and roadside thickets where they scurry about on the ground like mice taking advantage of every bit of cover. On the rare occasions when they appear in the open they are easily mistaken for song sparrows. Only the patient and alert observer will recognize that Lincoln's sparrow is a relatively common species in the province.

SWAMP SPARROW

SONG SPARROW

KAY HODGES

GROSBEAKS, BUNTINGS, FINCHES, SPARROWS — Family Fringillidae

SWAMP SPARROW
Melospiza georgiana subsp. (p. 500)

Scarce Summer Resident.
Length 5½ in.

DESCRIPTION: Ads. — Crown chestnut, often with gray median stripe and many black streaks; line over eye pale gray; line back of eye black; cheeks brown; sides and back of neck gray; rest of upperparts streaked with black, chestnut, and buffy-white; most feathers of wings and tail edged with chestnut; throat white bordered at sides with dusky; breast pale gray indistinctly streaked with dusky; flanks buffy; abdomen white.

IDENTIFICATION: Much like the song and Lincoln's sparrow above but wings and tail show more reddish-brown; lack of distinct streaks on underparts separates the swamp sparrow from both of these species.

RANGE: Eastern North America. Breeds from central B.C. and Newfoundland south to Nebraska and New Jersey. Winters in southeastern states, Texas and Mexico.

NESTING: On or near the ground in marshy places. Nest of coarse grass lined with finer grass. Eggs, 4-5, bluish-white spotted with black and brown. (Spruce Grove, May 27.)

REMARKS: The swamp sparrow breeds from the edge of the parklands to the northern boundary of Alberta. Its distribution is dependent upon suitable habitat but it is nowhere common. The swamp sparrow has not been recorded in the mountains and the foothills.

Although they build their nests on a hummock in the marsh, swamp sparrows usually choose a territory close to bushes. Alders and willows bordering streams which run through a swamp, or brushy margins of muskegs are favorite haunts. Like the Lincoln's sparrow which may also inhabit such spots swamp sparrows rarely show themselves. They spend most of their time on the ground or in the network of low branches and rather than fly when approached they scurry off into hiding in some dense thicket. It is surprising that they are so timid for their surroundings are almost inaccessible except to winged enemies. Even when singing the males usually choose a low perch on a tuft of grass or in the lower branches of a bush where it is difficult to trace the sound to its source. Their song may be as easily overlooked as the birds themselves. A single note is repeated rapidly, not as fast as in the chipping sparrow's song but more like the junco's although the effect is sweeter with a suggestion of the tinkle of glass. On migration swamp sparrows forsake their usual haunts and move through the trees and shrubbery with other migrating sparrows.

GROSBEAKS, BUNTINGS, FINCHES, SPARROWS — Family Fringillidae

SONG SPARROW

Common Summer Resident.

Melospiza melodia subsp. (p. 500)

Length 6¼ in.

DESCRIPTION: Ads.—Crown dark brown with medial stripe of dark gray and bordered by gray line over eye; rest of upperparts streaked with black, brown, and buffy giving a streaked dark brown effect, no wing bars; tail about 2½ in. dark brown; throat pale gray bordered with streaks of rusty-brown; cheeks gray edged with brown; rest of underparts white or buffy heavily streaked down sides and across breast with rusty-brown, some of the streaks forming a dark spot in middle of breast. Sexes alike. Im.—Like adults but more buffy and less rusty.

IDENTIFICATION: There is much color variation in song sparrows but the breast band of heavy dark streaks with dark spot in its center is good identification in all cases.

RANGE: North America. Breeds in nearly all the wooded parts of North America. Winters from southern Canada to Mexico, the largest numbers being found in the southern parts of this range.

NESTING: On the ground. Nest of shredded bark, grass, and rootlets, lined with fine grass and rootlets. Eggs, 4-5, greenish-white spotted and blotched with brown. (Red Deer, June 15.)

REMARKS: The song sparrow breeds in all parts of Alberta but is scarce in the mountains and the prairies. In the latter region it nests rarely in a few of the more thickly wooded river valleys; in the mountains a dark subspecies occurs in small numbers.

The favorite habitat of the song sparrow is loose brush such as is found along woodland roads and streams, at the margins of dense forests, and throughout the parklands. From the brush, however, it makes frequent excursions into adjacent fields or even into the rushes bordering a woodland slough. From the time it arrives in mid-April until it leaves late in October the song sparrow spends most of its time in the undergrowth or on the ground scratching about for seeds and insects. It is not at all wary; in fact curiosity usually brings it quietly into the outer branches for a closer look at an unobtrusive observer. But if alarmed it becomes agitated and utters a sharp, *peent-peent,* with such force that its whole body moves with each note.

The song sparrow is appropriately named. Words can do no justice to its song and in any case there are so many variations, even in songs from the same bird, that description is futile. Yet, despite the varied arrangements of the notes, there is a quality about them which makes the song easily recognizable. And if there is ever any doubt as to identity, a check is simple; the singer will persist in his performance until approached within a few yards.

478

GROSBEAKS, BUNTINGS, FINCHES, SPARROWS — Family Fringillidae

McCOWN'S LONGSPUR
Rhyncophanes mccownii

Fairly Common Summer Resident.
Length 6 in.

DESCRIPTION: Ad. m.—Top of head, line along side of throat, and large crescent on breast black; line over eye, throat, and abdomen white; cheeks, hindneck, and sides gray; back and wings pale brownish-gray streaked with dark brownish-gray; a large chestnut patch at bend of wing; middle two tail feathers black, remainder white tipped with black. Ad. f.—Upperparts including crown streaked as in male; only faint chestnut mark at bend of wing; underparts grayish-white with no black border along throat and only few black feathers on breast; tail as in male. Im.—A streaked grayish-brown bird best identified by tail markings which are same as in adult.

IDENTIFICATION: Males are distinctively marked. In any plumage McCown's longspurs are best identified in flight by large amount of white in tail, only a line down the middle and a line across the tip being dark. All species of longspurs can be distinguished from sparrows in the hand by the long nail on the hind toe from which their name is derived.

RANGE: Central North America. Breeds from southern Alberta and Saskatchewan south to Wyoming and North Dakota. Winters from Colorado and Kansas south to Mexico.

NESTING: On the ground. Nest a depression lined with fine grasses. Eggs, 3-4, grayish-white lightly streaked with black and brown. (Calgary, May 28.)

REMARKS: The breeding range of McCown's longspur in Alberta coincides rather closely with that of the chestnut-collared longspur extending north to Youngstown in the east and to Calgary in the west. The species is quite locally distributed. Wanderers have been taken well outside the usual range at Beaverhill Lake, Sandy Creek near Athabasca, and on an island in Lesser Slave Lake.

McCown's and chestnut-collared longspurs frequent the same type of habitat; in fact they are often found loosely associated in nesting colonies where a few dozen pairs establish territories in the same field, but McCown's longspurs are always less numerous. Although the males of the two species are quite different in appearance their habits are similar. Both prefer low perches either on the ground or on a fence but not on bushes, and both indulge in a beautiful flight song performed with wings and tail spread as they flutter to the ground. In August when adults and young of both species mingle with various species of sparrows as they migrate through southern Alberta the amateur ornithologist can spend some interesting but perhaps frustrating hours separating one from the other.

GROSBEAKS, BUNTINGS, FINCHES, SPARROWS — Family Fringillidae

LAPLAND LONGSPUR
Calcarius lapponicus subsp. (p. 500)

Common Migrant.
Length 6½ in.

DESCRIPTION: Ad. m.—Entire head and upper chest black except buffy line behind eye; chestnut collar across hindneck; back and wings streaked with black, brown, and buffy-white; rest of underparts and sides of neck white with black streaks on sides; outer tail feather mainly white, rest dark brownish-gray. Ad. f.—Upperparts buffy-brown streaked with dark brown and black; indistinct light medial stripe on crown and buffy collar on hindneck; underparts white flecked with black on throat and breast and streaked with brown on sides. Im. and fall ads.—Similar to female.

IDENTIFICATION: Spring males are somewhat similar to chestnut-collared longspurs but larger and lacking extensive black underparts. In the fall Lapland longspurs are buffy streaked sparrows similar to vesper sparrows but browner and lacking light eye ring. Hind toe has long nail.

RANGE: Northern hemisphere. Breeds in North America across continent north of tree limit. Winters from extreme southern Canada south to Texas and Kentucky.

NESTING: On the ground on the tundra. Nest a depression lined with grass, feathers, and hair. Eggs, 4-7, pale olive-buff speckled with brown.

REMARKS: The Lapland longspur is a regular migrant through all of Alberta. It stops over to feed on seeds in the grasslands and cultivated fields of the prairies and parklands but passes over the wooded regions rapidly. It is not a regular transient through the mountains although it has been seen at Banff and Jasper. Small numbers of Lapland longspurs remain in extreme southern Alberta south of the Milk river during particularly mild winters.

Early in April twittering hordes of Lapland longspurs sweep across the fields of southern Alberta in undulating flight until, over a particularly inviting piece of fallow or stubble, they mill about to tighten their ranks and settle to feed. As they run about or crouch on the ground their colors blend so well with their surroundings that a person may walk into the midst of a flock without seeing a single bird until hundreds spring into the air all around him. In the fall southbound Lapland longspurs in large loose flocks flit past the hunter hidden in a stubble field or alight for a drink near his blind beside a slough. They are dull colored sparrows then but the buffy feather edgings which obscure their bright colors will wear off by spring uncovering the handsome breeding plumage.

480

McCOWN'S LONGSPUR
female

LAPLAND LONGSPUR
female   *male*

GROSBEAKS, BUNTINGS, FINCHES, SPARROWS — Family Fringillidae

SMITH'S LONGSPUR   Scarce Migrant.
Calcarius pictus   Length 6½ in.

DESCRIPTION: Ad. m.—Head except throat black with spot on crown, line over eye, spot behind eye, and margin of throat white; throat, hindneck, and underparts yellowish-buff; back and wings streaked with dull black and buffy; one white wing bar; two outer tail feathers mainly white, remainder dull black. Ad. f.—Upperparts streaked with dull black and buffy; line over eye light buffy; underparts pale buff lightest on throat and streaked with reddish-brown across breast and down sides; tail as in male. Im.—Similar to female.

IDENTIFICATION: Males are somewhat similar to Lapland longspur but lack black throat and have more white on face. Females and immatures are similar to Lapland longspurs and are best identified in flight by the two white outer tail feathers; they are browner above and the underparts are definitely buffy instead of white.

RANGE: Interior of North America. Breeds on tundra from Yukon to Hudson Bay. Winters from Texas to Kansas.

NESTING: On the ground. Nest a depression lined with grass. Eggs, 3-6, white spotted with brown.

REMARKS: Smith's longspurs migrate through Alberta in small numbers each spring and fall sometimes in company with Lapland longspurs. But while the latter usually feed in cultivated fields Smith's longspurs prefer open prairies or grassy lake flats which resemble their tundra home. They migrate in loose flocks flying low over the fields and twittering as they go. It is said their note has a higher pitch than that of the Lapland longspur but it takes a keen ear to detect the difference. It is difficult to find them in the grass; when approached they crouch in concealment refusing to take flight until the observer is practically upon them.

Smith's longspurs occur fairly regularly in the Camrose and Tofield areas and have been recorded also at Brooks, Egg Lake, Swan Lake, Peace River, and Wood Buffalo Park. Although the records are not sufficiently numerous to be convincing it appears that Smith's longspurs migrate a little later in the spring and a little earlier in the fall than the main body of Lapland longspurs. Flocks of longspurs which settle into grassy prairies when stubble fields are handy should be identified carefully. In the spring identification is not too difficult but in the fall, when the markings on the head are not distinctive, special attention should be paid to the color of the underparts.

GROSBEAKS, BUNTINGS, FINCHES, SPARROWS — Family Fringillidae

CHESTNUT-COLLARED LONGSPUR   Common Summer Resident.
Calcarius ornatus   Length 6 in.

DESCRIPTION: Ad. m.—Chestnut collar across hind-neck; top of head, broad line back of eye, patch on side of neck, and entire breast black; throat and cheeks buff; patch on nape, line over eye, line across lower throat, and abdomen white; back and wings dark grayish-brown streaked with pale grayish-brown; outer three tail feathers mainly white with black edges toward tip, middle three mainly black with some white toward base. Ad. f.— Entire upperparts including crown striped as in male; underparts buffy-gray faintly streaked on sides of throat and on breast with dusky brown; tail as in male. Im.— Like female but more streaked above and below; tail as in adult.

IDENTIFICATION: Males are distinctively marked. In any plumage chestnut-collared longspurs are most easily identified in flight by the large amount of white extending right to the tip of the outer half of the tail. Long nail on hind toe.

RANGE: Great Plains region of North America. Breeds from southern parts of prairie provinces south to Wyoming and Minnesota. Winters in southwestern states and Mexico.

NESTING: On the ground. Nest a depression lined with grasses. Eggs, 3-5, greenish-white speckled with brown and lavender. (Calgary, May 30.)

REMARKS: As a breeding species the chestnut-collared longspur is widely but locally distributed in southern Alberta west to Lethbridge and Calgary and north to the southern fringe of the parklands. It is most apt to occur where virgin prairie still abounds. Occasionally it has nested at scattered points outside this area. Small groups of nesting chestnut-collared longspurs have been found as far north as Edmonton and Tofield; there is a single non-breeding record from Banff. These excursions are probably caused by destruction of nesting habitat farther south which forces the former occupants to look farther afield for suitable territory. It is possible that a permanent extension of breeding range may result from these sporadic invasions of new territory.

The chestnut-collared longspur is a typical prairie bird frequenting the same type of habitat as the horned lark and McCown's longspur. Usually a number of pairs nest in the same field forming a loosely associated colony. For their nesting territory they select short grass prairies or occasionally cultivated fields if the vegetation is short but they avoid buck-brush, tall grass, and damp areas. The singing perch of the male is a rock or a clump of dirt. From time to time however he rises into the air a dozen feet or so, then spreading his tail and setting his wings above his back he flutters slowly to the ground singing a tinkling melody. Somewhere in the vicinity his mate blends perfectly with the grass as she incubates her eggs. After the young have hatched both birds spend most of their time on the ground catching insects for the hungry family. At this time too the adults start to moult and in August when the whole group moves southward the male looks much like the others in his drab winter plumage.

483

SMITH'S LONGSPUR

ALLAN BROOKS

CHESTNUT-COLLARED LONGSPUR
female   *male*

S. MACDONALD

SNOW BUNTINGS

PARULA WARBLER
Parula americana

Accidental.
Length 4½ in.

A small warbler; upperparts blue-gray with yellowish-green patch on back; two white wing-bars; throat and breast bright yellow with band of dark brown across breast; abdomen white. Females are duller and usually lack breast band.

This is an eastern warbler rarely recorded west of Ontario. On June 6, 1958, an adult male parula warbler was collected in the foothills about fifteen miles west of Turner Valley. Except on migration the species is most likely to occur in conifers festooned with lichens.

SCARLET TANAGER
Piranga olivacea

Status unknown.
Length 7 in.

Male: entirely scarlet except for black wings and tail. Female: olive-green above and greenish-yellow below; wings and tail greenish-brown; similar to female western tanager but lacks wing-bars. Males lose their red plumage in the fall and resemble females with black wings and tails.

A female scarlet tanager struck a window in Calgary on Nov. 2, 1964, and died in captivity about a week later. This is the only authenticated record of the species in Alberta although sight records are occasionally reported. Tanagers would not normally be expected to remain in Alberta until November.

GROSBEAKS, BUNTINGS, FINCHES, SPARROWS — Family Fringillidae

SNOW BUNTING   Common Winter Resident.
Plectrophenax nivalis   subsp. (p. 500)   Length 7 in.

DESCRIPTION: The breeding plumage is white except a black mantle across back, black primaries, and black middle tail feathers. In winter the black feathers are edged with white and brown and the head and neck may be washed with gray or rusty or both; the underparts are always white except for a small rusty mark on each side of the breast.

IDENTIFICATION: Distinctively marked; no other small bird has such large areas of black and white. During winter the upper surface may be quite grayish but when the birds take flight the black and white wings and tail are distinctive.

RANGE: Circumpolar. Breeds in North America from tree limit north. Winters from central Canada to Colorado and Florida.

NESTING: On the ground on the tundra. Nest of grass lined with moss and feathers. Eggs, 4-6, white spotted with brown.

REMARKS: Snow buntings, popularly known as snowbirds, first appear in the settled regions of Alberta in October often travelling southward in company with flocks of Lapland longspurs but while the latter rarely stop north of the international boundary snow buntings regularly remain in southern Alberta throughout the winter. Their numbers vary greatly from year to year without any apparent correlation with the severity of the weather. They are gregarious birds; flocks of several hundred are not at all unusual. When the snow lies deep on the ground they pick seeds from grass and weeds which protrude above it but their favorite resort is a patch of bare fallow cleared of snow by strong winds or a patch of bare gravel on a road. Here they find the grit which is essential to the digestion of their food. Often they settle down to spend the night in a bare spot on a little-used road and scores may be killed as they rise blindly into the glare of a speeding car.

Throughout southern and central Alberta, including the foothills and mountains, snow buntings are winter residents. By early April large flocks have formed as northbound migrants join the resident population. Some of these flocks number in the thousands. Most have left by the end of the month but some late migrants may be seen in May; by this time most of the gray edges have worn from their feathers and the beautifully contrasting black and white breeding plumage shows at its best. In northern Alberta snow buntings are seen only on migration.

CHECK-LIST OF BIRDS OF ALBERTA

(including subspecies, based on the

1957 Check-list of the A.O.U.)

COMMON LOON. *Gavia immer* (Brunnich).

ARCTIC LOON. *Gavia arctica* (Linnaeus).

RED-THROATED LOON. *Gavia stellata* (Pontoppidan).

RED-NECKED GREBE. *Podiceps grisegena holbollii* Reinhart. Holboell's Grebe.

HORNED GREBE. *Podiceps auritus cornutus* Gmelin. American Horned Grebe.

EARED GREBE. *Podiceps caspicus californicus* Heermann. American Eared Grebe.

WESTERN GREBE. *Aechmophorus occidentalis* (Lawrence).

PIED-BILLED GREBE. *Podilymbus podiceps podiceps* (Linnaeus). Pied-billed Grebe.

WHITE PELICAN. *Palecanus erythrorhynchos* Gmelin.

DOUBLE-CRESTED CORMORANT. *Phalacrocorax auritus auritus* (Lesson). Eastern Double-crested Cormorant.

GREAT BLUE HERON. *Ardea herodias herodias* Linnaeus. Great Blue Heron.

CATTLE EGRET. *Bubulcus ibis* (Linnaeus).

COMMON EGRET. *Casmerodius albus egretta* (Gmelin). American Egret.

SNOWY EGRET. *Leucophoyx thula* subsp. Believed to be *brewsteri* (*Thayer and Bangs*), Brewster's Egret, but specimens have not been examined.

BLACK-CROWNED NIGHT HERON. *Nycticorax nycticorax hoactli* (Gmelin).

AMERICAN BITTERN. *Botaurus lentiginosus* (Rackett).

WHISTLING SWAN. *Olor columbianus* (Ord).

TRUMPETER SWAN. *Olor buccinator* Richardson.

CANADA GOOSE. *Branta canadensis parvipes* (Cassin). Athabasca Canada Goose. Breeds in northern Alberta southward to at least Athabasca but exact range unknown.
Branta canadensis moffitti Aldrich. Basin Canada Goose. Breeds in central and southern Alberta intergrading with *parvipes* in north-central Alberta.
Branta canadensis hutchinsii (Richardson). Hutchins' Goose. Scarce migrant.

BRANT. *Branta bernicla hrota* (Muller). Hybridizes with next species in western North America.

BLACK BRANT. *Branta nigricans* (Lawrence).

WHITE-FRONTED GOOSE. *Anser albifrons frontalis* Baird. White-fronted Goose.

SNOW GOOSE. *Chen hyperborea hyperborea* (Pallas). Lesser Snow Goose.

BLUE GOOSE. *Chen caerulescens* (Linnaeus).

ROSS' GOOSE. *Chen rossii* (Cassin).

MALLARD. *Anas platyrhynchos platyrhynchos* Linnaeus. Common Mallard.

BLACK DUCK. *Anas rubripes* Brewster.

GADWALL. *Anas strepera* Linnaeus.

CHECK LIST (Continued)

PINTAIL. *Anas acuta* Linnaeus.

GREEN-WINGED TEAL. *Anas carolinensis* Gmelin.

BLUE-WINGED TEAL. *Anas discors discors* Linnaeus.

CINNAMON TEAL. *Anas cyanoptera septentrionalium* Snyder and Lumsden. North American Cinnamon Teal.

EUROPEAN WIDGEON. *Mareca penelope* (Linnaeus).

AMERICAN WIDGEON. *Mareca americana* (Gmelin). Baldpate.

SHOVELER. *Spatula clypeata* (Linnaeus).

WOOD DUCK. *Aix sponsa* (Linnaeus).

REDHEAD. *Aythya americana* (Eyton).

RING-NECKED DUCK. *Aythya collaris* (Donovan).

CANVASBACK. *Aythya valisineria* (Wilson).

GREATER SCAUP. *Aythya marila nearctica* Stejneger.

LESSER SCAUP. *Aythya affinis* (Eyton).

COMMON GOLDENEYE. *Bucephala clangula americana* (Bonaparte). American Goldeneye.

BARROW'S GOLDENEYE. *Bucephala islandica* (Gmelin).

BUFFLEHEAD. *Bucephala albeola* (Linnaeus).

OLDSQUAW. *Clangula hyemalis* (Linnaeus).

HARLEQUIN DUCK. *Histrionicus histrionicus* (Linnaeus).

KING EIDER. *Somateria spectabilis* (Linnaeus).

WHITE-WINGER SCOTER. *Melanitta deglandi deglandi* (Bonaparte).

SURF SCOTER. *Melanitta perspicillata* (Linnaeus).

RUDDY DUCK. *Oxyura jamaicensis rubida* (Wilson). Ruddy Duck.

HOODED MERGANSER. *Lophodytes cucullatus* (Linnaeus).

COMMON MERGANSER. *Mergus merganser americanus* Cassin. American Merganser.

RED-BREASTED MERGANSER. *Mergus serrator serrator* Linnaeus. Red-breasted Merganser.

TURKEY VULTURE. *Cathartes aura septentrionalis* Wied. Turkey Vulture.

GOSHAWK. *Accipiter gentilis atricapillus* (Wilson). Eastern Goshawk.

SHARP-SHINNED HAWK. *Accipiter striatus velox* (Wilson). Sharp-shinned Hawk.

COOPER'S HAWK. *Accipiter cooperii* (Bonaparte).

RED-TAILED HAWK. *Buteo jamaicensis borealis* (Gmelin). Eastern Red-tailed Hawk. Breeds in northeastern Alberta.
   Buteo jamaicensis kriderii Hoopes. Krider's red-tailed Hawk. Breeds in southern Alberta but with some admixture of characteristics of *borealis* and *calurus*.
   Buteo jamaicensis calurus Cassin. Western Red-tailed Hawk. Breeds in the wooded sections of Western Alberta.
   Red-tailed Hawks of southern Alberta are not plainly referable to any subspecies but represent intergradation between *calurus*, *kriderii* and *borealis*.

488

CHECK LIST (Continued)

HARLAN'S HAWK. *Buteo harlani* (Audubon).

BROAD-WINGED HAWK. *Buteo platypterus platypterus* (Vieillot).
Broad-winged Hawk.

SWAINSON'S HAWK. *Buteo swainsoni* Bonaparte.

ROUGH-LEGGED HAWK. *Buteo lagopus s. johannis* (Gmelin).
American Rough-legged Hawk.

FERRUGINOUS HAWK. *Buteo regalis* (Gray).

GOLDEN EAGLE. *Aquila chrysaetos canadensis* (Linnaeus).
Golden Eagle.

BALD EAGLE. *Haliaeetus leucocephalus alascanus* Townsend.
Northern Bald Eagle.

MARSH HAWK. *Circus cyaneus hudsonius* (Linnaeus). Marsh Hawk.

OSPREY. *Pandion haliaetus carolinensis* (Gmelin). Osprey.

GYRFALCON. *Falco rusticolus obsoletus* Gmelin. Gyrfalcon.

PRAIRIE FALCON. *Falco mexicanus* Schlegel.

PEREGRINE FALCON. *Falco peregrinus anatum* Bonaparte. Duck Hawk.

PIGEON HAWK. *Falco columbarius richardsonii* Ridgway. Richardson's
Pigeon Hawk. Known to breed from the international boundary
north to the North Saskatchewan River. Has been seen in the
breeding season as far north as Belvedere and Fork Lake.

Falco columbarius bendirei Swann. Western Pigeon Hawk. Believed
to breed from about Athabasca northward and in the mountains.

SPARROW HAWK. *Falco sparverius sparverius* Linnaeus.
Eastern Sparrow Hawk.

BLUE GROUSE. *Dendragapus obscurus richardsonii* (Douglas).
Richardson's Grouse.

SPRUCE GROUSE. *Canachites canadensis canadensis* (Linnaeus).
Hudsonian Spruce Grouse. Breeds in the forested regions of
northern and western Alberta southward to the valley of the Bow.
Reported as occurring commonly in Jasper Park.

Canachites canadensis osgoodi Bishop. Alaska Spruce Grouse. Has
been taken in the breeding season at Lake Athabasca. Believed
to breed in the extreme northern part of the province.

Canachites canadensis franklinii (Douglas). Franklin's Grouse.
Breeds in the mountains.

RUFFED GROUSE. *Bonasa umbellus umbelloides* (Douglas). Gray
Ruffed Grouse. Breeds in southern and central Alberta, northward
to about Athabasca.

Bonasa umbellus yukonensis Grinnell. Yukon Ruffed Grouse. Breeds
in northern Alberta intergrading with *umbelloides* in the Peace
River, Lesser Slave Lake and north Athabasca districts.

WILLOW PTARMIGAN. *Lagopus lagopus albus* (Gmelin). Willow
Ptarmigan.

WHITE-TAILED PTARMIGAN. *Lagopus leucurus leucurus* (Richardson).
Northern White-tailed Ptarmigan.

CHECK LIST (Continued)

GREATER PRAIRIE CHICKEN. *Tympanuchus cupido pinnatus* Brewster.
Greater Prairie Chicken.

SHARP-TAILED GROUSE. *Pedioecetes phasianellus caurus* Friedmann.
Alaska Sharp-tailed Grouse. Breeds in northern Alberta southward
to the Peace River and probably Ft. McMurray region.
Pedioecetes phasianellus jamesi Lincoln. Plains Sharp-tailed Grouse.
Breeds in the southern half of the province.

SAGE GROUSE. *Centrocercus urophasianus urophasianus* (Bonaparte).

RING-NECKED PHEASANT. *Phasianus colchicus* Linnaeus. The Pheasant
in North America is a mixture of two or more subspecies.

CHUKAR. *Alectoris graeca* (Meisner). Several subspecies have been included in the introduced stock in North America.

GRAY (HUNGARIAN) PARTRIDGE. *Perdix perdix perdix* (Linnaeus).
European Gray Partridge.

TURKEY. *Meleagris gallopavo* Linnaeus. Wild Turkey. Specimens not
available for subspecific determination. Introduced from wild stock
obtained from South Dakota and therefore probably *Meleagris
gallopavo silvestris* Vieillot.

EUROPEAN COMMON CRANE. *Grus grus* (Linnaeus). Subspecies unknown.

WHOOPING CRANE. *Grus americana* (Linnaeus).

SANDHILL CRANE. *Grus canadensis canadensis* (Linnaeus).
Little Brown Crane. Transient.
Grus canadensis tabida (Peters). Sandhill Crane. Breeds in the
province.

VIRGINIA RAIL. *Rallus limicola limicola* Vieillot. Virginia Rail.

SORA. *Porzana carolina* (Linnaeus). Sora Rail.

YELLOW RAIL. *Coturnicops noveboracensis noveboracensis* (Gmelin).
Yellow Rail.

COOT. *Fulica americana americana* Gmelin. American Coot.

SEMIPALMATED PLOVER. *Charadrius semipalmatus* Bonaparte.

PIPING PLOVER. *Charadrius melodus circumcinctus* (Ridgway). Belted
Piping Plover.

KILLDEER. *Charadrius vociferus vociferus* Linnaeus. Killdeer.

MOUNTAIN PLOVER. *Eupoda montana* (Townsend).

AMERICAN GOLDEN PLOVER. *Pluvialis dominica dominica* (Muller).
American Golden Plover. Regular transient through the province.
Pluvialis dominica fulva (Gmelin). Pacific Golden Plover. Rare
straggler; only one record for the province.

BLACK-BELLIED PLOVER. *Squatarola squatarola* (Linnaeus).

RUDDY TURNSTONE. *Arenaria interpres morinella* (Linnaeus).
Ruddy Turnstone.

COMMON SNIPE. *Capella gallinago delicata* (Ord). Wilson's Snipe.

LONG-BILLED CURLEW. *Numenius americanus parvus* Bishop. Northern
Long-billed Curlew.

WHIMBREL. *Numenius phaeopus hudsonicus* Latham. Hudsonian Curlew.

UPLAND PLOVER. *Bartramia longicauda* (Bechstein).

SPOTTED SANDPIPER. *Actitis macularia* (Linnaeus).

CHECK LIST (Continued)

SOLITARY SANDPIPER. *Tringa solitaria solitaria* Wilson. Eastern Solitary Sandpiper. Breeds in the province.
Tringa solitaria cinnamomea (Brewster). Western Solitary Sandpiper. Regular transient.

WANDERING TATTLER. *Heteroscelus incanum* (Gmelin).

WILLET. *Catoptrophorus semipalmatus inornatus* (Brewster). Western Willet.

GREATER YELLOWLEGS. *Totanus melanoleucus* (Gmelin).

LESSER YELLOWLEGS. *Totanus flavipes* (Gmelin).

KNOT. *Calidris canutus rufa* (Wilson). American Knot.

PECTORAL SANDPIPER, *Erolia melanotos* (Vieillot).

WHITE-RUMPED SANDPIPER. *Erolia fuscicollis* (Vieillot).

BAIRD'S SANDPIPER. *Erolia bairdii* (Coues).

LEAST SANDPIPER. *Erolia minutilla* (Vieillot).

DUNLIN. *Erolia alpina pacifica* (Vieillot). Red-backed Sandpiper.

SHORT-BILLED DOWITCHER. *Limnodromus griseus hendersoni* Rowan. Inland Dowitcher. Breeds in the province.

LONG-BILLED DOWITCHER. *Limnodromus scolopaceus* (Say). Long-billed Dowitcher. Transient.

STILT SANDPIPER. *Micropalama himantopus* (Bonaparte).

SEMIPALMATED SANDPIPER. *Ereunetes pusillus* (Linnaeus).

BUFF-BREASTED SANDPIPER. *Tryngites subruficollis* (Vieillot).

MARBLED GODWIT. *Limosa fedoa* (Linnaeus).

HUDSONIAN GODWIT. *Limosa haemastica* (Linnaeus).

SANDERLING. *Crocethia alba* (Pallas).

AMERICAN AVOCET. *Recurvirostra americana* Gmelin.

RED PHALAROPE. *Phalaropus fulicarius* (Linnaeus).

WILSON'S PHALAROPE. *Steganopus tricolor* Vieillot.

NORTHERN PHALAROPE. *Lobipes lobatus* (Linnaeus).

PARASITIC JAEGER. *Stercorarius parasiticus* (Linnaeus).

LONG-TAILED JAEGER. *Stercorarius longicaudus* Vieillot.

GLAUCOUS GULL. *Larus hyperboreus hyperboreus* Gunnerus.

GLAUCOUS-WINGED GULL. *Larus glaucescens* Naumann.

HERRING GULL. *Larus argentatus smithsonianus* Coues. Herring Gull. Common migrant; breeds in the extreme northern part of the province.

CALIFORNIA GULL. *Larus californicus* Lawrence.

RING-BILLED GULL. *Larus delawarensis* Ord.

MEW GULL. *Larus canus brachyrhynchus* Richardson. Short-billed Gull.

FRANKLIN'S GULL. *Larus pipixcan* Wagler.

BONAPARTE'S GULL. *Larus philadelphia* (Ord).

SABINE'S GULL. *Xema sabini* (Sabine).

CHECK LIST (Continued)

FORSTER'S TERN. *Sterna forsteri* Nuttal.

COMMON TERN. *Sterna hirundo hirundo* Linnaeus. Common Tern.

ARCTIC TERN. *Sterna paradisaea* Pontoppidan.

CASPIAN TERN. *Hydroprogne caspia* (Pallas).

BLACK TERN. *Chlidonias niger surinamensis* (Gmelin). Black Tern.

ROCK DOVE (DOMESTIC PIGEON). *Columba livia* Gmelin.

MOURNING DOVE. *Zenaidura macroura marginella* (Woodhouse). Western Mourning Dove.

BLACK-BILLED CUCKOO. *Coccyzus erythropthalmus* (Wilson).

SCREECH OWL. *Otus asio* subsp.

GREAT HORNED OWL. *Bubo virginianus wapacuthu* (Gmelin). Arctic Horned Owl. Breeds in all parts but the mountains.
Bubo virginianus lagophonus (Oberholser). Northwestern Horned Owl. Breeds in the mountains.

SNOWY OWL. *Nyctea scandiaca* (Linnaeus).

HAWK OWL. *Surnia ulula caparoch* (Muller). American Hawk Owl.

PYGMY OWL. *Glaucidium gnoma californicum* Sclater. California Pygmy Owl.

BURROWING OWL. *Speotyto cunicularia hypogaea* (Bonaparte). Western Burrowing Owl.

BARRED OWL. *Strix varia varia* Barton. Northern Barred Owl.

GREAT GRAY OWL. *Strix nebulosa nebulosa* (Forster). Great Gray Owl.

LONG-EARED OWL. *Asio otus tuftsi* Godfrey. Western Long-eared Owl.

SHORT-EARED OWL. *Asio flammeus flammeus* (Pontoppidan). Short-eared Owl.

BOREAL OWL. *Aegolius funereus richardsoni* (Bonaparte). Richardson's Owl.

SAW-WHET OWL. *Aegolius acadicus acadicus* (Gmelin). Saw-whet Owl.

POOR-WILL. *Phalaenoptilus nuttallii nuttallii* (Audubon). Nuttall's Poor-will.

COMMON NIGHTHAWK. *Chordeiles minor minor* (Forster). Eastern Nighthawk. Breeds in northern Alberta from about Banff and Red Deer northward, intergrading with *sennetti* in southern Alberta.
Chordeiles minor sennetti Coues. Sennet's Nighthawk. Breeds in extreme southeastern Alberta, from about the Cypress Hills to the international border.
Chordeiles minor hesperis Grinnell. Pacific Nighthawk. Nighthawks of the Waterton Lakes Park Region are intermediate between *hesperis* and *sennetti.*

BLACK SWIFT. *Cypseloides niger borealis* (Kennerly). Black Swift.

RUBY-THROATED HUMMINGBIRD. *Archilochus colubris* (Linnaeus).

RUFOUS HUMMINGBIRD. *Selasphorus rufus* (Gmelin.)

CHECK LIST (Continued)

CALLIOPE HUMMINGBIRD. *Stellula calliope* (Gould).

KINGFISHER. *Megaceryle alcyon alcyon* (Linnaeus). Eastern Belted Kingfisher. Breeds throughout the province except in the southwestern
part, intergrading with *caurina* in the central parts of southern
Alberta.
Megaceryle alcyon caurina (Grinnell). Western Belted Kingfisher.
Breeds in extreme southwestern Alberta, intergrading with *alcyon*
along the northern and eastern boundaries of its range.

YELLOW-SHAFTED FLICKER. *Colaptes auratus luteus* Bangs. Northern
Flicker. Central Alberta, intergrading with *borealis* in the vicinity
of Athabasca and hybridizing with *C. cafer* along the western and
southern parts of its range.
Colaptes auratus borealis Ridgeway. Boreal Flicker. Northern Alberta, southward to the Peace River and Athabasca districts.

RED-SHAFTED FLICKER. *Colaptes cafer collaris* Vigors. Red-shafted
Flicker. Pure *cafer* is to be expected only in the mountains. Eastward
in the foothills and throughout the southern part of the province
most flickers show a mixture of the characters of the yellow-shafted
and red-shafted flickers.

PILEATED WOODPECKER. *Dryocopus pileatus abieticola* (Bangs).
Northern Pileated Woodpecker.

RED-HEADED WOODPECKER. *Melanerpes erythrocephalus caurinus*
Brodkorb. Western Red-headed Woodpecker.

LEWIS' WOODPECKER. *Asyndesmus lewis* (Gray).

YELLOW-BELLIED SAPSUCKER. *Sphyrapicus varius varius* (Linnaeus).
Yellow-bellied Sapsucker. Common breeder.
Sphyrapicus varius nuchalis Baird. Red-naped Sapsucker. Breeds
in the mountains from near Banff southward.

HAIRY WOODPECKER. *Dendrocopos villosus septentrionalis* (Nuttall).
Northern Hairy Woodpecker. Throughout the province except the
mountains of the southwest.
Dendrocopos villosus monticola (Anthony). Rocky Mountain Hairy
Woodpecker. Southwestern mountains, from about Canmore to the
international boundary.

DOWNY WOODPECKER. *Dendrocopos pubescens medianus* (Swainson).
Northern Downy Woodpecker.
Dendrocopos pubescens nelsoni (Oberholser). Nelson's Downy
Woodpecker. Due to the overlapping of characters between the two
above subspecies in Alberta taxonomists have found it difficult to
classify the Alberta Downy Woodpeckers. Most of them appear to be
intermediate between *medianus* and *nelsoni*.
Dendrocopos pubescens leucurus (Hartlaub). Batchelder's Downy
Woodpecker. Breeds in the extreme southwestern part of the
province.

BLACK-BACKED THREE-TOED WOODPECKER. *Picoides arcticus*
(Swainson). Arctic Three-toed Woodpecker.

NORTHERN THREE-TOED WOODPECKER. *Picoides tridactylus
fasciatus* Baird. Alaska Three-toed Woodpecker.

EASTERN KINGBIRD. *Tyrannus tyrannus* (Linnaeus).

CHECK LIST (Continued)

WESTERN KINGBIRD. *Tyrannus verticalis* Say.

SCISSOR-TAILED FLYCATCHER. *Muscivora forficata* (Gmelin).

EASTERN PHOEBE. *Sayornis phoebe* (Latham).

SAY'S PHOEBE. *Sayornis saya saya* (Bonaparte). Breeds in the province. *Sayornis saya yukonensis* Bishop. Yukon Phoebe. Most certainly a migrant through the province and a possible breeder in the north-western part.

YELLOW-BELLIED FLYCATCHER. *Empidonax flaviventris* (Baird and Baird).

TRAILL'S FLYCATCHER. *Empidonax traillii traillii* (Audubon). Alder Flycatcher.

LEAST FLYCATCHER. *Empidonax minimus* (Baird and Baird).

HAMMOND'S FLYCATCHER. *Empidonax hammondii* (Xantus).

DUSKY FLYCATCHER. *Empidonax oberholseri* Phillips. Formerly Wright's Flycatcher.

WESTERN FLYCATCHER. *Empidonax difficilis difficilis* Baird.

WESTERN WOOD PEWEE. *Contopus sordidulus veliei* Coues.

OLIVE-SIDED FLYCATCHER. *Nuttallornis borealis* (Swainson).

HORNED LARK. *Eremophila alpestris arcticola* (Oberholser). Pallid Horned Lark. Breeds in the mountains. Scarce migrant elsewhere.
Eremophila alpestris hoyti (Bishop). Hoyt's Horned Lark. Common migrant and fairly common winter resident in extreme southern Alberta.
Eremophila alpestris leucolaema (Coues). Desert Horned Lark. Breeds commonly from the international boundary in the south, northward through the prairies. Northern boundary of range and zone of intergradation with *enthymia* not known.
Eremophila alpestris enthymia Oberholser. Saskatchewan Horned Lark. Breeds at Clyde, Tofield and Camrose. Probably intergrades with *leucolaema* in the southern parklands but specimens from that area are needed for confirmation.

VIOLET-GREEN SWALLOW. *Tachycineta thalassina lepida* Mearns. Violet-green Swallow.

TREE SWALLOW. *Iridoprocne bicolor* (Vieillot).

BANK SWALLOW. *Riparia riparia riparia* (Linnaeus). Bank Swallow.

ROUGH-WINGED SWALLOW. *Stelgidopteryx ruficollis serripennis* (Audubon). Rough-winged Swallow.

BARN SWALLOW. *Hirundo rustica erythrogaster* Boddaert.

CLIFF SWALLOW. *Petrochelidon pyrrhonota hypopolia* Oberholser. Great Basin Cliff Swallow.

PURPLE MARTIN. *Progne subis subis* (Linnaeus). Purple Martin.

GRAY JAY. *Perisoreus canadensis albescens* Peters. Alberta Jay. The common breeding Canada Jay of Alberta. Found in all heavily forested regions except the mountains, intergrading with montane races in the western foothills.
Perisoreus canadensis pacificus (Gmelin). Alaska Jay. Resident in the mountains from the Jasper region to near Waterton Lakes Park where it intergrades with *bicolor*.

CHECK LIST (Continued)

Perisoreus canadensis bicolor Miller. Idaho Jay. Resident in extreme southwestern Alberta intergrading with *pacificus* north of Waterton Lakes Park.

BLUE JAY. *Cyanocitta cristata bromia* Oberholser. Northern Blue Jay.

STELLER'S JAY. *Cyanocitta stelleri annectens* (Baird). Black-headed Jay.

BLACK-BILLED MAGPIE. *Pica pica hudsonia* (Sabine). American Magpie.

COMMON RAVEN. *Corvus corax principalis* Ridgway. Northern Raven.

COMMON CROW. *Corvus brachyrhynchos brachyrhynchos* Brehm. Eastern Crow. Probably the breeding subspecies in northeastern Alberta, southward to about Red Deer. The exact limit of its range in Alberta is not known.

Corvus brachyrhynchos hesperis Ridgway. Western Crow. Known to breed in the Peace River district, in the mountains and throughout southern Alberta south of Red Deer. The exact zone of intergradation with *brachyrhynchos* is not known.

CLARK'S NUTCRACKER. *Nucifraga columbiana* (Wilson).

BLACK-CAPPED CHICKADEE. *Parus atricapillus septentrionalis* Harris. Long-tailed Chickadee.

MOUNTAIN CHICKADEE. *Parus gambeli grinnelli* van Rossem. Grinnell's Chickadee.

BOREAL CHICKADEE. *Parus hudsonicus columbianus* Rhoads. Columbian Chickadee. Breeds in the mountains.

Parus hudsonicus farleyi Godfrey. Alberta Brown-headed Chickadee. Breeds in the mixed-wood forests east of the mountains.

WHITE-BREASTED NUTHATCH. *Sitta carolinensis cookei* Oberholser.

RED-BREASTED NUTHATCH. *Sitta canadensis* Linnaeus.

BROWN CREEPER. *Certhia familiaris montana* Ridgway. Brown Creeper.

DIPPER. *Cinclus mexicanus unicolor* Bonaparte. Dipper.

HOUSE WREN. *Troglodytes aedon parkmanii* Audubon. Western House Wren.

WINTER WREN. *Troglodytes troglodytes hiemalis* Vieillot. Eastern Winter Wren. Northern Alberta, from about Belvedere to the northern boundary.

Troglodytes troglodytes pacificus Baird. Western Winter Wren. Breeds in the mountains.

LONG-BILLED MARSH WREN. *Telmatodytes palustris iliacus* Ridgway. Alberta Marsh Wren.

SHORT-BILLED MARSH WREN. *Cistothorus platensis stellaris* (Naumann). Short-billed Marsh Wren.

ROCK WREN. *Salpinctes obsoletus obsoletus* (Say). Common Rock Wren.

MOCKINGBIRD. *Mimus polyglottos* subsp. No specimens are available for subspecific determination.

CATBIRD. *Dumetella carolinensis* (Linnaeus). Catbird.

CHECK LIST (Continued)

BROWN THRASHER. *Toxostoma rufum longicauda* (Baird). Western Brown Thrasher.

SAGE THRASHER. *Oreoscoptes montanus* (Townsend).

ROBIN. *Turdus migratorius migratorius* Linnaeus. Eastern Robin. Northern and central Alberta, south to about Banff and the Red Deer River. *Turdus migratorius propinquus* Ridgway. Western Robin. Southern Alberta, intergrading with *migratorius* in central Alberta.

VARIED THRUSH. *Ixoreus naevius meruloides* (Swainson). Northern Varied Thrush.

HERMIT THRUSH. *Hylocichla guttata faxoni* Bangs and Penard. Eastern Hermit Thrush.

SWAINSON'S THRUSH. *Hylocichla ustulata swainsoni* (Tschudi). Olive-backed Thrush. The breeding subspecies of the province except the Peace River and Lesser Slave Lake areas.
Hylocichla ustulata incana Godfrey. Yukon Olive-backed Thrush.
Known to breed in the Peace River and Lesser Slave Lake areas.

GRAY-CHEEKED THRUSH. *Hylocichla minima minima* (Baird).

VEERY. *Hylocichla fuscescens salicicola* Ridgway. Willow Thrush.

MOUNTAIN BLUEBIRD. *Sialia currucoides* (Bechstein).

TOWNSEND'S SOLITAIRE. *Myadestes townsendi townsendi* (Audubon). Townsend's Solitaire.

GOLDEN-CROWNED KINGLET. *Regulus satrapa satrapa* Lichtenstein Eastern Golden-crowned Kinglet. Breeds in most of the heavily forested regions east of the mountains and in northern Alberta.
Regulus satrapa amoenus van Rossem. Golden-crowned Kinglet. Breeds in the Rocky Mountain regions.

RUBY-CROWNED KINGLET. *Regulus calendula calendula* (Linnaeus). Eastern Ruby-crowned Kinglet.

WATER PIPIT. *Anthus spinoletta pacificus* Todd. Western Pipit. Breeds in the mountains and is a common migrant elsewhere in the province.

SPRAGUE'S PIPIT. *Anthus spragueii* (Audubon).

BOHEMIAN WAXWING. *Bombycilla garrula pallidiceps* Reichenow. Bohemian Waxwing.

CEDAR WAXWING. *Bombycilla cedrorum* Vieillot.

NORTHERN SHRIKE. *Lanius excubitor invictus* Grinnell. Northwestern Shrike.

LOGGERHEAD SHRIKE. *Lanius ludovicianus excubitorides* Swainson. White-rumped Shrike.

STARLING. *Sturnus vulgaris vulgaris* Linnaeus. Starling.

SOLITARY VIREO. *Vireo solitarius solitarius* (Wilson) Blue-headed Vireo. Breeds in northern Alberta.
Vireo solitarius cassinii Xantus. Cassin's Vireo. There is a specimen from Canmore in the National Museum of Canada.

RED-EYED VIREO. *Vireo olivaceus* (Linnaeus).

PHILADELPHIA VIREO. *Vireo philadelphicus* (Cassin).

496

WARBLING VIREO. *Vireo gilvus gilvus* (Vieillot). Eastern Warbling Vireo. Known from southern Alberta east of the mountains; may occur in the eastern wooded sections of northern Alberta.

> *Vireo gilvus swainsonii* Baird. Western Warbling Vireo. Known to breed in the mountains and in western Alberta, from the international boundary north to the Peace River district. May occur northward to the border in the western part.

BLACK-AND-WHITE WARBLER. *Mniotilta varia* (Linnaeus).

TENNESSEE WARBLER. *Vermivora peregrina* (Wilson).

ORANGE-CROWNED WARBLER. *Vermivora celata celata* (Say). Orange-crowned Warbler. Breeds in northern Alberta southward to about Lac La Nonne and Edmonton.

> *Vermivora celata orestera.* Oberholser. Rocky Mountain Orange-crowned Warbler. Breeds locally in southern Alberta and in the mountains. The exact ranges of the two subspecies are not known.

PARULA WARBLER. *Parula americana* (Linnaeus).

YELLOW WARBLER. *Dendroica petechia aestiva* (Gmelin). Eastern Yellow Warbler. Breeds in the plains region of southern Alberta, northward through the parklands to Camrose and possibly farther north.

> *Dendroica petechia amnicola* Batchelder. Newfoundland Yellow Warbler. Breeds in the mountains and in northern Alberta, north of the North Saskatchewan River.

MAGNOLIA WARBLER. *Dendroica magnolia* (Wilson).

CAPE MAY WARBLER. *Dendroica tigrina* (Gmelin).

BLACK-THROATED BLUE WARBLER. *Dendroica caerulescens caerulescens* (Gmelin). Black-throated Blue Warbler.

MYRTLE WARBLER. *Dendroica coronata coronata* (Linnaeus). Myrtle Warbler. Breeds in the province.

> *Dendroica coronata hooveri* McGregor. Alaska Myrtle Warbler. Migrant and possible breeder in the western parts of the mountains.

AUDUBON'S WARBLER. *Dendroica auduboni memorabilis* Oberholser.

TOWNSEND'S WARBLER. *Dendroica townsendi* (Townsend).

BLACK-THROATED GREEN WARBLER. *Dendroica virens virens* (Gmelin). Black-throated Green Warbler.

BLACKBURNIAN WARBLER. *Dendroica fusca* (Muller).

CHESTNUT-SIDED WARBLER. *Dendroica pensylvanica* (Linnaeus).

BAY-BREASTED WARBLER. *Dendroica castanea* (Wilson).

BLACKPOLL WARBLER. *Dendroica striata* (Forster).

PINE WARBLER. *Dendroica pinus pinus* (Wilson). Northern Pine Warbler.

PALM WARBLER. *Dendroica palmarum palmarum* (Gmelin). Western Palm Warbler.

OVENBIRD. *Seiurus aurocapillus cinereus* Miller. Gray Ovenbird.

NORTHERN WATERTHRUSH. *Seiurus noveboracensis notabilis* Ridgway. Grinnell's Waterthrush.

CONNECTICUT WARBLER. *Oporornis agilis* (Wilson).

CHECK LIST (Continued)

MOURNING WARBLER. *Oporornis philadelphia* (Wilson).

MACGILLIVRAY'S WARBLER. *Oporornis tolmiei tolmiei* (Townsend).

YELLOWTHROAT. *Geothlypis trichas campicola* Behle and Aldrich. Northern Plains Yellowthroat.

YELLOW-BREASTED CHAT. *Icteria virens auricollis* (Deppe) Long-tailed Chat.

WILSON'S WARBLER. *Wilsonia pusilla pusilla* (Wilson). Wilson's Warbler. Forested areas east and north of the mountains.

Wilsonia pusilla pileolata (Pallas). Pileolated Warbler. Mountains.

CANADA WARBLER. *Wilsonia canadensis* (Linnaeus).

AMERICAN REDSTART. *Setophaga ruticilla tricolora* (Muller). Northern American Redstart.

HOUSE SPARROW. *Passer domesticus domesticus* (Linnaeus). English Sparrow.

BOBOLINK. *Dolichonyx oryzivorus* (Linnaeus).

WESTERN MEADOWLARK. *Sturnella neglecta neglecta* Audubon.

YELLOW - HEADED BLACKBIRD. *Xanthocephalus xanthocephalus* (Bonaparte).

REDWINGED BLACKBIRD. *Agelaius phoeniceus arctolegus* Oberholser. Giant Redwing.

BALTIMORE ORIOLE. *Icterus galbula* (Linnaeus).

BULLOCK'S ORIOLE. *Icterus bullockii bullockii* (Swainson).

RUSTY BLACKBIRD. *Euphagus carolinus carolinus* (Muller).

BREWER'S BLACKBIRD. *Euphagus cyanocephalus* (Wagler).

COMMON GRACKLE. *Quiscalus quiscula versicolor* Vieillot. Bronzed Grackle.

BROWN-HEADED COWBIRD. *Molothrus ater artemisiae* Grinnell. Nevada Cowbird.

WESTERN TANAGER. *Piranga ludoviciana* (Wilson).

SCARLET TANAGER. *Piranga olivacea* (Gmelin).

ROSE-BREASTED GROSBEAK. *Pheucticus ludovicianus* (Linnaeus).

BLACK-HEADED GROSBEAK. *Pheucticus melanocephalus melanocephalus* (Swainson).

INDIGO BUNTING. *Passerina cyanea* (Linnaeus).

LAZULI BUNTING. *Passerina amoena* (Say).

DICKCISSEL. *Spiza americana* (Gmelin).

EVENING GROSBEAK. *Hesperiphona vespertina vespertina* (Cooper). Eastern Evening Grosbeak. The subspecies to be expected in all wooded areas except the mountains.

Hesperiphona vespertina brooksi Grinnell. Western Evening Grosbeak. Mountains.

PURPLE FINCH. *Carpodacus purpureus purpureus* (Gmelin).

CASSIN'S FINCH. *Carpodacus cassinii* Baird.

498

CHECK LIST (Continued)

HOUSE FINCH. *Carpodacus mexicanus frontalis* (Say). Common House Finch.

PINE GROSBEAK. *Pinicola enucleator alascensis* Ridgway. Alaska Pine Grosbeak. Winter visitant in northern and central Alberta.
> *Pinicola enucleator montana* Ridgway. Rocky Mountain Pine Grosbeak. Resident in mountains; probably a visitant to the eastern parts in winter.

GRAY-CROWNED ROSY FINCH. *Leucosticte tephrocotis tephrocotis* (Swainson). Gray-crowned rosy finch. Breeds in Rocky Mountain regions.
> *Leucosticte tephrocotis littoralis* Baird. Hepburn's rosy finch. Scarce winter visitor.

HOARY REDPOLL. *Acanthis hornemanni exilipes* (Coues). Hoary Redpoll.

COMMON REDPOLL. *Acanthis flammea flammea* (Linnaeus).

PINE SISKIN. *Spinus pinus pinus* (Wilson). Northern Pine Siskin.

AMERICAN GOLDFINCH. *Spinus tristis pallidus* Mearns. Pale Goldfinch.

RED CROSSBILL. *Loxia curvirostra sitkensis* Grinnell. Sitka Crossbill. There are specimens from the Jasper region but nothing is known regarding its status in the province.
> *Loxia curvirostra bendirei* Ridgway. Bendire's Crossbill. Occurs and may breed in the Cypress Hills and southern parts of the mountains.

WHITE-WINGED CROSSBILL. *Loxia leucoptera leucoptera* Gmelin.

RUFOUS-SIDED TOWHEE. *Pipilo erythrophthalmus arcticus* (Swainson). Arctic Towhee.

LARK BUNTING. *Calamospiza melanocorys* Stejneger.

SAVANNAH SPARROW. *Passerculus sandwichensis anthinus* Bonaparte. Western Savannah Sparrow. Known to breed in the Jasper region. Has been taken in migration in central Alberta, and at Ft. Chipewyan in early June, where it may breed.
> *Passerculus sandwichensis nevadensis* Grinnell. Nevada Savannah Sparrow. Breeds throughout most of the province.

GRASSHOPPER SPARROW. *Ammodramus savannarum perpallidus* (Coues). Western Grasshopper Sparrow.

BAIRD'S SPARROW. *Ammodramus bairdii* (Audubon).

LECONTE'S SPARROW. *Passerherbulus caudacutus* (Latham).

SHARP-TAILED SPARROW. *Ammospiza caudacuta nelsoni* (Allen). Nelson's Sparrow.

VESPER SPARROW. *Pooecetes gramineus confinis* Baird. Western Vesper Sparrow.

LARK SPARROW. *Chondestes grammacus strigatus* Swainson. Western Lark Sparrow.

SLATE-COLORED JUNCO. *Junco hyemalis hyemalis* (Linnaeus). Slate-colored Junco. Breeds in the mixed - wood belt of western and northern Alberta east of the mountains.
> *Junco hyemalis cismontanus* Dwight. Cassiar Junco. Breeds in the mountains at Jasper Park.

OREGON JUNCO. *Junco oreganus montanus* Ridgway. Montana Junco. Breeds in the mountains from the international boundary to the

499

Jasper region but with an admixture of *hyemalis* blood in the northern part of its range. Occasionally seen in migration in other parts of the province.

Junco oreganus mearnsi Ridgway. Mearn's Pink-sided Junco. Breeds in the Cypress Hills of southeastern Alberta. In migration occasionally elsewhere.

TREE SPARROW. *Spizella arborea ochracea* Brewster. Western Tree Sparrow.

CHIPPING SPARROW. *Spizella passerina boreophila* Oberholser. Canadian Chipping Sparrow.

CLAY-COLORED SPARROW. *Spizella pallida* (Swainson).

BREWER'S SPARROW. *Spizella breweri breweri* Cassin. Brewer's Sparrow. Breeds in the prairie section of southern Alberta.

Spizella breweri taverneri Swarth and Brooks. Timberline Sparrow. Known to breed above timberline in Jasper and Banff Parks and may possibly breed in the mountains southward to the international boundary.

HARRIS' SPARROW. *Zonotrichia querula* (Nuttall).

WHITE-CROWNED SPARROW. *Zonotrichia leucophrys gambelii* (Nuttall). Gambel's Sparrow. Breeds in the mountains at Jasper Park, in the western Peace River district and at Ft. Chipewyan.

Zonotrichia leucophrys oriantha Oberholser. Breeds in the Cypress Hills and southern mountains and foothills, intergrading with *gambelii* north of Waterton Lakes Park.

GOLDEN-CROWNED SPARROW. *Zonotrichia atricapilla* (Gmelin).

WHITE-THROATED SPARROW. *Zonotrichia albicollis* (Gmelin).

FOX SPARROW. *Passerella iliaca zaboria* Oberholser. Yukon Fox Sparrow. Breeds in northern and north-central Alberta.

Passerella iliaca altivagans Riley. Alberta Fox Sparrow. Breeds in the mountains in the Jasper Park Region.

Passerella iliaca schistacea Baird. Slate-colored Fox Sparrow. Breeds in the southwestern mountains intergrading with *altivagans* in the Banff region.

LINCOLN'S SPARROW. *Melospiza lincolnii lincolnii* (Audubon). Lincoln's sparrow.

SWAMP SPARROW. *Melospiza georgiana ericrypta* Oberholser. Western Swamp Sparrow.

SONG SPARROW. *Melospiza melodia juddi* Bishop. Dakota Song Sparrow. Breeds throughout the province except in the mountains.

Melospiza melodia inexpectata Riley. Yellowhead Song Sparrow. Breeds in the mountains.

McCOWN'S LONGSPUR. *Rhyncophanes mccownii* (Lawrence).

LAPLAND LONGSPUR. *Calcarius lapponicus lapponicus* (Linnaeus). Lapland Longspur. Scarce migrant.

Calcarius lapponicus alascensis Ridgway. Alaska Longspur. Common migrant and scarce winter resident in the extreme southern part of the province.

SMITH'S LONGSPUR. *Calcarius pictus* (Swainson).

CHESTNUT-COLLARED LONGSPUR. *Calarius ornatus* (Townsend).

SNOW BUNTING. *Plectrophenax nivalis nivalis* (Linnaeus). Eastern Snow Bunting.

HYPOTHETICAL LIST

Material evidence of the occurrence of the following species in Alberta has not been obtained to date:

YELLOW-BILLED LOON, *Gavia adamsi*
GREAT WHITE HERON, *Ardea occidentalis*
WHITE-FACED GLOSSY IBIS, *Plegadis guarauna*
EMPEROR GOOSE, *Philacte canagica*
COMMON SCOTER, *Oidemia nigra americana*
CALIFORNIA CONDOR, *Gymnogyps californianus*
SWALLOW-TAILED KITE, *Elanoides forficatus*
ROCK PTARMIGAN, *Lagopus mutus*
BOB-WHITE, *Colinus virginianus*
AMERICAN WOODCOCK, *Philohela minor*
ESKIMO CURLEW, *Numenius borealis*
WESTERN SANDPIPER, *Ereunetes mauri*
BLACK-NECKED STILT, *Himantopus mexicanus*
POMARINE JAEGER, *Stercorarius pomarinus*
IVORY GULL, *Pagophila eburnea*
PASSENGER PIGEON, *Ectopistes migratorius*
CHIMNEY SWIFT, *Chaetura pelagica*
VAUX'S SWIFT, *Chaetura vauxi*
WHITE-THROATED SWIFT, *Aeronautes saxatalis*
WILLIAMSON'S SAPSUCKER, *Sphyrapicus thyroideus*
CRESTED FLYCATCHER, *Myiarchus crinitus*
CHESTNUT-BACKED CHICKADEE, *Parus rufescens*
PYGMY NUTHATCH, *Sitta pygmaea*
EASTERN BLUEBIRD, *Sialia sialis*
BLUE-GRAY GNATCATCHER, *Polioptila caerulea*
NASHVILLE WARBLER, *Vermivora ruficapilla*
BLACK-THROATED GRAY WARBLER, *Dendroica nigrescens*

EUROPEAN COMMON CRANE   Accidental.
Grus grus   Length 48 in.

A large crane; head and most of foreneck dark bluish-gray; face and sides of neck white; remainder of body pale ashy-gray; primaries black. At a distance the common crane may appear almost white, like a whooping crane, but dark foreneck is distinctive.

On Dec. 11, 1957, a common crane appeared near Cavendish and remained in the vicinity until at least Dec. 20, 1957. On March 20, 1958, a common crane was seen near Stirling Lake, south of Lethbridge. Photographs were secured on each of these occasions. On Sept. 19, 1958, a common crane was seen in company with sandhill cranes near Athabasca. These occurrences, together with a sighting of a common crane in Alaska on April 24, 1958, suggest the probability that all of these records were of a single individual which made at least one northward and two southward migratory trips through Alberta to Alaska. It is interesting to speculate whether this may have been a wild bird which had wandered well out of its normal range or whether it was a bird which had escaped from captivity in North America. No evidence of the latter has yet been produced.

INDEX

Numbers in black face type refer to illustrations

INDEX — Continued

INDEX — Continued

INDEX — Continued

INDEX — Continued

INDEX — Continued

INDEX — Continued

508

INDEX — Continued

509

INDEX — Continued

510

INDEX — Continued

AS OF 1958

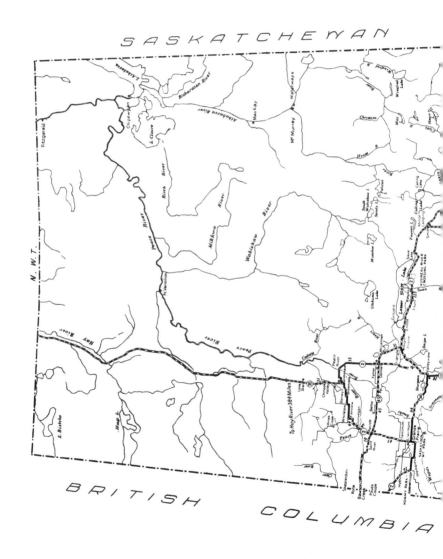